Interactive Homework Workbook

Grade 4

Scott Foresman • Addison Wesley

enVisionMATH™ California

Scott Foresman is an imprint of PEARSON

pearsonschool.com

Glenview, Illinois • Boston, Massachusetts • Chandler, Arizona • Shoreview, Minnesota • Upper Saddle River, New Jersey

ISBN – 13: 978-0-328-38444-0

ISBN – 10: 0-328-38444-5

3 4 5 6 7 8 9 10 V004 12 11 10 09

Contents

Topic 1 Numeration 1

Topic 2 Addition and Subtraction Number Sense 11

Topic 3 Multiplication and Division: Meanings and Facts 29

Topic 4 Multiplying by 1-Digit Numbers. 50

Topic 5 Variables and Expressions 65

Topic 6 Multiplying by 2-Digit Numbers. 75

Topic 7 Dividing by 1-Digit Divisors. 89

Topic 8 Lines, Angles, Shapes, and Solids 112

Topic 9 Fraction Meanings and Concepts. 131

Topic 10 Addition and Subtraction of Fractions 147

Topic 11 Fraction and Decimal Concepts 155

Topic 12 Operations with Decimals. 168

Topic 13 Solving Equations. 179

Topic 14 Integers. 189

Topic 15 Measurement, Perimeter, and Area. 197

Topic 16 Data and Graphs. 213

Topic 17 Length and Coordinates 225

Topic 18 Formulas and Equations. 233

Topic 19 Congruence and Symmetry 245

Topic 20 Probability. 253

Step Up to Grade 5. 261

Name ____________________

Thousands

Use a place-value chart to help you write a number in standard form.

Write four hundred twenty thousand, three hundred fifty-nine in standard form.

Step 1 Write 420 in the thousands period.

Step 2 Write 359 in the ones period.

The standard form is 420,359.

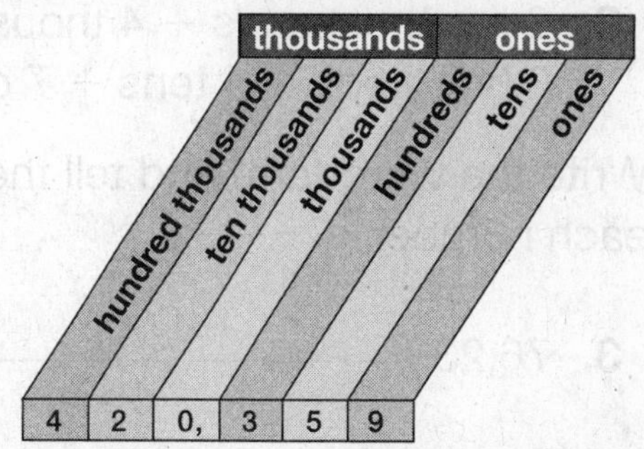

Each digit in 420,359 has a different *place value* and *value.* The *place value* of the digit 3 is the hundreds place. This digit has a *value* of 300.

Write each number in standard form.

1. 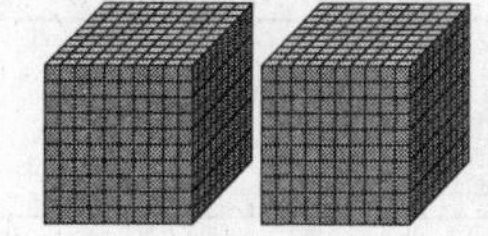  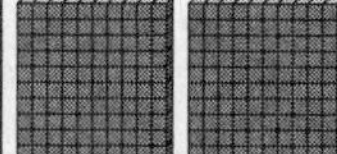  ____________

2. 7 ten thousands + 5 thousands + 8 hundreds + 1 ten + 0 ones ____________

Write the word form and tell the value of the underlined digit for each number.

3. 4,<u>6</u>32 ____________________

____

4. <u>7</u>,129 ____________________

____

5. 13,57<u>2</u> ____________________

____

6. **Number Sense** Write a six-digit number with a 5 in the ten thousands place and a 2 in the ones place. ____________

Name ____________________

Practice

1-1

Thousands

Write each number in standard form.

1. 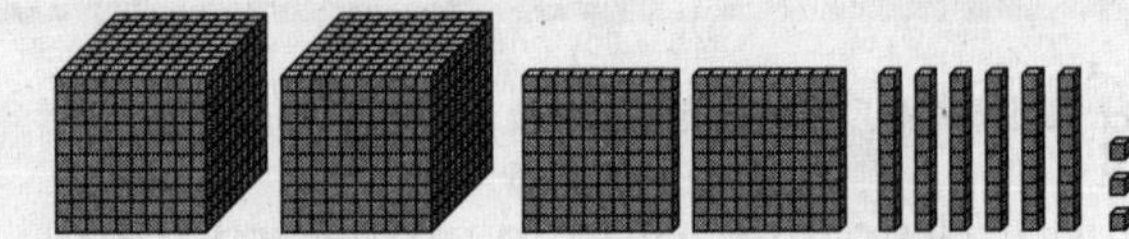 ____________________

2. 8 ten thousands + 4 thousands + 9 hundreds + 4 tens + 7 ones ____________________

Write the word form and tell the value of the underlined digit for each number.

3. 7<u>6</u>,239 ____________________

____

4. 823,<u>7</u>74 ____________________

____

5. **Number Sense** Write the number that has 652 in the ones period and 739 in the thousands period. ____________________

During a weekend at the Movie Palace Theaters, 24,875 tickets were sold. Add the following to the number of tickets sold.

6. 100 tickets ____________________ 7. 1,000 tickets ____________________

8. Which of the following numbers has a 5 in the ten thousands place?

A 652,341 **B** 562,341 **C** 462,541 **D** 265,401

9. **Writing to Explain** Explain how you know the 6 in the number 364,021 is not in the thousands place.

____

____

Name ____________________

Reteaching
1-2

Millions

Here are different ways to represent 555,612,300.

Place-value chart:

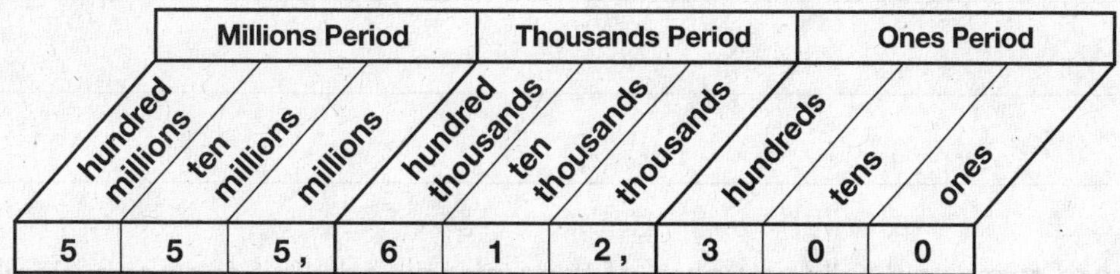

5	5	5,	6	1	2,	3	0	0

Expanded form: 555,612,300 = 500,000,000 + 50,000,000 + 5,000,000 + 600,000 + 10,000 + 2,000 + 300

Word form: 555,612,300 = five hundred fifty-five million, six hundred twelve thousand, three hundred

The 6 is in the hundred thousands place. Its value is 600,000.

1. Write nine hundred seventy-six million, four hundred thirty-three thousand, one hundred eleven in standard form. ____________

2. Write 80,000,000 + 700,000 + 30,000 + 200 + 90 + 7 in standard form. ____________

3. Write the word form and tell the value of the underlined digit in 33<u>7</u>,123,421.

____

____

____

____

4. **Number Sense** In the number 213,954,670, which digit has the second greatest value? What is its value?

____

Name ______________________

Millions

Write the number in standard form and in word form.

1. 300,000,000 + 70,000,000 + 2,000,000 + 500,000 + 10,000 + 2,000 + 800 + 5

Write the word form and tell the value of the underlined digit for each number.

2. 4,$\underline{6}$00,028

3. 488,423,0$\underline{4}$6

4. Number Sense Write the number that is one hundred million more than 15,146,481.

5. The population of a state was estimated to be 33,871,648. Write the word form.

6. Which is the expanded form for 43,287,005?

A 4,000,000 + 300,000 + 20,000 + 8,000 + 700 + 5

B 40,000,000 + 3,000,000 + 200,000 + 80,000 + 7,000 + 5

C 400,000,000 + 30,000,000 + 2,000,000 + 8,000 + 500

D 4,000,000 + 30,000 + 2,000 + 800 + 70 + 5

7. Writing to Explain In the number 463,211,889, which digit has the greatest value? Explain.

Name ________________________________

Comparing and Ordering Whole Numbers

You can use a number line to compare two numbers. Which is greater, 33,430 or 33,515?

Step 1 Plot the first number on a number line:

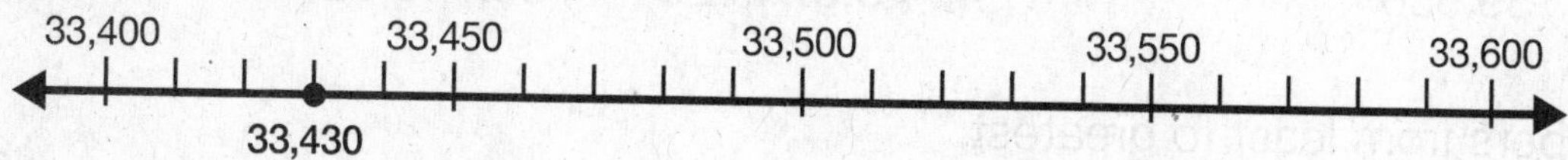

Step 2 Plot the second number on the same number line:

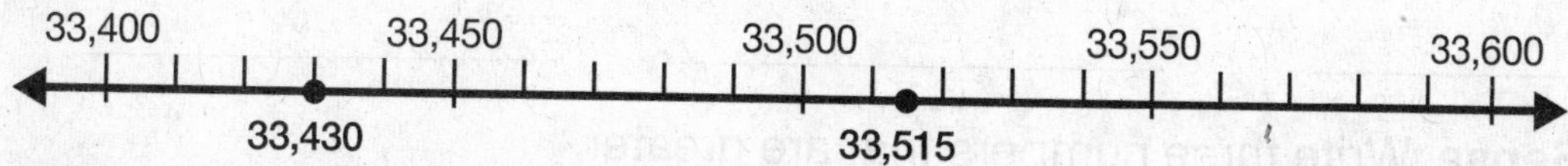

Step 3 Compare the numbers. Remember, as you move to the right on a number line, the numbers increase.
Looking at the number line, 33,515 is to the right of 33,430, so 33,515 > 33,430.

You can use place value to order numbers from greatest to least. Write the numbers, lining up places. Begin at the left and find the greatest digit. If necessary, continue comparing the other digits:

	Continue comparing.	Write from greatest to least.
42,078		
37,544	37,554	42,078
24,532	39,222	39,222
39,222	39,222 > 37,544	37,544
		24,532

Compare. Write > or < for each ◯.

1. 3,211 ◯ 4,221 **2.** 35,746 ◯ 35,645 **3.** 355,462 ◯ 535,845

4. Order the numbers from greatest to least. 62,500 62,721 63,001 61,435

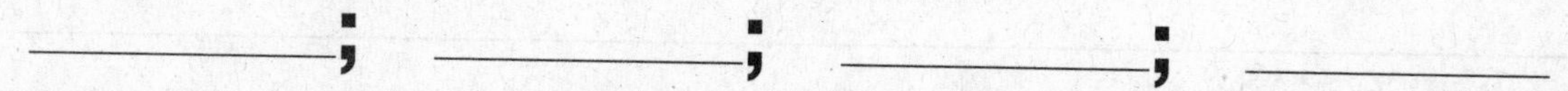

5. Number Sense Write 3 numbers that are greater than 12,000 but less than 13,000.

Name ______________________

Practice
1-3

Comparing and Ordering Whole Numbers

Compare. Write > or < for each ◯.

1. 2,854,376 ◯ 2,845,763

2. 6,789 ◯ 9,876

3. 59,635 ◯ 59,536

4. 29,374,125 ◯ 30,743,225

Order the numbers from least to greatest.

5. 45,859,211 4,936,211 43,958,211

____________ ____________ ____________

6. Number Sense Write three numbers that are greater than 1,543,000 and less than 1,544,000.

____________ ____________ ____________

7. Put the planets in order from the one closest to the sun to the one farthest from the sun.

____

____

____

____

____

The Five Closest Planets to the Sun

Planet	Distance (miles)
Earth	93,000,000
Jupiter	483,000,000
Mars	142,000,000
Mercury	36,000,000
Venus	67,000,000

8. Which number has the greatest value?

A 86,543,712 **B** 82,691,111 **C** 85,381,211 **D** 86,239,121

9. Writing to Explain Tell how you could use a number line to determine which of two numbers is greater.

____

____

Name ______________________________

Reteaching 1-4

Understanding Zeros in Place Value

To compare and order numbers with zeros, you can write the numbers in their expanded form and compare.

For Exercises **1** through **4**, compare the numbers. Write each number in expanded form. Then write < or > for each.

1. 4,009 ◯ 4,090

____

2. 9,008 ◯ 9,800

____

3. 15,500 ◯ 15,055

____

4. 78,040 ◯ 78,004

____

For Exercises **5** through **10**, compare the numbers. Put < or > for each.

5. 5,090 ◯ 5,009

6. 12,080 ◯ 12,800

7. 10,306 ◯ 10,360

8. 25,400 ◯ 25,040

9. 45,004 ◯ 45,400

10. 40,504 ◯ 45,004

For Exercises **11** through **14**, order the numbers from least to greatest.

11. 4,800 4,080 4,008

____

12. 46,000 40,600 40,060

____

13. 67,000 60,070 60,007

____

14. 70,008 78,000 70,080

____

15. Number Sense Write a 4-digit number with a 0 in the hundreds place and a 0 in the tens place. Now write another number, using the same four digits and tell which number is larger.

____

Name ______________________________

Practice 1-4

Understanding Zeros in Place Value

For Exercises **1** through **8**, write > or < for each ◯.

1. 1,400 ◯ 1,004

2. 3,070 ◯ 3,700

3. 16,050 ◯ 16,005

4. 22,040 ◯ 22,400

5. 100,040 ◯ 104,000

6. 6,010 ◯ 6,001

7. 9,090 ◯ 9,009

8. 21,910 ◯ 21,091

For Exercises **9** through **16**, order the numbers from greatest to least.

9. 1,002 1,020 1,200

____

10. 4,400 4,004 4,040

____

11. 7,101 7,110 7,011

____

12. 1,040 1,400 1,004

____

13. 13,007 31,700 13,700 13,070

____

14. 19,800 91,008 91,080 91,800

____

15. 80,050 80,005 80,500 85,000

____

16. 12,045 12,450 12,405 14,205

____

17. Jamie is playing a computer game. Her scores were 105,011, 110,501, and 105,110. What was her highest score?

____

18. Which number below is **NOT** between 43,050 and 45,300?

A 45,030 **B** 45,003 **C** 43,500 **D** 43,005

19. **Writing to Explain** Dennis said 901,100 is greater than 910,001 because 100 is greater than 1. Is he correct?

____

Name ____________________

Reteaching
1-5

Make an Organized List

Brian has four passes to a theme park. He could take himself and three friends. The group of friends for him to choose from includes Art, Ned, Jeff, and Belinda. How many different combinations are possible?

Read and Understand

Step 1: What do you know?

There are four friends: Art, Ned, Jeff, and Belinda.

Step 2: What are you trying to find?

Find out how many different combinations of friends Brian can take.

Plan and Solve

Step 3: What strategy will you use?

Strategy: Make an organized list

Answer: There are four combinations.

Brian, Art, Ned, Jeff, and Belinda. Brian has to be in each combination.

List the choices:

Brian, Art, Ned, Belinda
Brian, Art, Ned, Jeff
Brian, Art, Jeff, Belinda
Brian, Ned, Jeff, Belinda

Look Back and Check

Is your work correct?

Yes, because each combination uses Brian. The way the list is organized shows that all ways were found.

Finish solving the problem.

1. Ann, Mara, Jenny, Tina, and Sue are sisters. Two of the five sisters must help their father at his business each Saturday. How many combinations of two sisters are possible?

____

____

____

Ann	Mara	Jenny	Tina
Ann	Jenny		

Name ____________________

Practice

1-5

Make an Organized List

Make an organized list to solve each problem. Write each answer in a complete sentence.

1. Tonya and Lauren are designing a soccer uniform. They want to use two colors on the shirt. Their choices are green, orange, yellow, purple, blue, and silver. How many ways can they choose two colors?

2. Yancey collects plastic banks. He has three different banks: a pig, a cow, and a horse. How many ways can Yancey arrange his banks on a shelf?

3. Kevin has a rabbit, a ferret, a gerbil, and a turtle. He feeds them in a different order each day. In how many different orders can Kevin feed his pets?

Name ___________________________

Reteaching **2-1**

Understanding Rounding

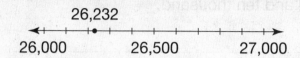

26,232

26,000 26,500 27,000

You can round by using a number line or place value. On a number line, tell if 26,232 is closer to 26,000 or 27,000.

Using place value, find the rounding place and look at the digit to the right of it. If that digit is 5 or more, you round up; if it is less than 5, you round down.

Example 1
To round 26,987 to the nearest thousandth, look at the number to the right of the thousandths place. It is 9, so 26,987 rounds up to 27,000.

Round each number to the nearest hundredth and the nearest thousand.

1. 23,315 ___________________________

2. 63,756 ___________________________

3. 556,299 ___________________________

4. 5,673,356 ___________________________

5. 8,945,457 ___________________________

Round each number to the place of the underlined digit.

6. 4,<u>3</u>45 ____________ **7.** 34,<u>6</u>78 ____________

8. 7<u>8</u>,911 ____________ **9.** 6<u>5</u>6,890 ____________

10. 3,456,9<u>8</u>7 ____________ **11.** 3<u>4</u>5,175 ____________

12. Number Sense Write three numbers that round to 3,000 when rounded to the nearest thousand.

____

Name ______________________

Practice

2-1

Understanding Rounding

Round each number to the nearest thousand and ten thousand.

1. 68,354 ______________________

2. 857,836 ______________________

3. 6,172,438 ______________________

Round each number to the nearest hundred thousand.

4. 782,954 ______________________

5. 5,416,755 ______________________

6. Round the height of Mount Cameroon to the nearest thousand.

____

7. Round the height of Mount Kilimanjaro to the nearest ten thousand.

____

African Mountains

Mountain	Height (in feet)
Mount Kilimanjaro	19,340
Mount Cameroon	13,435
Mount Kenya	17,058
Mount Meru	14,979

8. Which is 346,759 rounded to the nearest ten thousand?

A 300,000 **B** 346,000 **C** 350,000 **D** 400,000

9. Writing to Explain Explain how you would round 265,588 to the nearest ten thousand.

____

____

Name ___________________________

Reteaching

2-2

Rounding Whole Numbers

Round 8,742,883 to the nearest million.

You can use place value or a number line to help you round numbers. On the number line below, 8,742,883 is between 8,000,000 and 9,000,000. The halfway number is 8,500,000.

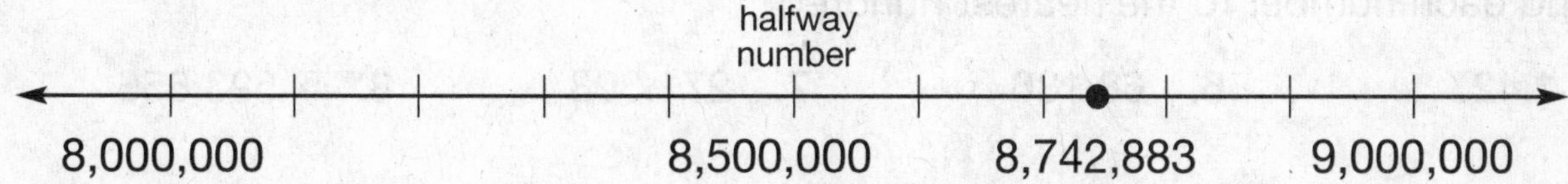

8,742,883 is closer to 9,000,000 than to 8,000,000.

Therefore, 8,742,883 rounds up to 9,000,000.

When the number you want to round is greater than or equal to the halfway number, round up.

Round to the nearest hundred thousand. Draw a number line on a separate sheet of paper to help you.

1. 387,422 ______________

2. 3,124,607 ______________

3. 1,111,022 ______________

Round to the nearest million. Use place value to help you.

4. 27,643,087 ______________

5. 14,117,362 ______________

6. 5,500,000 ______________

Name ______________________

Practice

2-2

Rounding Whole Numbers

Round each number to the nearest ten.

1. 16,326 ________ **2.** 412,825 ________ **3.** 6,512,162 ________ **4.** 42,084,097 ________

Round each number to the nearest hundred.

5. 1,427 ________ **6.** 68,136 ________ **7.** 271,308 ________ **8.** 7,593,656 ________

Round each number to the nearest thousand.

9. 18,366 ________ **10.** 409,614 ________ **11.** 48,229,930 ________ **12.** 694,563,239 ________

Round each number to the underlined place.

13. 12,$\underline{1}$08 ________ **14.** $\underline{5}$70,274 ________ **15.** 9,$\underline{3}$33,625 ________ **16.** 5$\underline{3}$4,307,164 ________

17. What is 681,542 rounded to the nearest hundred thousand?

A 600,000 **B** 680,000 **C** 700,000 **D** 780,000

18. Writing to Explain Mrs. Kennedy is buying pencils for each of 315 students at Hamilton Elementary. The pencils are sold in boxes of tens. How can she use rounding to decide how many pencils to buy?

____

____

____

Name ________________________

Reteaching **2-3**

Using Mental Math to Add or Subtract

There are different strategies for adding and subtracting with mental math.

Addition Strategies

With breaking apart you can add numbers in any order.

235 + 158	Break apart 158. 158 = 5 + 153
235 + 5 = 240	Add one part to make a ten.
240 + 153 = 393	Add the other part.

With compensation you can add or subtract to make tens.

235 + 158	Add 2 to make a ten. 158 + 2 = 160
235 + 160 = 395	
395 − 2 = 393	Subtract 2 from the answer because 2 was added earlier.

Subtraction Strategies

Using compensation

162 − 48	Add 2 to make 50.
162 − 50 = 112	2 + 48 = 50
112 + 2 = 114	Since you subtracted 2 too many, add 2 to the answer.

Using counting on

400 − 185	Add 5 to make 190. 185 + 5 = 190
190 + 10 = 200	Make the next 100.
200 + 200 = 400	Add 200 to make 400.
5 + 10 + 200 = 215	Find the total of what you added.

Add or subtract. Use mental math.

1. 67 + 31 = ______ **2.** 86 − 14 = ______

3. 29 + 43 = ______ **4.** 206 − 78 = ______

5. Reasoning How can you write 72 + (8 + 19) to make it easier to add? ______

Marble Collection	
red	425
blue	375
green	129
yellow	99

Use mental math to solve.

6. How many more blue marbles are there than yellow marbles? ______

7. What is the number of red and green marbles? ______

Name ______________________

Practice
2-3

Using Mental Math to Add or Subtract

Add or subtract. Use mental math.

1. 89 + 46 ______

2. 101 − 49 ______

3. 400 + 157 ______

4. 722 + 158 ______

5. 120 − 33 ______

6. 900 − 187 ______

7. 299 + 206 ______

8. 878 + 534 ______

9. 554 − 59 ______

10. Reasoning How can you write 52 + (8 + 25) to make it easier to add? ______

11. Selena's family went on a trip. The total hotel bill was $659. The cost of the airfare was $633. Use mental math to find the total cost for the hotel and the airfare. ______

12. One year 76 people helped at the town cleanup. The next year 302 people helped. How many more people helped in the second year? Use mental math to find the answer. ______

13. Stanley wants to collect 900 sports cards. So far, he has collected 428 baseball cards and 217 football cards. How many more cards does Stanley need to complete his collection?

A 255 **B** 472 **C** 645 **D** 683

14. Writing to Explain Explain how you could add 678 + 303 using mental math.

______

______

______

Name ______________________

Reteaching
2-4

Estimating Sums and Differences of Whole Numbers

Rounding can be used to estimate sums and differences.

To estimate 1,436 + 422:

Rounding

1,436 rounds to 1,400
422 rounds to 400
1,400 + 400 = 1,800

To estimate 3,635 − 1,498:

Rounding

3,635 rounds to 3,600
1,498 rounds to 1,500
3,600 − 1,500 = 2,100

Estimate each sum or difference.

1. 265 + 426

2. 348 + 122

3. 562 − 223

4. 824 − 590

5. 2,189 + 388

6. 1,329 + 5,345

7. 877 − 475

8. 9,245 − 4,033

9. 788 + 212 = ____________

10. 9,769 − 4,879 = ____________

11. 65,328 − 14,231 = ____________

12. 32,910 + 4,085 = ____________

13. **Number Sense** Is 976 − 522 more or less than 400? Explain how you can tell without actually subtracting.

____

14. The fourth-graders are helping raise money for the local animal shelter. They hoped to raise $1,000. So far they have made $465 in bake sales and $710 in T-shirt sales. About how much more than $1,000 have they raised? ____________

Name ______________________

Practice

2-4

Estimating Sums and Differences of Whole Numbers

Estimate each sum or difference.

1. 627 + 95

2. 829 − 292

3. 987 − 233

4. 1,568 + 352

5. 4,263 − 1,613 ______

6. 7,502 + 2,187 ______

7. 24,141 − 2,177

8. 64,099 − 55,555

9. 83,595 + 18,999

______ ______ ______

10. About how much larger is the largest ocean than the smallest ocean?

______

Ocean Area	
Ocean	**Area (million sq km)**
Arctic Ocean	13,986
Atlantic Ocean	82,217
Indian Ocean	73,481
Pacific Ocean	165,384

11. About how many million square kilometers do all the oceans together cover?

______

12. Mallory is a pilot. Last week she flew the following round trips in miles: 2,020; 1,358; 952; 2,258; and 1,888. Which of the following is a good estimate of the miles Mallory flew last week?

A 6,000 mi **B** 6,800 mi **C** 7,600 mi **D** 8,600 mi

13. Writing to Explain Explain how you would estimate to subtract 189 from 643.

______

______

Name ______________________

Reteaching

2-5

Problem Solving: Missing or Extra Information

Some problems contain too much or too little information. If a problem has missing information, you cannot solve it. If a problem has extra information, you need to figure out what information is needed to solve the problem.

Step 1: Read and Understand

Mark has $40. Nora has $45. How much money will Mark have left if he buys a CD for $15?

To solve this problem, you need to find out how much money Mark will have left over after he buys a CD.

Step 2: Plan and Solve

Decide which information you need to solve the problem and what is extra information.

You need to know how much money Mark has and how much the CD costs. You do not need to know how much money Nora has. Then, subtract the amount of money Mark spent on the CD from the amount of money he had.

$40 - 15 = 25$

Mark has $25 left.

Larissa volunteers at a wildlife group. One of her jobs is to photocopy a flier and give copies to her friends and neighbors. Last month Larissa made 45 copies. There were 15 colored and 30 in black and white. This month Larissa made 75 copies.

1. Do you have enough information to find out how many copies Larissa made in the last 2 months? Explain.

____

____

2. In order to raise money for the National Pet Association, Karl plans to sell bags of pet treats. He will fill 100 bags of treats. He made bags of treats for cats and bags of treats for dogs. How many dog treats did Karl use?

   What information did you not use to solve this problem?

____

3. Do you have enough information to find out how many bags of dog treats Karl made?

____

____

Name ______________________

Practice **2-5**

Problem Solving: Missing or Extra Information

For **1** through **4**, decide if each problem has extra information or not enough information. Tell any information that is not needed or that is missing. Solve if you have enough information.

1. Kendall pitches for his school's baseball team. Kendall pitches every game, and he averages 5 strikeouts per game. Each game lasts about 2 hours long. If Kendall pitches in 7 games during the season how many strikeouts will he have?

____

2. **Geometry** Yolanda is putting up a fence for her dog in the shape of a square. Each foot of fencing costs $7. If Yolanda is planning to have each side of the fence be 10 feet long how many feet of fencing will Yolanda need?

____

3. Gretchen sings and plays guitar in a band after school. If Gretchen sings half of the songs the band knows, how many songs does the band know?

____

4. A store is selling printer paper for $3.25 per package. How much does it cost to buy a box of construction paper if there are 10 packages in a box?

____

5. What do you need to know if you're trying to find the year George Washington was born and you know he died in 1799?

A The current year

B The exact date he died

C How old he was when he died

D There is enough information

6. **Writing to Explain** If you wanted to write a word problem about how much money the fourth-grade class collected at their bake sale, what information would you need to include?

____

Name ______________________________

Adding Whole Numbers

You can add more than two numbers when you line up the numbers by place value and add one place at a time.

Add 3,456 + 139 + 5,547.

Estimate: 3,000 + 100 + 6,000 = 9,100

Step 1	Step 2	Step 3
Line up numbers by place value. Add the ones. Regroup if needed.	Add the tens. Regroup if needed.	Add the hundreds, then the thousands. Continue to regroup.
2 (carried) 3,456 139 + 5,547 2 22 becomes 2 tens and 2 ones.	1 2 (carried) 3,456 139 + 5,547 42	1 1 2 (carried) 3,456 139 + 5,547 9,142
	Keep digits in neat columns as you add.	9,142 is close to the estimate of 9,100.

Add.

1. 945 + 124 + 343

2. 2,588 + 373 + 866

3. 12,566 + 8,222 + 5,532

4. 2,955 + 9,017 + 248

5. 16,699 + 3,311 + 32,484

6. 3,881 + 1,735 + 364

7. Number Sense Jill added 450 + 790 + 123 and got 1,163. Is this sum reasonable?

____

____

Name ______________________

Practice
2-6

Adding Whole Numbers

Add.

1. 486 + 875 + 45

2. 4,334 + 4,948 + 890

3. 938 + 1,487 + 8,947

4. 7,226 + 1,587 + 72,984

5. 54,236 + 223 + 7,856

6. 80 + 960 + 4 + 1,986

7. 27,987 + 2,096 + 15,098 + 7,945

8. 8,738 + 5,234 + 836 + 237

9. **Number Sense** Luke added 429 + 699 + 314 and got 950. Is this sum reasonable?

____

10. What is the combined length of the three longest glaciers?

____

World's Longest Glaciers

Glaciers	Length (miles)
Lambert-Fisher Ice Passage	320
Novaya Zemlya	260
Arctic Institute Ice Passage	225
Nimrod-Lennox-King	180

11. What is the total combined length of the four longest glaciers in the world?

____

12. Which is the sum of 3,774 + 8,276 + 102?

A 1,251 **B** 12,152 **C** 13,052 **D** 102,152

13. **Writing to Explain** Leona added 6,641 + 1,482 + 9,879. Should her answer be more than or less than 15,000?

____

Name ______________________

Reteaching 2-7

Subtracting Whole Numbers

Here is how to subtract. Find 7,445 − 1,368

Estimate: 7,000 − 1,000 = 6,000

Step 1	Step 2	Step 3	Step 4
7,445 − 1,368 = 7 (regrouped: 3 15)	7,445 − 1,368 = 77 (regrouped: 3 13 15)	7,445 − 1,368 = 077 (regrouped: 3 13 15)	7,445 − 1,368 = 6,077 (regrouped: 3 13 15)
You cannot subtract 8 ones from 5 ones. You must regroup. Regroup 4 tens as 3 tens and 10 ones. Subtract 8 ones from 15 ones.	You cannot subtract 6 tens from 3 tens. You must regroup. Regroup 4 hundreds as 3 hundreds and 10 tens. Subtract 6 tens from 13 tens.	Subtract 3 hundreds from 3 hundreds.	Subtract 1 thousand from 7 thousand. 6,077 + 1,368 = 7,445 (carries: 1 1) You can check your answer using addition.

Subtract.

1. 624 − 379
2. 759 − 211
3. 814 − 662
4. 391 − 208
5. 4,772 − 1,671
6. 8,335 − 4,188
7. 4,219 − 1,379
8. 5,216 − 2,158

9. **Estimation** Carlos has 2,175 marbles. Emily has 1,833 marbles. Carlos says that he has about 1,000 more marbles than Emily. Is Carlos correct? Explain your answer.

____

____

____

Name ______________________

Practice 2-7

Subtracting Whole Numbers

Subtract.

1. 7,242 − 158

2. 520 − 203

3. 848 − 257

4. 6,797 − 1,298

5. 753 − 218

6. 7,392 − 4,597

7. 3,898 − 1,299

8. 3,721 − 459

9. Which of the following best describes the answer to the subtraction problem? 3,775 − 1,831

A The answer is less than 1,000.

B The answer is about 1,000.

C The answer is greater than 1,000.

D You cannot tell from the information given.

10. **Writing to Explain** The Environmental Club's goal is to collect 1,525 cans by the end of the summer. The number of cans they collected each week is shown in the table below. How can you find the number of cans they need to collect in week 4 to meet their goal?

Week Number	Number of cans collected
1	378
2	521
3	339
4	

____

____

Name ______________________________

Reteaching **2-8**

Subtracting Across Zeros

Here is how to subtract across zeros.

Find 606 − 377.

Estimate: 600 − 400 = 200

Step 1	Step 2	Step 3	Step 4
606 − 377	5 10 ~~60~~6 − 377	9 5 ~~10~~ 16 ~~606~~ − 377	9 5 ~~10~~ 16 ~~606~~ − 377 229
You cannot subtract 7 ones from 6 ones, so you must regroup.	Since there is a zero in the tens place, you must regroup using the hundreds. Regroup 6 hundreds as 5 hundreds and 10 tens.	Regroup 10 tens and 6 ones as 9 tens and 16 ones.	Subtract. 1 1 229 + 377 606 You can check your answer by using addition.

Subtract.

1. 707 − 58

2. 950 − 47

3. 800 − 638

4. 3,506 − 866

5. 4,507 − 3,569

6. 3,076 − 1,466

7. 8,106 − 2,999

8. 6,083 − 1,492

9. Reasonableness Lexi subtracts 9,405 from 11,138. Should her answer be greater than or less than 2,000? Explain your answer.

____

____

Name ______________________

Practice 2-8

Subtracting Across Zeros

Subtract.

1. 906 − 45

2. 3,091 − 1,361

3. 4,000 − 2,557

4. 800 − 139

5. 1,070 − 593

6. 8,904 − 3,596

7. 3,007 − 2,366

8. 523 − 203

9. 7,403 − 3,254 ______

10. 5,067 − 2,987 ______

11. 6,790 − 1,298 ______

12. Robert set a goal to swim 1,000 laps in a swimming pool during his summer break. Robert has finished 642 laps. How many more laps does he have to swim in order to meet his goal?

A 332 **B** 358 **C** 468 **D** 472

13. Writing to Explain If 604 − 72 = ______, then 532 + ______ = 604. Explain the process of checking your work.

____

____

____

____

Name ______________________

Reteaching

2-9

Draw a Picture and Write an Equation

Read the question and follow the steps to develop a problem-solving strategy.

In the morning, a grocery store had 28 apples on display. By the end of the day, 11 apples had been purchased. How many apples were left?

Step 1: Read/Understand

- Find the information you are given. [There were 28 apples; now there are 11 fewer apples.]
- Find the information you need to figure out. [The number of apples that are left]

Step 2: Plan

- Draw a picture that helps you visualize the problem you are trying to solve.

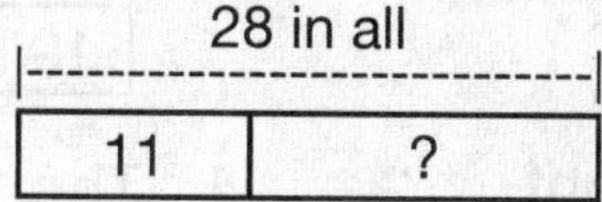

Step 3: Solve

- Figure out which operation you need to use to solve the problem, and write an equation. [Subtraction; 28 − 11 = ?]
- Solve the equation to answer the problem. [28 − 11 = 17; 17 apples were left.]

1. Erika put 12 flakes of fish food in her fish tank before school, and 13 more when she got home. How many flakes did she put in the tank? Use the steps below. ______

Step 1:

- What information are you given?

______

- What information do you need to figure out?

______

Step 2:

- Draw a picture.

Step 3:

- Choose an operation and write an equation.

______

- Solve the equation.

______

Solve the following problems. Draw pictures to help you.

2. Roy is reading a book that is 68 pages. He has read 24 pages so far. How many more pages does he have to read to finish the book? ______

3. There are 29 students in the school band. During practice, 6 new students joined the band. How many students are in the band now? ______

4. Jaycee's teacher gave her a box of 96 pens. She gave 17 of the pens to her classmates. How many pens were left in the box? ______

Name ______________________

Practice
2-9

Draw a Picture and Write an Equation

For **1–4** write an equation and solve. Use the picture to help you.

1. A remote control car has a speed of 5 feet per second. How many feet will the car travel in 6 seconds?

____

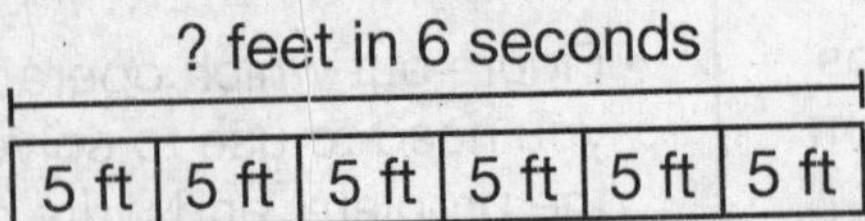

2. Danny has 45 minutes to take a math test. If Danny finishes half the test in 19 minutes, how many minutes does he have left to finish it?

____

45 minutes

19 minutes	? minutes left

3. While shopping, Janet bought a shirt for $8, a pair of jeans for $22, mittens for $5, and a hat for $10. How much money did Janet spend?

____

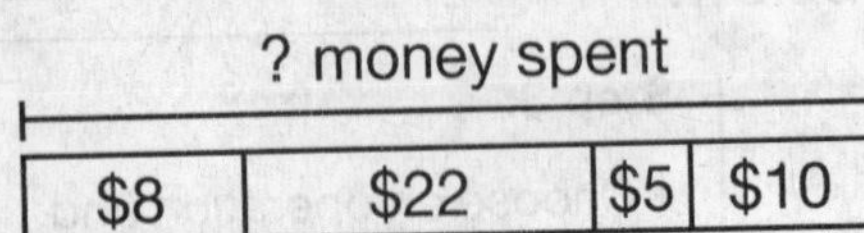

4. The 175th anniversary of the completion of the Erie Canal was in the year 2000. If it took 8 years to dig the Canal, in what year did the digging of the Erie Canal begin?

____

Year 2000

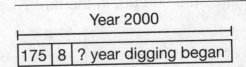

175	8	? year digging began

5. The average length of a song on a certain CD is 3 minutes. The CD has 12 songs. Write an equation for the length of the whole CD. Draw a picture to help you.

A 12×3 **B** $12 + 3$ **C** $12 \div 3$ **D** $12 - 3$

6. Writing to Explain It takes Jinny 56 minutes to drive to her friend's house. She drove 15 minutes and then stopped at a store. She then drove another 10 minutes. What do you need to do to find the amount of time she has left to drive?

____

____

____

Name ______________________

Reteaching **3-1**

Meanings for Multiplication

Addition sentence:

5 + 5 + 5 + 5 = 20

Multiplication sentence:

4 × 5 = 20

There are 4 rows of 5.

There are 3 boxes. There are 7 books in each box.

There are 3 groups of 7.

Addition sentence:

7 + 7 + 7 = 21

Multiplication sentence:

3 × 7 = 21

Write an addition sentence and a multiplication sentence for each picture.

1.

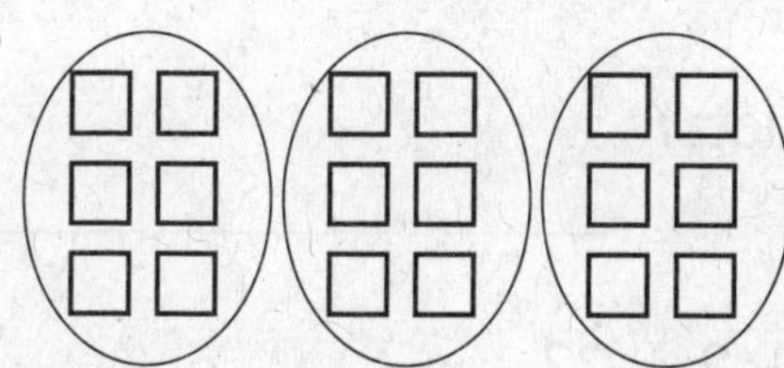

____

2.

____

Write a multiplication sentence for each addition sentence.

3. 10 + 10 + 10 + 10 = 40 ______________________

4. 3 + 3 + 3 + 3 + 3 + 3 = 18 ______________________

5. **Number Sense** Explain how multiplication can help you find 7 + 7 + 7.

____

Name ______________________

Practice
3-1

Meanings for Multiplication

Write an addition sentence and a multiplication sentence for the picture.

1. 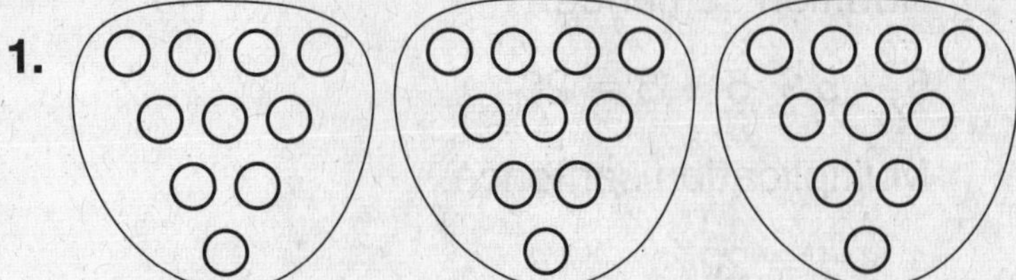
____
____

Write a multiplication sentence for each addition sentence.

2. 4 + 4 + 4 + 4 = 16 ______________

3. 10 + 10 + 10 + 10 + 10 + 10 = 60 ______________

4. **Number Sense** How could you use multiplication to find 7 + 7 + 7?

____

5. A classroom desk has 4 legs. How many legs do 5 desks have altogether? ______________

6. Danielle planted 3 seeds in each of 6 different pots. How many seeds did she plant? ______________

7. Which is the multiplication sentence for 2 + 2 + 2 + 2?

A $4 \times 4 = 16$

B $2 \times 2 = 4$

C $4 \times 2 = 8$

D $2 \times 6 = 12$

8. **Writing to Explain** Explain how you can use multiplication to find 2 + 2 + 2 + 2.

____

____

____

Name ______________________

Patterns for Facts

Reteaching
3-2

Pattern		**Example**
All multiples of two are even numbers.		2, 18, 44
All multiples of 5 end in 0 or 5.		25, 100, 220
For all multiples of nine, the sum of the digits is always a multiple of 9.	27 $2 + 7 = 9$ 63 $6 + 3 = 9$	

1. 9×5 = ____

2. 2×8 = ____

3. 5×8 = ____

4. 9×4 = ____

5. 9×3 = ____

6. 2×7 = ____

7. 5×3 = ____

8. 5×6 = ____

9. 9×2 = ____

10. 5×7 = ____

11. 6×3 = ____

12. 2×6 = ____

Item	Number in Package
Baseball cards	5
Stickers	2
Coupons	9

13. How many baseball cards are in 4 packages?

____

14. How many stickers do you get if you buy 9 packages?

____

15. How many coupons do you get if you buy 7 packages?

____

Name ____________________

Practice
3-2

Patterns for Facts

1. 5×4

2. 2×3

3. 9×7

4. 5×2

5. 8×2

6. 5×3

7. 9×8

8. 9×4

9. $9 \times 6 =$ _____

10. $2 \times 7 =$ _____

11. $5 \times 5 =$ _____

Algebra Find the missing number.

12. _____ $\times 9 = 45$

13. $2 \times$ _____ $= 14$

14. A package of baseball cards includes 5 cards. How many baseball cards are in 5 packages?

____

15. What is the value of the missing number?
$9 \times \square = 36$

A 6 **B** 4 **C** 3 **D** 2

16. Writing to Explain Milton needs to find the product of two numbers. One of the numbers is 9. The answer also needs to be 9. How will he solve this problem? Explain.

____

____

____

Name ______________________

Reteaching 3-3

Multiplication Properties

You can use the Properties of Multiplication to help you find products.

Commutative Property of Multiplication

You can multiply any two numbers in any order.

$2 \times 3 = 3 \times 2$

Identity Property of Multiplication

When you multiply any number by 1, the product is that number.

$7 \times 1 = 7$

Zero Property of Multiplication

When you multiply any number by 0, the product is also 0.

$3 \times 0 = 0$

1. $7 \times 3 = 3 \times$ ______

2. $4 \times 0 =$ ______

3. $5 \times 4 = 4 \times$ ______

4. $2 \times 1 =$ ______

5. $0 \times 7 =$ ______

6. $8 \times 3 = 3 \times$ ______

7. $9 \times 1 = 1 \times$ ______

8. $1 \times 5 =$ ______

9. Number Sense How do you know that $35 \times 5 = 5 \times 35$ without finding products?

____

____

____

10. Writing to Explain Explain how you know that in ? × 6,273 = 6,273, the ? will be 1.

____

Name ______________________

Practice 3-3

Multiplication Properties

1. $\begin{array}{r} 0 \\ \times\ 4 \\ \hline \end{array}$

2. $\begin{array}{r} 1 \\ \times\ 3 \\ \hline \end{array}$

3. $\begin{array}{r} 7 \\ \times\ 1 \\ \hline \end{array}$

4. $\begin{array}{r} 5 \\ \times\ 0 \\ \hline \end{array}$

5. $\begin{array}{r} 1 \\ \times\ 8 \\ \hline \end{array}$

6. $\begin{array}{r} 3 \\ 0 \\ \hline \end{array}$

7. $\begin{array}{r} 4 \\ \times\ 1 \\ \hline \end{array}$

8. $\begin{array}{r} 6 \\ \times\ 0 \\ \hline \end{array}$

9. $1 \times 1 =$ ______________

10. $9 \times 0 =$ ______________

11. $0 \times 0 =$ ______________

Algebra Find the missing number. Tell which property can help you.

12. ______ $\times 9 = 0$

13. $1 \times$ ______ $= 4$

14. Ray has 4 boxes with 5 pens in each box. Kevin has 5 boxes with 4 pens in each. Who has more pens?

____

15. Which property can help you find the missing number? ______ $\times 9 = 0$

____

16. **Writing to Explain** Milton needs to find the product of two numbers. One of the numbers is 6. The answer also needs to be 6. How will you solve this problem? Explain.

____

____

____

Name ______________________

Reteaching **3-4**

3, 4, 6, 7, and 8 as Factors

You can use breaking apart to help find the product.

Example How many baseball cards do you have if you have 4 packages with 6 cards in each package?

You need to find 4×6.

4 groups of 6 are the same as 4 groups of 3 plus 4 groups of 3.

$4 \times 3 = 12$

$4 \times 3 = 12$

$4 \times 6 = (4 \times 3) + (4 \times 3)$

$= 12 + 12$

$= 24$

You have 24 baseball cards.

Use breaking apart to find each product.

1. $3 \times 5 =$ ______ **2.** $9 \times 4 =$ ______

3. $6 \times 6 =$ ______ **4.** $3 \times 7 =$ ______

5. $5 \times 7 =$ ______ **6.** $8 \times 4 =$ ______

7. $6 \times 7 =$ ______ **8.** $7 \times 8 =$ ______

Compare. Use <, >, or = to fill in each ◯.

9. 7×4 ◯ 7×5 **10.** 6×6 ◯ 3×7

11. 8×3 ◯ 3×8 **12.** 9×5 ◯ 12×3

13. Number Sense Explain how 9×4 can help you find 9×8.

____

____

____

Name ______________________

Practice 3-4

3, 4, 6, 7, and 8 as Factors

For **1** through **8**, fill in each ____ .

1. $3 \times 10 = (2 \times 10) + (1 \times \_\_\_)$

2. $2 \times \_\_\_ = (2 \times 5) + (2 \times 1)$

3. $4 \times 7 = (4 \times \_\_\_) + (4 \times 2)$

4. $11 \times 8 = (11 \times 5) + (11 \times \_\_\_)$

5. $3 \times 6 = (3 \times 1) + (3 \times \_\_\_)$

6. $6 \times 6 = (6 \times \_\_\_) + (6 \times 4)$

7. $7 \times \_\_\_ = (7 \times 4) + (7 \times 3)$

8. $1 \times 8 = (1 \times \_\_\_) + (1 \times 3)$

For **9** through **20**, use breaking apart to find each product.

9. 5×5 ____

10. 3×6 ____

11. 4×2 ____

12. 7×3 ____

13. 7×2 ____

14. 6×6 ____

15. 7×7 ____

16. 6×7 ____

17. 8×3 ____

18. 10×6 ____

19. 6×12 ____

20. 4×6 ____

For **21** through **29**, compare using <, >, or = to fill in each ◯.

21. 3×4 ◯ 6×1

22. 5×8 ◯ 6×7

23. 3×6 ◯ 9×2

24. 8×4 ◯ 7×4

25. 7×5 ◯ 12×3

26. 5×6 ◯ 3×10

27. 1×8 ◯ 2×3

28. 4×5 ◯ 2×10

29. 8×6 ◯ 7×7

30. Candice has placed her seashells into 4 rows with 5 seashells in each row. How many seashells does she have? ____

31. A chessboard has 8 rows and 8 columns. Each row has 4 white squares and 4 black squares. Which expression below would give you the number of black squares on a chessboard?

A 8×8 **B** 8×4 **C** 4×4 **D** $8 + 8$

32. Writing to Explain Using the breaking apart method, what is the best way to multiply 8 by 7?

____

Name ______________________________

Reteaching **3-5**

Look for a Pattern

What pattern do you see?

1 A 2 B 3 C 4 D 5 E 6 F

The numbers alternate with letters of the alphabet, in order. The pattern would continue like this:

7 G 8 H 9 I

What pattern do you see?

A	B	C
1	1	1
2	2	4
3	3	9
4	4	16
5		25

The number in column A is multiplied by the number in column B. Column C is the product.

The last number in column B would be 5.

Look for a pattern. Draw the next two shapes.

1.

Look for a pattern. Write the three missing numbers.

2. 2, 4, 6, 8, ______, ______, ______

3. 2, 7, 12, 17, ______, ______, ______

4. 60, 52, 44, 36, ______, ______, ______

5. 88, 77, 66, 55, ______, ______, ______

Name ______________________

Practice

3-5

Look for a Pattern

Look for a pattern. Draw the next two shapes.

1. 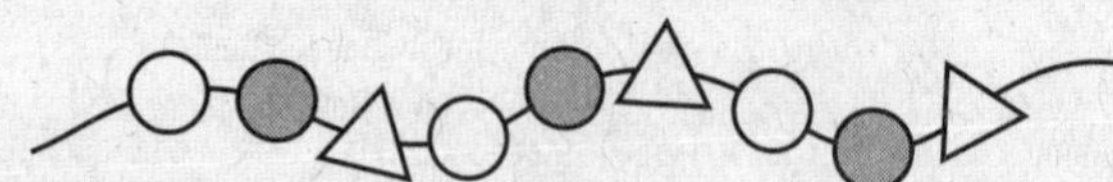

2. 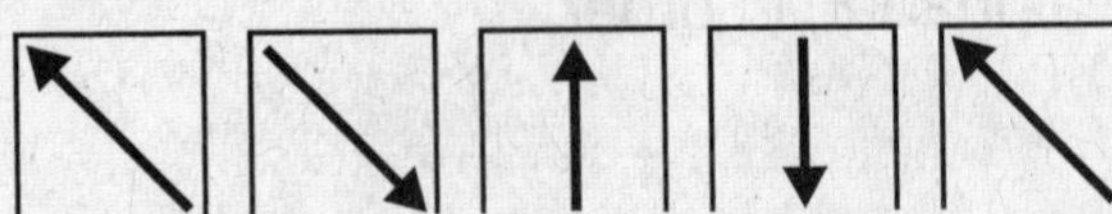

Look for a pattern. Write the missing numbers.

3. 5, 8, 11, 14, 17, ______, ______

4. 4, 6, 10, 16, 24, ______, ______

Look for a pattern. Complete each number sentence.

5. 80 + 8 = 88

808 + 80 = 888

8,008 + 880 = __________

80,808 + 8,080 = __________

6. 10 + 1 = 11

100 + 1 = 101

1,000 + 1 = __________

10,000 + 1 = __________

Look for a pattern. Write the missing numbers.

7. Sally went to purchase tiles for her kitchen floor. She measured the floor to find how many tiles she needed to cover the floor. Sally decided to make a pattern. She chose 10 red tiles, 20 beige tiles, 30 white tiles, ______ black tiles, and ______ gray tiles to complete a pattern for the kitchen floor.

8. Reasoning Fill in the missing amounts to update Carl's savings passbook.

Carl's Savings Account

Date	Deposit	Balance
4/7	$25	$945
4/14		$995
4/21	$25	
4/30	$50	
5/7		$1,095

Name ______________________

Reteaching
3-6

Meanings for Division

When you divide, you separate things into equal groups.

Doris is making 8 box lunches, each with the same number of strawberries. She has a total of 32 strawberries. How many strawberries should go in each lunch?

What you think: Doris will have to place an equal number of strawberries in each box. She must put 32 strawberries into 8 equal groups. How many strawberries are in each group?

What you show: 8 equal groups

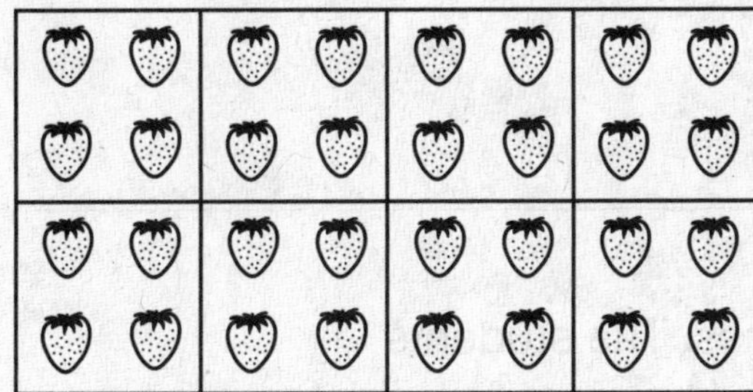

32 strawberries divided into 8 separate groups leaves 4 strawberries in each group.

What you write: $32 \div 8 = 4$

32 is the dividend, the number that is being divided.

8 is the divisor, the number the dividend is being divided by.

4 is the quotient, or the answer to the division problem.

Each lunch should have 4 strawberries.

Draw pictures to solve each problem.

1. You put 15 marbles into 3 groups. How many marbles are in each group?

   ____

2. You need to put 20 ice cubes into 5 glasses. How many cubes should go into each glass?

   ____

Name ____________________

Meanings for Division

Draw pictures to solve each problem.

1. There are 12 small gift bags. Each bag can hold 1 toy and some stickers. There are 36 stickers. If an equal number of stickers is put in each bag, how many stickers will be in each bag?

   ____

2. One egg carton holds 12 eggs. How many cartons are you able to fill with 60 eggs?

   ____

3. There are 21 students in Mr. Tentler's class. The students divided themselves evenly into 3 groups. How many students are in each group?

   ____

4. Calvin read an 18-page chapter in his social studies book in 2 hours. If he read the same number of pages each hour, how many pages did he read per hour?

   A 3 pages **B** 6 pages **C** 9 pages **D** 12 pages

5. **Writing to Explain** A class is planning a party. A pizza restaurant cuts each pizza into 8 slices. There are 32 students. How many pizzas does the class need to order for each student to have a slice? Explain.

   ____

   ____

   ____

Name ______________________________

Reteaching

3-7

Relating Multiplication and Division

Multiplication and division are related, just like addition and subtraction are related.

This is the fact family for 5, 6, and 30:

$5 \times 6 = 30$ $30 \div 6 = 5$

$6 \times 5 = 30$ $30 \div 5 = 6$

Complete each fact family.

1. $2 \times$ = ______10

______ × ______ = 10

10 ÷ 5 = ______

10 ÷ ______ = ______

2. 9 × ______ = 27

______ × ______ = 27

27 ÷ 3 = ______

27 ÷ ______ = ______

3. 8 × ______ = 72

______ × ______ = 72

72 ÷ 8 = ______

72 ÷ ______ = ______

4. 6 × ______ = 48

______ × ______ = 48

48 ÷ 8 = ______

48 ÷ ______ = ______

Write a fact family for each set of numbers.

5. 7, 4, 28

____

6. 5, 8, 40

____

7. Number Sense What multiplication facts are part of the fact family for 12 ÷ 3 = 4?

____

Name ______________________________

Practice

3-7

Relating Multiplication and Division

Complete each fact family.

1. $7 \times$ _____ $= 42$

_____ $\times$ _____ $= 42$

$42 \div 6 =$ _____

$42 \div$ _____ $=$ _____

2. $9 \times$ _____ $= 36$

_____ $\times$ _____ $= 36$

$36 \div 4 =$ _____

$36 \div$ _____ $=$ _____

Write a fact family for each set of numbers.

3. 6, 3, 18

____

4. 5, 5, 25

____

5. Reasoning Why does the fact family for 81 and 9 have only two number sentences?

____

____

____

6. Which number sentence completes the fact family?

$9 \times 6 = 54$ $54 \div 9 = 6$ $54 \div 6 = 9$

A $9 \times 9 = 81$ **B** $6 \times 9 = 54$ **C** $6 \times 6 = 36$ **D** $8 \times 6 = 48$

7. Writing to Explain Find two ways to divide 16 evenly. Explain.

____

____

Name ______________________________

Reteaching **3-8**

Special Quotients

There are special rules for dividing numbers by 1 and by 0.

Rule: A number divided by 1 is that number.

Examples: $4 \div 1 = 4$ $55 \div 1 = 55$

Rule: A number divided by itself (except 0) is 1.

Examples: $17 \div 17 = 1$ $135 \div 135 = 1$

Rule: Zero divided by a number (except 0) is 0.

Examples: $0 \div 4 = 0$ $0 \div 15 = 0$

Rule: You cannot divide a number by zero.

Examples: $7 \div 0$ cannot be done $12 \div 0$ cannot be done

1. $0 \div 2 =$ ______ **2.** $4 \div 4 =$ ______

3. $0 \div 7 =$ ______ **4.** $9 \div 9 =$ ______

5. $0 \div 3 =$ ______ **6.** $10 \div 10 =$ ______

7. $0 \div 11 =$ ______ **8.** $11 \div 1 =$ ______

Compare. Use >, <, or = for each ◯.

9. $6 \div 6$ ◯ $3 \div 3$ **10.** $7 \div 1$ ◯ $8 \div 8$

11. $0 \div 5$ ◯ $3 \div 1$ **12.** $0 \div 4$ ◯ $0 \div 9$

13. $5 \div 5$ ◯ $0 \div 5$ **14.** $7 \div 7$ ◯ $9 \div 9$

15. $8 \div 1$ ◯ $0 \div 8$ **16.** $9 \div 9$ ◯ $9 \div 1$

17. $0 \div 12$ ◯ $12 \div 1$ **18.** $0 \div 11$ ◯ $0 \div 15$

19. **Number Sense** If $a \div 4 = 0$, what do you know about *a*? ______

Name ______________________

Practice

3-8

Special Quotients

1. $0 \div 10 =$ ______ **2.** $7 \div 1 =$ ______ **3.** $8 \div 8 =$ ______

4. $9 \div 9 =$ ______ **5.** $0 \div 5 =$ ______ **6.** $5 \div 1 =$ ______

7. $1\overline{)4}$ ______ **8.** $8\overline{)0}$ ______ **9.** $3\overline{)3}$ ______ **10.** $1\overline{)6}$ ______

11. Number Sense If $x \div 9 = 1$, how do you know what x is? Explain.

____

____

12. Kenneth has 22 math problems to do for homework. He has 12 problems done. How many more problems does he have left? If he completes 1 problem every minute, how many more minutes does he have to work?

____

13. There are 8 people who would like to share a box of granola bars that contains 8 bars. How many granola bars does each person get if they share equally?

____

14. Which is the quotient of $20 \div 20$?

A 20 **B** 2 **C** 1 **D** 0

15. Writing to Explain Write the rule that applies to the following number sentence: $0 \div 7 = 0$.

____

____

____

____

____

Name ______________________

Using Multiplication Facts to Find Division Facts

Tile Floor Darren is laying a tile floor in the hallway. The pattern for the floor is shown to the right.

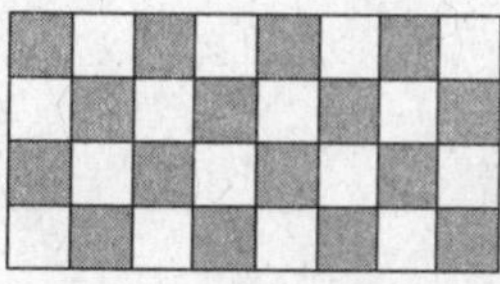

First, use Darren's tile floor to write a multiplication story for $4 \times 8 = 32$.

Darren's tile floor has 4 rows with 8 pieces of tile in each row. How many pieces of tile are there in all?

Second, use Darren's tile floor to write a division story for $32 \div 4 = 8$.

Darren has 32 small triangles. He needs 4 for each shaded square. How many shaded squares can he make with the small triangles?

Use the data in the table to write a multiplication or a division story for each number fact. Solve.

Building Supplies	Number in a Box
Fasteners	6
Bolts	12

1. 6×4

____

____

____

2. $12 \div 4$

____

____

____

Name ______________________________

Using Multiplication Facts to Find Division Facts

Solve.

1. 12 ÷ 3 = ________
2. 20 ÷ 5 = ________
3. 50 ÷ 10 = ________
4. 27 ÷ 9 = ________
5. 6 ÷ 2 = ________
6. 16 ÷ 8 = ________
7. 63 ÷ 9 = ________
8. 36 ÷ 4 = ________
9. 48 ÷ 6 = ________
10. 32 ÷ 8 = ________
11. 25 ÷ 5 = ________
12. 18 ÷ 2 = ________

Use the data in the table to write a multiplication story for the number fact. Solve.

First Aid Kit	
Supply	**Number in Kit**
Bandages	4
Cleanser Pads	6
Cotton Balls	12

13. 2 × 6 =

____

____

____

14. Which is the quotient of 28 ÷ 7?

A 14 **B** 9 **C** 6 **D** 4

15. **Writing to Explain** Write a division story for 12 and 3.

____

____

____

Name ______________________________

Reteaching
3-10

Problem Solving: Draw a Picture and Write an Equation

Read the question and follow the steps to solve.
Bryan has 24 bottles of water. He and his friends have 8 backpacks. If he puts the same number of bottles into each backpack, how many bottles will be in each?

Step 1: Read/Understand

- Find the information the problem gives you. [There are 24 bottles of water and 8 backpacks.]
- Find the information the problem wants you to figure out. [The number of bottles in each backpack]

Step 2: Plan and Solve

- Draw a picture to help you visualize the problem.

24 in all

?	?	?	?	?	?	?	?

- Figure out which operation you need to use. [Division]
- Write an equation. [$24 \div 8 = ?$] Solve. [$? = 3$ bottles]

Step 3: Check

- Check your answer by using the inverse operation. [I used division to solve the problem, so I need to use multiplication to check my answer. If 8 divides into 24 three times, then 8×3 should equal 24. $8 \times 3 = 24$. The answer checks.]

1. **Strategy Practice** Joeli has 10 quarters. She wants to buy postcards to mail to her friends. Each postcard costs 2 quarters. How many postcards can she buy?

- What does the question tell you?

____

- What does the question ask you to find?

____

- Draw a picture. Write an equation. Solve and check.

____

Solve the following problems. Draw a picture to help.

2. Mack has 36 photos. His album can fit 9 photos per page. How many pages will he need to use? ______

3. There are 3 buses taking 96 students on a field trip. If each bus has the same number of students, how many students are on each bus? ______

Name ______________________

Practice
3-10

Problem Solving: Draw a Picture and Write an Equation

Draw pictures to solve each problem.

1. Terrence has 16 trophies and he wants to put an equal number on 4 shelves. How many trophies will he have on each shelf?

____

2. Jody is making a sculpture of her dog. If the sculpture is 6 inches long and her dog is 7 times as long as the sculpture, how long is Jody's dog?

____

3. Lisa has 45 megabytes of space left on her flash drive. She has 5 files that are the same size that will fill up the space. How many megabytes are the files?

____

4. A store is displaying boxes of a new video game in 7 rows. If the store has 49 copies of the game, how many games are in each row?

____

5. Mrs. Lopez is 54 and has a daughter who is six years more than a third of her age. Which expression below shows how old Mrs. Lopez's daughter is?

A $54 + 6 \div 3$ **B** $54 \div 3 + 6$ **C** $54 \div 6 + 3$ **D** $54 + 3 \div 6$

6. **Writing to Explain** Jillian wants to organize her CD collection into wooden crates. Each crate holds 8 CDs. Jillian has 48 CDs. How can she use a picture to figure out how many crates she needs?

____

____

____

Name ____________________

Reteaching **4-1**

Using Patterns to Multiply by Multiples of 10 and 100

Patterns can help you multiply by numbers that are multiples of 10 or 100.

3 × 5 = 15	2 × 4 = 8	5 × 7 = 35
3 × **50** = **150**	2 × **40** = **80**	5 × **70** = **350**
3 × **500** = 1,5**00**	2 × **400** = **800**	5 × **700** = 3,5**00**

To find each of the products above, first complete the basic multiplication fact, then write the same number of zeros seen in the factor that is a multiple of 10. For example:

3 × 500 = 1,500

First find 3 × 5.	**3 × 5 = 15**
Then, count the number of zeros in the multiple of 10.	**500 has 2 zeros.**
Write 2 zeros to form the product.	**1,500**

Find each product. Use mental math.

1. 8 × 80 = ________ **2.** 6 × 60 = ________

3. 7 × 90 = ________ **4.** 5 × 200 = ________

5. 3 × 40 = ________ **6.** 7 × 200 = ________

7. 500 × 6 = ________ **8.** 600 × 9 = ________

9. 3 × 800 = ________ **10.** 600 × 7 = ________

11. **Number Sense** To find 8 × 600, multiply 8 and 6, then write ___ zeros to form the product.

Name ____________________

Practice
4-1

Using Patterns to Multiply by Multiples of 10 and 100

Find each product. Use mental math.

1. 6 × 70 = ________
2. 80 × 2 = ________
3. 40 × 9 = ________
4. 10 × 3 = ________
5. 4 × 500 = ________
6. 300 × 9 = ________
7. 8 × 600 = ________
8. 7 × 400 = ________
9. 6 × 200 = ________
10. 800 × 5 = ________
11. 6 × 800 = ________
12. 400 × 3 = ________

13. **Number Sense** How many zeros will the product of 7 × 500 have? ________

Mr. Young has 30 times as many pencils as Jack. The whole school has 200 times as many pencils as Jack. If Jack has 2 pencils, how many pencils does

14. Mr. Young have?

____

15. the whole school have?

____

16. Find 3 × 100.

A 30 **B** 300 **C** 3,000 **D** 30,000

17. **Writing to Explain** Wendi says that the product of 5 × 400 will have 2 zeros. Is she correct? Explain.

____

____

____

Name ______________________________

Using Mental Math to Multiply

You can multiply mentally by using compatible numbers or breaking apart numbers.

Find 4 × 19 using compatible numbers.

Step 1: Substitute a compatible number for 19 that is easy to multiply by 4.

19 × 4
↓ Add 1 to make 20.
20 × 4

Step 2: Find the new product.

20 × 4 = 80

Step 3: Now adjust. Subtract 1 group of 4.
80 − 4 = 76.

4 × 19 = 76

Find 2 × 76 by breaking apart numbers.

Step 1: Use place value to break apart 76 into 70 and 6.

2 × 76

Step 2: Think of 2 × 76 as 2 × 70 and 2 × 6.

2 × 70 + 2 × 6

140 + 12

Step 3: Add the partial products to get the total.

140 + 12 = 152

2 × 76 = 152

Use mental math to find each product.

1. 5 × 32 = ____________

2. 7 × 53 = ____________

3. 66 × 2 = ____________

4. 92 × 4 = ____________

5. 31 × 8 = ____________

6. 4 × 29 = ____________

7. 18 × 5 = ____________

8. 6 × 49 = ____________

9. 68 × 3 = ____________

10. 4 × 19 = ____________

11. 17 × 5 = ____________

12. 31 × 6 = ____________

13. Algebra In ***a*** × ***b*** = 120, ***a*** is a one-digit number and ***b*** is a two-digit number. What numbers could ***a*** and ***b*** represent?

____

____

Name ______________________

Practice 4-2

Using Mental Math to Multiply

Use compatible numbers to find each product.

1. $34 \times 4 =$ ______ **2.** $53 \times 7 =$ ______ **3.** $41 \times 6 =$ ______

4. $76 \times 5 =$ ______ **5.** $83 \times 3 =$ ______ **6.** $28 \times 8 =$ ______

7. $94 \times 2 =$ ______ **8.** $16 \times 4 =$ ______ **9.** $46 \times 5 =$ ______

Use breaking apart to find each product.

10. $15 \times 6 =$ ______ **11.** $95 \times 4 =$ ______ **12.** $29 \times 6 =$ ______

13. $83 \times 7 =$ ______ **14.** $36 \times 2 =$ ______ **15.** $79 \times 4 =$ ______

16. $42 \times 8 =$ ______ **17.** $17 \times 5 =$ ______ **18.** $86 \times 9 =$ ______

19. **Reasonableness** Quinn used breaking apart to find the product of 37×4. Her answer was 124. What did she do incorrectly?

____

____

____

20. Davidson's Bakery uses 9 dozen eggs to make cookies each day. How many eggs do they use?

A 90 **B** 98 **C** 108 **D** 112

21. **Writing to Explain** Find the product of 53×6. Explain how you found the product.

____

____

____

Name ______________________

Using Rounding to Estimate

You can use rounding to estimate products.

Estimate 7 × 28.

Using **rounding numbers**
Round 28 to 30.
7 × 30
7 × 30 = 210

Estimate each product.

1. 6 × 88 is close to 6 × ______

2. 59 × 4 is close to ______ × 4

3. 7 × 31 ______

4. 38 × 5 ______

5. 21 × 6 ______

6. 3 × 53 ______

7. 5 × 790 ______

8. 488 × 6 ______

9. **Number Sense** Estimate to tell if 5 × 68 is greater than or less than 350. Tell how you decided.

____

____

10. Estimate how many of Part C would be made in 4 months.

____

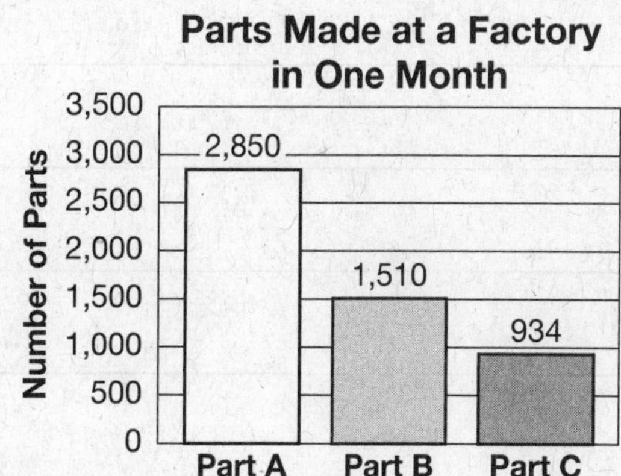

11. Estimate how many of Part B would be made in 3 months.

____

12. Estimate how many of Part A would be made in 9 months.

____

Name ______________________

Practice 4-3

Using Rounding to Estimate

Estimate each product.

1. 38 × 2 ________

2. 7 × 47 ________

3. 54 × 6 ________

4. 121 × 2 ________

5. 548 × 8 ________

6. 823 × 3 ________

7. 7 × 289 ________

8. 183 × 4 ________

9. 2 × 87 ________

10. 673 × 8 ________

The distance between San Francisco, California, and Salt Lake City, Utah, is 752 miles.

11. About how many miles would a car drive if it made 4 trips?

____

12. About how many miles would a car drive if it made 9 trips?

____

13. Vera has 8 boxes of paper clips. Each box has 275 paper clips. About how many paper clips does Vera have?

A 240 **B** 1,600 **C** 2,400 **D** 24,000

14. **Writing to Explain** A wind farm generates 330 kilowatts of electricity each day. About how many kilowatts does the wind farm produce in a week? Explain.

____

____

____

____

Name ____________________

Reteaching
4-4

Using an Expanded Algorithm

You can use arrays of place-value blocks to multiply.

Find the product for 3 × 14.

What You Show	What You Write
3 × 10 = 30 3 × 4 = 12 30 + 12 = 42	14 × 3 12 3 × 4 ones +30 3 × 1 tens 42

Draw an array for each problem to find the partial products and the product. Complete the calculation.

1. 18 × 4

2. 21 × 6

3. 17 × 6

4. 11 × 2

5. 23 × 5

6. 14 × 3

7. Number Sense What two simpler problems can you use to find 9 × 38? (Hint: think about the tens and ones.)

____

Name ________________________________

Practice
4-4

Using an Expanded Algorithm

Use the array to find the partial products. Add the partial products to find the product.

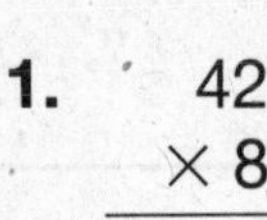

1. $\begin{array}{r} 42 \\ \times\ 8 \\ \hline \end{array}$

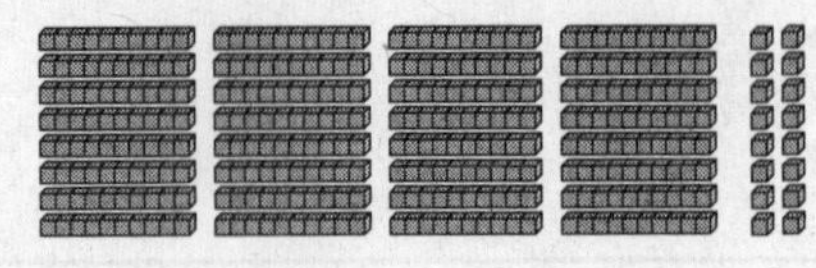

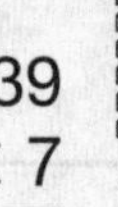

2. $\begin{array}{r} 39 \\ \times\ 7 \\ \hline \end{array}$

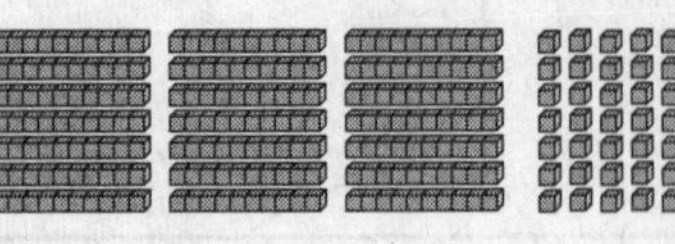

3. $\begin{array}{r} 21 \\ \times\ 4 \\ \hline \end{array}$

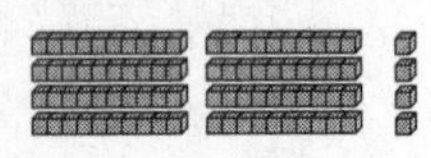

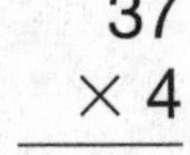

4. $\begin{array}{r} 37 \\ \times\ 4 \\ \hline \end{array}$

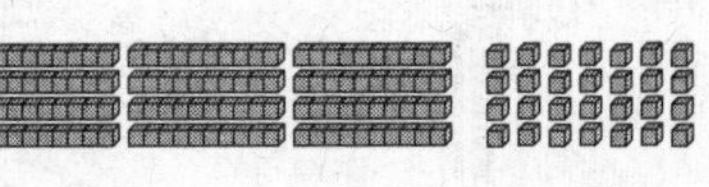

5. 7 × 14 = ______________

6. 3 × 52 = ______________

7. 4 × 42 = ______________

8. 5 × 26 = ______________

9. 6 × 62 = ______________

10. 9 × 76 = ______________

11. Alex can type 72 words per minute. How many words can Alex type in 5 minutes? ______________

12. Find 8 × 44

A 282 **B** 312 **C** 352 **D** 372

13. Writing to Explain Explain how you can use an array to find partial products for 4 × 36.

____

____

____

Name ______________________

Reteaching **4-5**

Multiplying 2-Digit by 1-Digit Numbers

Here is how to multiply a 2-digit number by a one-digit number using paper and pencil.

Find 3 × 24.	What You **Think**	What You **Write**
Step 1 Multiply the ones. Regroup if necessary.	3 × 4 = 12 ones Regroup 12 ones as 1 ten 2 ones.	$\begin{array}{r} {}^{1}\\ 24 \\ \times\ 3 \\ \hline 2 \end{array}$
Step 2 Multiply the tens. Add any extra tens.	3 × 2 tens = 6 tens 6 tens + 1 ten = 7 tens	$\begin{array}{r} {}^{1}\\ 24 \\ \times\ 3 \\ \hline 72 \end{array}$

Is your answer reasonable?

Exact: 3 × 24 = 72

Round 24 to 20.

Estimate: 3 × 20 = 60 Since 72 is close to 60, the answer is reasonable.

Find each product. Decide if your answer is reasonable.

1. $\begin{array}{r} 13 \\ \times\ 3 \\ \hline \end{array}$

2. $\begin{array}{r} 17 \\ \times\ 7 \\ \hline \end{array}$

3. $\begin{array}{r} 24 \\ \times\ 5 \\ \hline \end{array}$

4. $\begin{array}{r} 48 \\ \times\ 8 \\ \hline \end{array}$

5. $\begin{array}{r} 62 \\ \times\ 6 \\ \hline \end{array}$

6. $\begin{array}{r} 36 \\ \times\ 5 \\ \hline \end{array}$

7. $\begin{array}{r} 88 \\ \times\ 5 \\ \hline \end{array}$

8. $\begin{array}{r} 52 \\ \times\ 8 \\ \hline \end{array}$

9. **Estimation** Use estimation to decide which has the greater product: 813 × 6 or 907 × 5. ______________

Name ______________________

Practice **4-5**

Multiplying 2-Digit by 1-Digit Numbers

Find each product. Decide if your answer is reasonable.

1.

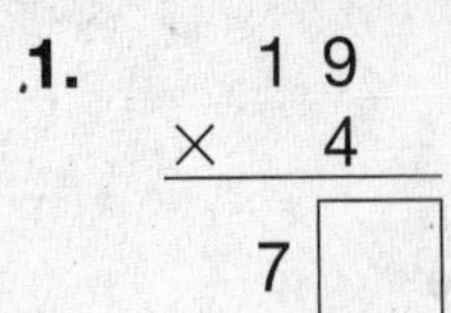

2.

2 3
× 7
☐ 6 ☐

3.

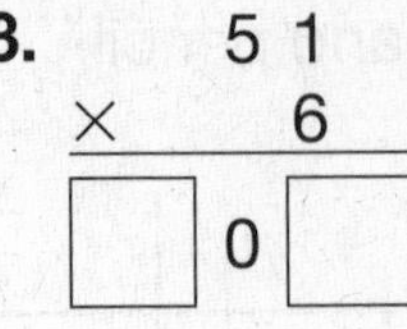

4. 39 × 7

5. 48 × 5

6. 53 × 7

7. 29 × 8

8. 42 × 6 = ______________

9. 89 × 8 = ______________

10. 77 × 9 = ______________

11. 94 × 4 = ______________

12. **Number Sense** Penny says that 4 × 65 = 260. Explain how you would estimate to check the reasonableness of Penny's answer.

____

____

13. A large dump truck uses about 18 gallons of fuel in 1 hour of work. How many gallons of fuel are needed if the truck works for 5 hours? ______________

14. Which of the following is a reasonable estimate for 6 × 82?

A 48 **B** 480 **C** 540 **D** 550

15. **Writing to Explain** Tyrone has 6 times as many marbles as his sister Pam. Pam has 34 marbles. Louis has 202 marbles. Who has more marbles, Tyrone or Louis? Explain how you found your answer.

____

____

Name ____________________

Multiplying 3-Digit by 1-Digit Numbers

Here is how to multiply larger numbers.

	Example A	Example B
Step 1 Multiply the ones. Regroup if necessary.	1 154 x 4 6	2 214 x 7 8
Step 2 Multiply the tens. Add any extra tens. Regroup if necessary.	21 154 x 4 16	2 214 x 7 98
Step 3 Multiply the hundreds. Add any extra hundreds.	21 154 x 4 616	2 214 x 7 1,498

Find each product. Estimate to check reasonableness.

1. 185 × 4

2. 517 × 4

3. 741 × 3

4. 413 × 6

5. 625 × 6

6. 381 × 5

7. 711 × 8

8. 802 × 5

9. Number Sense How could you use the product of 108 and 4 to find the product of 324 and 4?

____

10. A factory can make 241 footballs in 1 week. How many can it make in 9 weeks?

____

Name ______________________

Practice
4-6

Multiplying 3-Digit by 1-Digit Numbers

Find each product. Estimate for reasonableness.

1. 352 × 3

2. 385 × 4

3. 482 × 8

4. 632 × 5

5. 219 × 6

6. 768 × 7

7. 521 × 4

8. 848 × 9

9. 7 × 211 = ______

10. 6 × 517 = ______

If the baseball players in the table score the same number of runs each season, how many runs will

Runs Scored in 2001	
Player	**Runs Scored**
A	128
B	113
C	142

11. Player A score in 5 seasons?

____

12. Player C score in 8 seasons?

____

13. How many bottles of water would Tim sell if he sold 212 bottles each week for 4 weeks?

A 800 **B** 840 **C** 848 **D** 884

14. **Writing to Explain** If you know that 8 × 300 = 2,400, how can you find 8 × 320? Explain.

____

____

____

Name ______________________

Reteaching
4-7

Multiplying Greater Numbers by 1-Digit Numbers

Multiply 1,442 × 6.

Step 1 Multiply the ones. Regroup if you can.	**Step 2** Multiply the tens. Add. Regroup if you can.	**Step 3** Multiply the hundreds. Add. Regroup if you can.	**Step 4** Multiply the thousands. Add.
1 1,442 × 6 2	2 1 1,442 × 6 52	2 2 1 1,442 × 6 652	2 2 1 1,442 × 6 8,652

1. 1,343 × 4

2. 1,489 × 6

3. 9,893 × 6

4. 7,721 × 7

5. 3,563 × 5

6. 36,563 × 7

7. 23,764 × 5

8. 17,687 × 9

9. 3,648 × 6 ________

10. 8,795 × 7 ________

11. 6,998 × 7 ________

12. 22,304 × 3 ________

13. 78,424 × 9 ________

14. 11,542 × 5 ________

15. 37,204 × 4 ________

16. 50,273 × 6 ________

17. 13,455 × 3 ________

18. There are 2,345 passengers on each of 6 cruise ships.

How many passengers are there altogether? ________________

Name ______________________

Practice 4-7

Multiplying Greater Numbers by 1-Digit Numbers

1. $\begin{array}{r} 2,143 \\ \times \quad 5 \\ \hline \end{array}$

2. $\begin{array}{r} 3,121 \\ \times \quad 4 \\ \hline \end{array}$

3. $\begin{array}{r} 11,256 \\ \times \quad 6 \\ \hline \end{array}$

4. $\begin{array}{r} 32,017 \\ \times \quad 7 \\ \hline \end{array}$

5. $\begin{array}{r} 5,502 \\ \times \quad 8 \\ \hline \end{array}$

6. $\begin{array}{r} 87,483 \\ \times \quad 9 \\ \hline \end{array}$

7. $\begin{array}{r} 18,471 \\ \times \quad 6 \\ \hline \end{array}$

8. $\begin{array}{r} 36,572 \\ \times \quad 8 \\ \hline \end{array}$

9. 3,765 × 4 ________

10. 6 × 7,648 ________

11. 5 × 12,264 ________

12. There are 36,200 pencils on each of 4 shelves at the office supply manufacturer's warehouse.

How many pencils are there altogether? ________________

13. Algebra Find the value of 7*n* when *n* is 7,565? ________________

Use the pictograph for Exercises 14 and 15.

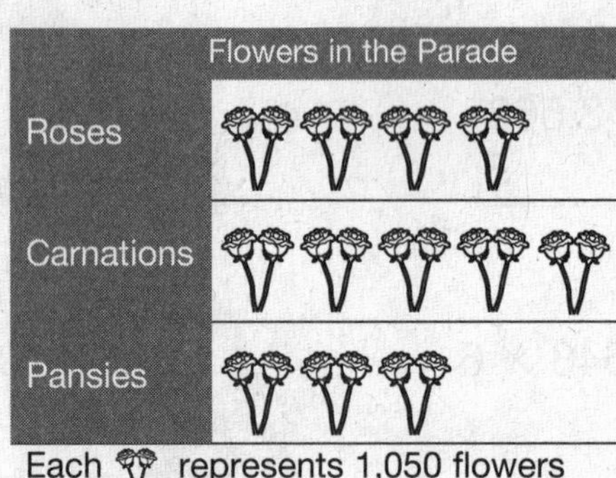

14. How many carnations are on the floats in the parade?

A 3,150 carnations
B 4,200 carnations
C 5,150 carnations
D 5,250 carnations

15. Explain It Karen said there were 4,050 pansies in the parade. Explain her error.

____

____

____

Name ______________________________

Reteaching

4-8

Problem Solving: Reasonableness

After you solve a problem, it is important to check your answer to see whether it is reasonable.

Read and Understand

There are 5 animals on a farm. Each animal eats 105 pounds of food per week. How much food does the farmer have to buy each week?

? pounds of food in all

105	105	105	105	105

Plan and Solve

Multiply to find the answer. $5 \times 105 = 525$

Check for Reasonableness

Ask yourself, "Did I answer the right question?" Estimate to check your answer. $5 \times 100 = 500$. The answer is reasonable because 500 is close to 525.

Solve the following problems. Check your answers for reasonableness.

1. Marisa multiplied 32×60 and got a product of 192. Explain why Marisa's answer is not reasonable.

____

____

____

2. Jaime practiced swimming for 11 hours every week for 8 weeks. How many hours did he practice all summer? How can you check your answer?

____

____

____

Name ______________________

Practice **4-8**

Reasonableness

For Exercises **1** and **2**, use reasonableness to decide if each answer is correct. Explain why the answer is reasonable or not. If the answer is incorrect, give the correct answer.

1. Johan is selling baseball cards for 45¢ apiece. He is selling 8 cards and says he'll make $32.40.

____

____

2. Each of the 23 students in Mr. Small's class read 8 books last month. Mr. Small estimated the total number of books read was between 160 and 230.

____

____

Julia is planting sunflowers. Use the table to the right to solve Exercises **3–5**.

Weeks	Height in inches
1	16
2	32
3	48
4	64
5	

3. How large will the sunflower be after the 5th week?

____

4. How can you use reasonableness to check your answer?

____

5. Viktor divided 63 by 7 and said his answer is 10. Which statement below shows why his answer is not reasonable?

A Viktor subtracted.

B Viktor answered the wrong question.

C Viktor estimated, he didn't solve.

D Viktor is correct.

6. **Writing to Explain** The world's largest sunflower was about 300 inches tall. Julia says her sunflower will be that tall in 10 weeks because after 2 weeks her sunflower was 32 inches and $32 \times 10 = 320$. Is Julia correct? If not what did she do wrong?

____

____

Name ____________________

Reteaching

5-1

Variables and Expressions

How do you use expressions containing variables?

To use an expression with a variable, replace the variable with a value and compute.

Suppose $n = 6$.

Substitute 6 for n.

Then, add.

$36 + n$

$36 + 6 = 42$

You can also use a table.

t	$t - 15$
28	13
41	26
19	4
35	20

$28 - 15 = 13$

$41 - 15 = 26$

Substitute 35 for the expression $t - 15$.

$35 - 15 = 20$.

The missing number is 20.

Copy and complete the table.

	w	$w + 16$
1.	6	$6 + 16 =$
2.	9	$9 + 16 =$
3.	☐	☐ $+ 16 = 30$

4. Number Sense Does the expression $d - 12$ have a greater value when $d = 42$ or when $d = 46$?

Find the missing number in each table.

5.

e	16	22	26	31
$e \times 3$	48	66	78	

6.

g	100	72	56	12
$g \div 2$	50		28	6

Name ____________________

Practice 5-1

Variables and Expressions

Copy and complete the table.

	k	$k \times 7$
1.	5	$5 \times 7 = \square$
2.	9	$9 \times 7 = \square$
3.	11	$\square \times 7 = 77$
4.	13	$\square \times 7 = 91$

Complete the table for each problem.

5.

x	60	72	42	36
$x \div 6$	10	12	7	

6.

b	14	18	23	27
$b + 9$		27	32	36

7.

z	5	8	10	12
$z \times 8$	40		80	96

8.

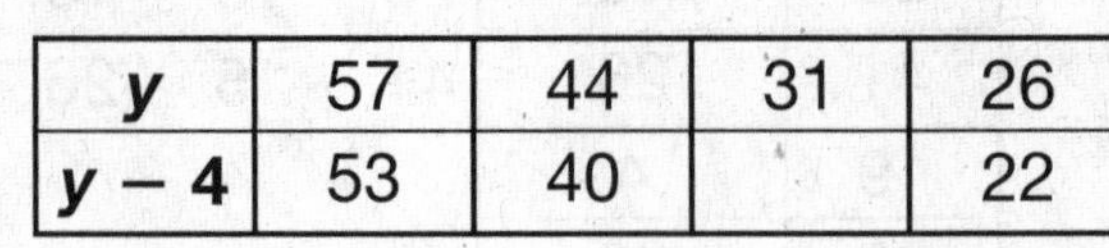

y	57	44	31	26
$y - 4$	53	40		22

9. When $c = 4$, what is the value of the expression $72 \div c$?

A 18 **B** 20 **C** 24 **D** 28

10. Writing to Explain Explain how you could show five less than a number using an expression.

____

____

Name ______________________

Reteaching

5-2

Equality

Equality is important for finding values of expressions.

Example

Marty has a total of 21 books in his collection. He gave x number of books to friends, and received 2 from his teacher. If $x = 3$, how many books does Marty have left on his bookshelf?

Find the value of $21 - x + 2$, when $x = 3$.
$21 - 3 + 2 = 20$, when Marty has 20 books on his bookshelf.

Find the value of each expression if $p = 6$.

1. $3 + p$ ______ **2.** $p - 3$ ______ **3.** $4 + p - 5$ ______

4. $8 - p + 2$ ______ **5.** $p + p - 6$ ______ **6.** $3 + 7 + p$ ______

Find the value of each expression if $k = 4$.

7. $9 + k - 5$ ______ **8.** $k + k - k$ ______ **9.** $k + 7 + 5$ ______

10. $25 + k - 6$ ______ **11.** $k + 45 - 20$ ______ **12.** $73 - k + k$ ______

13. Zach and Alyssa sold raffle tickets for class. Between the two of them they sold n number of tickets. Alyssa sold 36 tickets. How many tickets did Zach sell if $n = 78$? ______________

14. Josh mows lawns in his neighborhood to make money. On Saturday Josh mowed x amount of lawns and on Sunday he mowed $x + 2$. If $x = 3$, how many lawns did Josh cut over the weekend?

____

15. There are 14 basketball games in the season. At the end of the season, the Tigers won k number of games and had one tie. How many games did the Tigers lose if $k = 10$?

____

Name ______________________

Practice

5-2

Equality

In **1** through **9**, find the value of each expression for $z = 4$.

1. $5 + z$ ______ **2.** $z - 4 + 7$ ______ **3.** $z - z$ ______

4. $z + 1 + z$ ______ **5.** $12 - z$ ______ **6.** $10 - 5 + z$ ______

7. $z - z + z$ ______ **8.** $8 - z + z$ ______ **9.** $96 + z$ ______

In **10** through **18**, find the value of each expression for $y = 9$.

10. $y + y - y$ ______ **11.** $y - 0 + 1$ ______ **12.** $y - 4$ ______

13. $y + 14$ ______ **14.** $y + y + 9$ ______ **15.** $15 + y + 15$ ______

16. $y - 6 - 3$ ______ **17.** $y - y + 1$ ______ **18.** $1 + y - 4$ ______

In **19** through **27**, find the value of each expression for $x = 17$.

19. $x - 7$ ______ **20.** $x - 14 + x$ ______ **21.** $x - 9 - 7$ ______

22. $x + 12 + 101$ ______ **23.** $x + x$ ______ **24.** $x + x - x$ ______

25. $x + 3 - 20$ ______ **26.** $x - x$ ______ **27.** $x - x + x$ ______

28. What does $A + B + C$ equal if $A = 6$, $B = 3$, and $B = C$? ______

29. Thomas has q books. His sister Tara has 12 fewer books than he has. Which expression below shows how many books Tara has?

A $q - 12$ **B** $12 - q$ **C** $q + 12$ **D** $12 + q$

30. Writing to Explain Why is the value of $a - 1$ always less than the value of a?

____

Name ______________________

Reteaching 5-3

Expressions with Parentheses

When an expression contains more than two terms and different operations, **parentheses ( )** can be used to show which computation should be done first.

Example

Amy is making necklaces and bracelets and selling them to raise money. Amy raised \$26 selling necklaces and \$14 selling bracelets. She spent \$5 on beads and \$3 on the string. How much money did Amy raise?

Write a number sentence, group the different operations together, and use parentheses to show the two groups.

(14 + 26) − (3 + 5) =

Find the value of the expressions in parentheses first.

40 − 8 Then subtract. 32

Amy raised \$32 selling necklaces and bracelets.

Find the value of each expression.

1. 7 + (7 − 4) ____ **2.** (3 + 6) − 4 ____ **3.** (8 + 4) − (4 + 3) ____

4. 9 + (16 − 5) ____ **5.** (32 − 8) − 14 ____ **6.** (17 + 3) − (4 + 3) ____

7. (34 − 12) + (16 − 5) ____ **8.** 9 − (5 − 4) ____ **9.** (45 − 15) − (13 − 6) ____

Choose where to put parentheses to make each number sentence true.

10. 20 − 5 + 3 = 12 **11.** 14 + 12 − 6 = 20 **12.** 24 − 8 + 13 = 3

13. 15 − 7 + 6 = 14 **14.** 36 − 14 + 7 = 15 **15.** 43 + 12 − 26 = 29

16. Writing to Explain Explain how you would solve this problem: (9 + 14) − (7 + 4).

____

____

____

Name ______________________________

Expressions with Parentheses

For **1** through **16**, find the value of each expression.

1. (6 + 7) − 2 ______

2. 12 − (9 − 7) ______

3. (45 + 1) + 1 ______

4. (15 − 2) + 1 ______

5. 31 + (31 − 7) ______

6. 30 − (13 + 3) ______

7. (11 + 6) − 1 ______

8. 4 + (10 − 5) ______

9. (4 + 10) − 1 ______

10. 40 − (90 − 70) ______

11. 76 + (9 + 7) ______

12. 62 − (9 − 7) ______

13. 17 − (8 − 3) ______

14. 29 − (17 + 1) ______

15. 4 − (99 − 97) ______

16. 3 + (5 − 5) ______

17. Patricia and Rick are planning a hike. Rick can carry 22 pounds in his backpack and Patricia can carry 5 pounds less than Rick. How much weight can they carry together? ______

18. Callie rode her bike 3 miles less than Cory. Cory rode his bike 7 miles less than Katie. Katie rode her bike 14 miles. Which expression shows the number of miles that Callie rode?

A (14 − 7) − 3

B 14 − (7 − 3)

C (14 + 7) − 3

D 14 + (7 − 3)

19. **Writing to Explain** Tony was asked to compare two expressions. He wrote: "10 − (6 − 4) < 10 − (6 + 4) because a minus sign always decreases a number and a plus sign increases a number." Is he correct? Explain your answer.

____

____

____

____

Name ____________________

Reteaching
5-4

Simplifying Expressions

When an expression contains more than one operation, **parentheses ( )** can be used to show which computation should be done. Parentheses are one type of **grouping symbol**.

Do the computation inside the parentheses first.

Evaluate **(**2 + 8**)** × 3.

$10 \times 3 = 30$

Evaluate 2 + **(**8 × 3**)**.

$2 + 24 = 26$

Some expressions contain more than one set of parentheses.

Do the computation inside each pair of parentheses first.

Evaluate **(**4 + 9**)** − **(**30 ÷ 5**)**.

$13 - 6 = 7$

After you solve the computations inside the parentheses, use the order of operations to choose which computation to solve next:

Multiplication

Division

Addition

Subtraction

1. (16 + 4) ÷ 10 ____________

2. (16 ÷ 4) + (10 − 3) ____________

3. 48 ÷ (2 × 3) ____________

4. 27 − (5 × 3) ____________

5. (4 × 6) ÷ 6 + 5 ____________

6. (36 ÷ 6) × 4 ____________

7. Evaluate 11 × (8 − *n*) for *n* = 4. ____________

Name ______________________

Practice **5-4**

Simplifying Expressions

1. $(18 \div 9) + 7$ ________

2. $(4 + 3) \times (9 - 2)$ ________

3. $32 \div (8 + 8)$ ________

4. $(26 - 17) \times (9 \div 3)$ ________

5. $64 \div (5 + 1 + 2)$ ________

6. $27 \div (3 \times 3) + 7$ ________

Rewrite with parentheses to make each sentence true.

7. $42 + 12 \div 6 = 44$ ______________________

8. $33 - 14 + 4 = 15$ ______________________

9. $32 \div 8 \times 2 = 8$ ______________________

Evaluate each expression for $w = 9$.

10. $72 \div (w + 0)$ ________

11. $(12 + w) \div 3$ ________

12. $(0 + w) \times 2$ ________

13. Write an expression to show how much Gretchen paid for drama, action, and comedy videos if she paid $4 each at a sale.

____

Gretchen's Video Purchases	
Mystery	6
Action	3
Comedy	5
Drama	2
Romance	2

14. Which statement is true when $x = 7$?

A $63 \div x = 21$

B $(x - 6) - (1 \times 1) = 1$

C $0 \div x = 7$

D $(2 + 7) \times (12 - x) = 45$

15. **Writing to Explain** Evaluate the expression $7 + (32 \div 16) \times 4 - 6$. What steps did you use to find the answer?

____

____

Name ____________________

Act It Out and Use Logical Reasoning

A class plans a recycling drive to raise funds for the school sports teams. Everyone in the class will collect bottles. The bottles will be either clear, brown, or green. Every collection has some of each color bottle. Mike collected 4 brown bottles, twice as many clear bottles as brown bottles, and 24 bottles in all. How many of each type of bottle did Mike collect?

Use colored cubes to show the objects and solve the problem.

Understand What do you need to find? You need to find how many of each color bottle Mike has in his collection.

Plan How can you solve the problem? You can use objects to show what you know and use reasoning to make conclusions.

Solve There are 4 brown bottles and twice as many clear bottles as brown bottles, so there are 8 clear bottles in Mike's collection. There are 12 brown and clear bottles together and 24 bottles in all. So there has to be 12 green bottles.

1. How many times more green bottles than brown bottles did Mike collect?

____

____

2. Jenny collected:
   16 green bottles
   the same number of clear bottles as brown bottles
   30 bottles in all
   How many of each color bottle did Jenny collect?

____

Name ______________________

Practice **5-5**

Act It Out and Use Logical Reasoning

For **1** through **4**, use logical reasoning to find the amounts of quarters, Q, dimes, D, and nickels N in each collection.

1. Tammy's collection:	**2.** Sara's collection:
$\frac{1}{3}$ as many dimes as nickels 3 more quarters than nickels 17 coins in all Q =___ D =___ N =___	5 quarters Twice as many dimes as quarters 16 coins in all Q =___ D =___ N =___
3. John's collection:	**4.** Stacey's collection:
10 coins in all 2 fewer quarters than dimes 2 quarters Q =___ D =___ N =___	15 coins in all Three times as many nickels as dimes 7 quarters Q =___ D =___ N =___

5. Erin's aquarium has guppies, zebrafish, and goldfish. She has 3 more guppies than zebrafish and she has twice as many zebrafish as goldfish. If she has 23 fish, how many of each type does she have?

____

6. Marco bought bananas, apples, and peaches at the supermarket. He bought twice as many pounds of bananas as apples, he bought 2 pounds more of apples than of peaches, and he bought 3 pounds of peaches. How many total pounds of fruit did he buy?

A 16 pounds

B 18 pounds

C 20 pounds

D 22 pounds

Name ______________________________

Reteaching
6-1

Using Mental Math to Multiply 2-Digit Numbers

You can multiply with mental math by using basic facts and patterns.

Example A: $5 \times 5 = 25$

$5 \times 5\mathbf{0} = 25\mathbf{0}$

The product contains the number of zeros in each factor.

Example B: $5 \times 6 = 30$

$5 \times 6\mathbf{0} = 30\mathbf{0}$

$5\mathbf{0} \times 6\mathbf{0} = 3{,}0\mathbf{00}$

$5\mathbf{0} \times 6\mathbf{00} = 30{,}\mathbf{000}$

When the product of a basic fact includes a zero, such as $5 \times 6 = 30$, that zero is not part of the pattern.

Multiply. Use mental math.

1. $20 \times 20 =$ ______

2. $50 \times 10 =$ ______

3. $40 \times 40 =$ ______

4. $30 \times 80 =$ ______

5. $60 \times 600 =$ ______

6. $50 \times 900 =$ ______

7. $70 \times 300 =$ ______

8. $70 \times 600 =$ ______

9. $40 \times 500 =$ ______

10. Number Sense Tell what numbers go in the blanks.

To find 90×300, multiply ______ and ______ .

Then write ______ zeros at the end.

Name ____________________

Practice 6-1

Using Mental Math to Multiply 2-Digit Numbers

Multiply. Use mental math.

1. 4 × 30 = ________ **2.** 5 × 90 = ________

3. 9 × 200 = ________ **4.** 6 × 500 = ________

5. 3 × 600 = ________ **6.** 0 × 600 = ________

7. 90 × 70 = ________ **8.** 70 × 400 = ________

9. 50 × 800 = ________ **10.** 30 × 800 = ________

11. 90 × 500 = ________ **12.** 30 × 4,000 = ________

13. Number Sense How many zeros are in the product of 60 × 900? Explain how you know.

____

____

Truck A can haul 400 lb in one trip. Truck B can haul 300 lb in one trip.

14. How many pounds can Truck A haul in 9 trips? ________

15. How many pounds can Truck B haul in 50 trips? ________

16. How many pounds can Truck A haul in 70 trips?

A 280 **B** 2,800 **C** 28,000 **D** 280,000

17. Writing to Explain There are 9 players on each basketball team in a league. Explain how you can find the total number of players in the league if there are 30 teams.

____

____

____

Name ______________________

Estimating Products

Estimate 11 × 94.

Using rounding

Round 11 to 10.

Round 94 to 90.

10 × 90 = 900

11 × 94 is about 900.

Using compatible numbers

Replace 11 with 10.

Replace 94 with 100.

10 × 100 = 1,000

11 × 94 is about 1,000.

Use rounding to estimate each product.

1. 62 × 82 ______

2. 59 × 48 ______

3. 74 × 302 ______

4. 47 × 790 ______

5. 498 × 63 ______

6. 687 × 38 ______

7. 18 × 412 ______

8. 385 × 75 ______

9. 62 × 147 ______

Use compatible numbers to estimate each product.

10. 32 × 83 ______

11. 37 × 22 ______

12. 51 × 296 ______

13. 65 × 34 ______

14. 108 × 81 ______

15. 43 × 620 ______

16. 426 × 71 ______

17. 59 × 701 ______

18. 87 × 87 ______

19. **Number Sense** To estimate the product of 37 × 99, Chris multiplied 40 × 100. Tell how you know if this is an underestimate or an overestimate.

____

____

Name ______________________________

Practice 6-2

Estimating Products

Use rounding to estimate each product.

1. 38 × 29 __________ **2.** 71 × 47 __________

3. 54 × 76 __________ **4.** 121 × 62 __________

5. 548 × 28 __________ **6.** 823 × 83 __________

7. 67 × 289 __________ **8.** 183 × 34 __________

Use compatible numbers to estimate each product.

9. 28 × 87 __________ **10.** 673 × 85 __________

11. 54 × 347 __________ **12.** 65 × 724 __________

13. 81 × 643 __________ **14.** 44 × 444 __________

15. 72 × 285 __________ **16.** 61 × 761 __________

17. Vera has 8 boxes of paper clips. Each box has 275 paper clips. About how many paper clips does Vera have?

A 240 **B** 1,600 **C** 2,400 **D** 24,000

18. **Writing to Explain** A wind farm generates 550 kilowatts of electricity each day. About how many kilowatts does the wind farm produce in a week? Explain.

____

____

____

Name ______________________________

Arrays and an Expanded Algorithm

Here is how to find the product of 12 × 24 using an array.

Draw a rectangle 24 units long by 12 units wide.

Divide the rectangle by tens and ones for each factor. Find the number of squares in each smaller square.

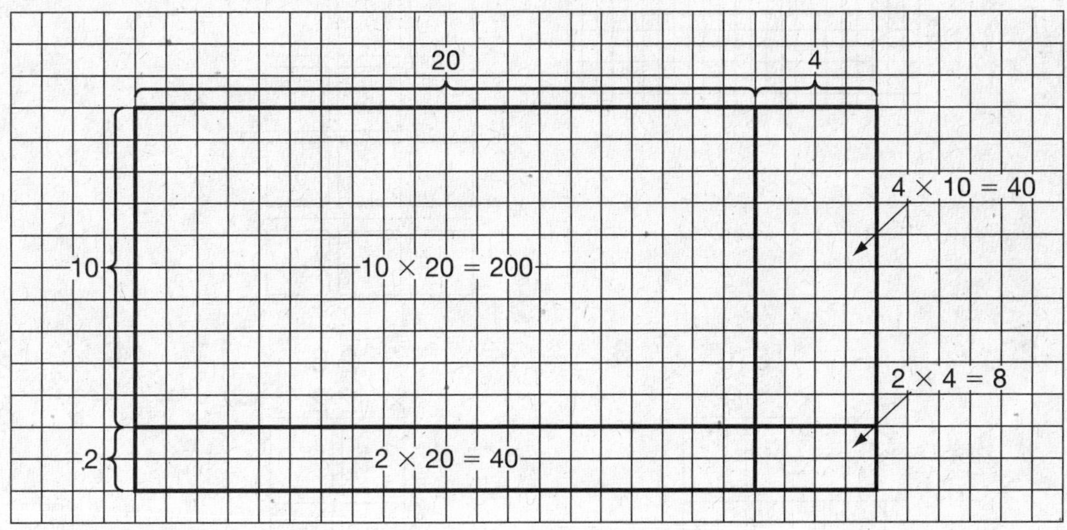

Then add the numbers of the squares in the four rectangles:

200 + 40 + 40 + 8 = 288

So, 12 × 24 = 288.

Divide the rectangle by tens and ones for each factor. Then complete the calculation.

1.

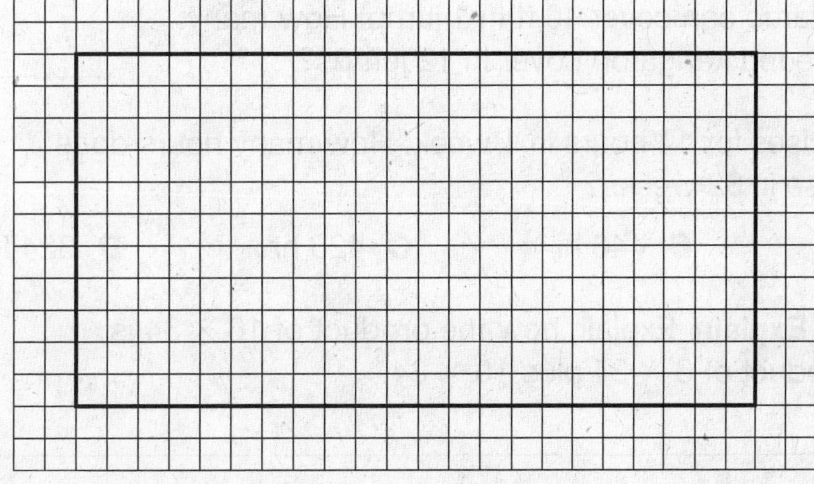

$$\begin{array}{r} 22 \\ \times\ 11 \\ \hline \end{array}$$

Name ______________________

Practice 6-3

Arrays and an Expanded Algorithm

Use the grid to draw a rectangle. Then complete the calculation.

1.

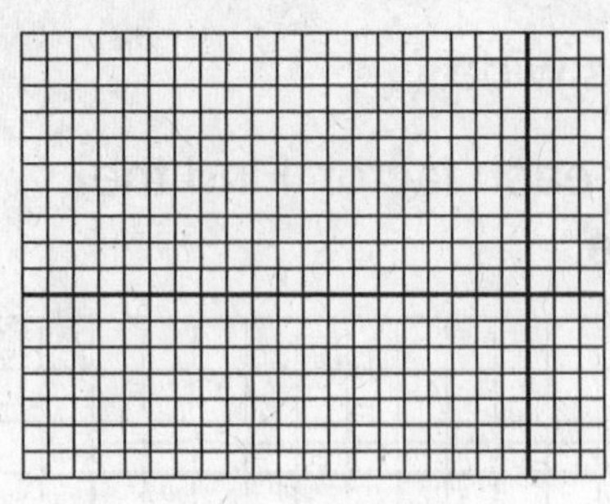

$$\begin{array}{r} 23 \\ \times\ 17 \\ \hline \end{array}$$

2.

$$\begin{array}{r} 31 \\ \times\ 19 \\ \hline \end{array}$$

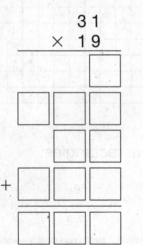

3.

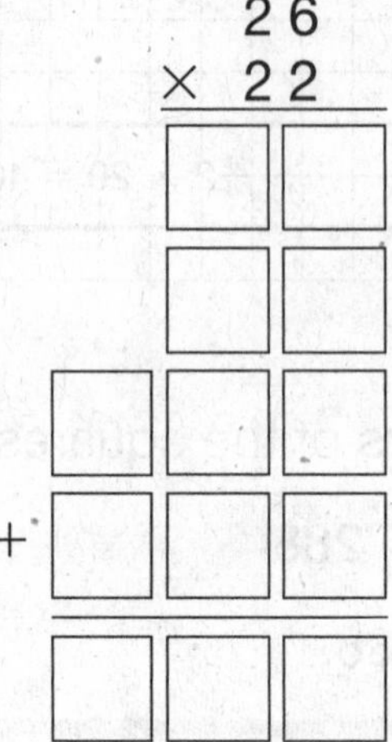

$$\begin{array}{r} 26 \\ \times\ 22 \\ \hline \end{array}$$

4.

$$\begin{array}{r} 33 \\ \times\ 14 \\ \hline \end{array}$$

5. 24 × 57 = ______________

6. 44 × 48 = ______________

7. A red kangaroo can cover 40 ft in 1 jump. How many feet can the red kangaroo cover in 12 jumps? ______________

8. Barb exercises for 14 hours in 1 week. How many hours does she exercise in 32 weeks?

A 496 hr **B** 448 hr **C** 420 hr **D** 324 hr

9. **Writing to Explain** Explain how the product of 16 × 34 is like the product of 6 × 34 plus 10 × 34.

____

Name ______________________________

Multiplying 2-Digit Numbers and Multiples of Ten

To find the product of 60 and 26, you can use breaking apart.

Mark off a section of a grid to show 60 × 26.

Count the number of rows.
Count the number of squares in each row.

There are 60 rows.
There are 26 squares per row.

Draw a line to separate the factor 26 into the tens place and the ones place. Show 26 as 20 + 6.

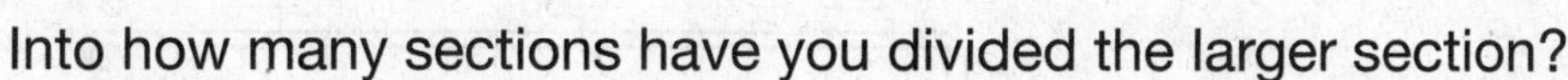

Into how many sections have you divided the larger section?

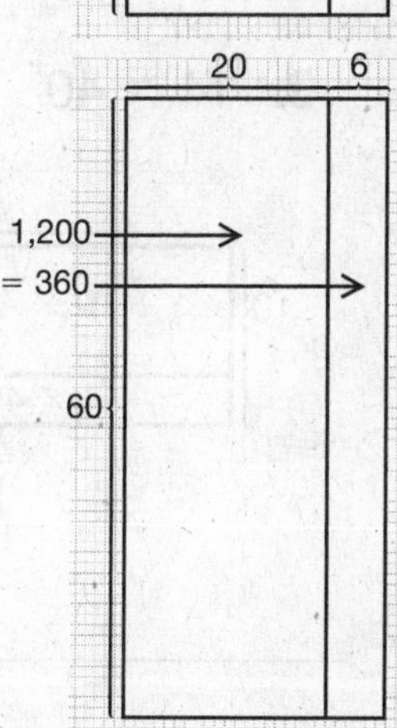

There are 2 sections. Mark one section 60 × 20 and the other section 60 × 6.

Multiply to find the products.

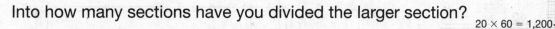

60 rows of 20	1,200	Add.
60 rows of 6	× 360	
	1,560	

Use grid models to break apart each product and solve.

1. 23 × 40 ______________________________
2. 16 × 30 ______________________________
3. 34 × 50 ______________________________
4. 60 × 47 ______________________________
5. 17 × 80 ______________________________
6. 70 × 31 ______________________________

Name ______________________

Practice

6-4

Multiplying 2-Digit Numbers and Multiples of Ten

Use the grid to show the partial products. Multiply to find the product.

1. 23 × 50

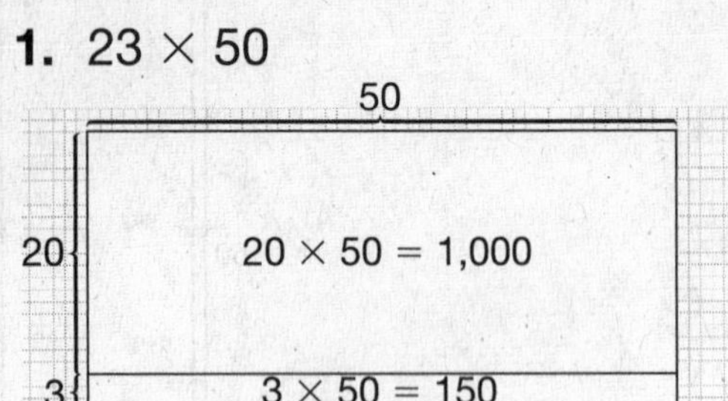

____

2. 30 × 82

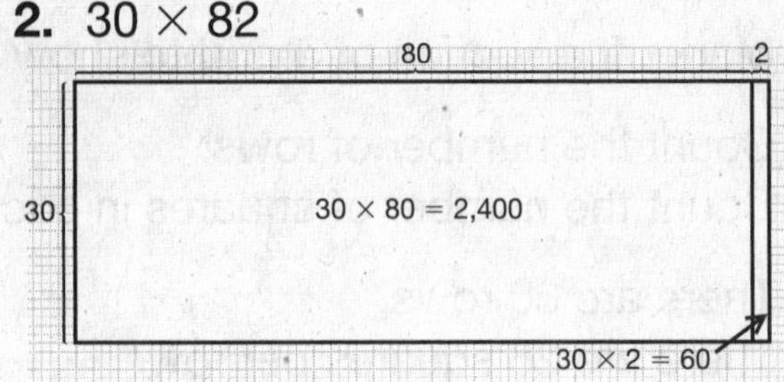

3. 14 × 40

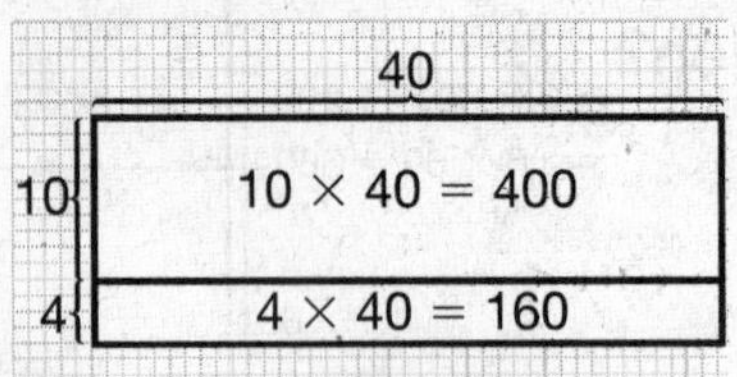

____

4. 20 × 63

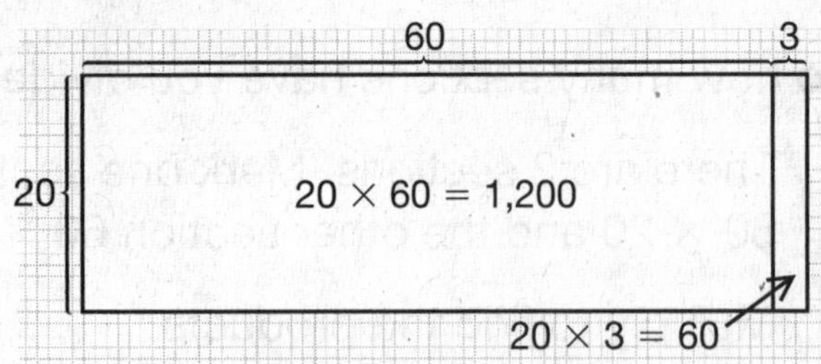

____

5. Martika works as a legal secretary. She earns $20 an hour. How much does Martika earn if she works 32 hours? ______________

6. Which numbers are the partial products of 77 × 30?

A 210 and 700 **B** 2,100 and 210 **C** 511 and 2,100 **D** 4,900 and 210

7. Writing to Explain Explain how you can find the product of 40 × 16 by breaking apart the numbers.

____

____

____

Name ___________________________

Reteaching **6-5**

Multiplying 2-Digit Numbers by 2-Digit Numbers

There are 24 cars in a race. Each car has a 13-person crew in the pit area. How many pit-area workers are at the race?

Step 1

Multiply the ones.

Regroup as necessary.

$$\begin{array}{r} {}^{1}\\ 24\\ \times 13\\ \hline 72 \end{array}$$

Step 2

Multiply the tens.

Regroup as necessary.

$$\begin{array}{r} {}^{1}\\ 24\\ \times 13\\ \hline 72\\ 240 \end{array}$$

Step 3

Add the partial products.

$$\begin{array}{r} {}^{1}\\ 24\\ \times 13\\ \hline 72\\ 240\\ \hline 312 \end{array}$$

24 × 13 = 312, so there are 312 pit-area workers at the race.

1. $\begin{array}{r} 38\\ \times\ 26\\ \hline \end{array}$ **2.** $\begin{array}{r} 67\\ \times\ 27\\ \hline \end{array}$ **3.** $\begin{array}{r} 47\\ \times\ 85\\ \hline \end{array}$ **4.** $\begin{array}{r} 88\\ \times\ 32\\ \hline \end{array}$

5. Writing to Explain Corina multiplied 62 × 22 and got a product of 1,042. Explain why Corina's answer is not reasonable.

____

____

____

____

____

____

Name ______________________

Practice 6-5

Multiplying 2-Digit Numbers by 2-Digit Numbers

1. $\begin{array}{r} 54 \\ \times\ 17 \\ \hline \end{array}$

2. $\begin{array}{r} 36 \\ \times\ 20 \\ \hline \end{array}$

3. $\begin{array}{r} 53 \\ \times\ 12 \\ \hline \end{array}$

4. $\begin{array}{r} 48 \\ \times\ 46 \\ \hline \end{array}$

5. $\begin{array}{r} 37 \\ \times\ 83 \\ \hline \end{array}$

6. $\begin{array}{r} 62 \\ \times\ 17 \\ \hline \end{array}$

7. $\begin{array}{r} 91 \\ \times\ 49 \\ \hline \end{array}$

8. $\begin{array}{r} 28 \\ \times\ 56 \\ \hline \end{array}$

9. $\begin{array}{r} 70 \\ \times\ 39 \\ \hline \end{array}$

10. $\begin{array}{r} 58 \\ \times\ 90 \\ \hline \end{array}$

11. $\begin{array}{r} 97 \\ \times\ 42 \\ \hline \end{array}$

12. $\begin{array}{r} 64 \\ \times\ 88 \\ \hline \end{array}$

13. A carton holds 24 bottles of juice. How many juice bottles are in 15 cartons?

____

Vegetable	Weight of 1 Bushel
Asparagus	24 lb
Beets	52 lb
Carrots	50 lb
Sweet corn	35 lb

14. How much do 21 bushels of sweet corn weigh?

____

15. How much do 18 bushels of asparagus weigh?

____

16. How much more do 13 bushels of beets weigh than 13 bushels of carrots?

____

17. Which of the following is a reasonable answer for 92 × 98?

A 1,800 **B** 9,000 **C** 10,000 **D** 90,000

18. **Writing to Explain** Garth is multiplying 29 × 16. He has 174 after multiplying the ones and 290 after multiplying the tens. Explain how Garth can find the final product.

____

Name ______________________________

Multiplying Greater Numbers by 2-Digit Numbers

You multiply a 3- or 4-digit number the same way you multiply a 2-digit number.

Find 457 × 32.

Step 1 Multiply by the ones. Regroup as needed.

$$\begin{array}{r} {\scriptstyle 1\,1} \\ \mathbf{457} \\ \underline{\times\ \mathbf{32}} \\ \mathbf{914} \end{array}$$

Step 2 Write a zero in the ones place. Multiply by the tens digit. Regroup as needed.

$$\begin{array}{r} {\scriptstyle 1\,2} \\ {\scriptstyle 1\,1} \\ \mathbf{457} \\ \underline{\times\ 32} \\ 914 \\ \mathbf{13{,}710} \end{array}$$

Step 3 Add the products.

$$\begin{array}{r} {\scriptstyle 1\,2} \\ {\scriptstyle 1\,1} \\ 457 \\ \underline{\times\ 32} \\ \mathbf{914} \\ \underline{+\ \mathbf{13{,}710}} \\ \mathbf{14{,}624} \end{array}$$

Here's WHY it Works:

$$\begin{aligned} 457 \times 32 &= 457 \times (30 + 2) \\ &= (457 \times 30) + (457 \times 2) \\ &= 13{,}710 + 914 \\ &= 14{,}624 \end{aligned}$$

Check by estimating. 500 × 30 = 15,000; The answer is reasonable because 15,000 is close to 14,624.

---

1. $\begin{array}{r} 442 \\ \underline{\times\ 15} \end{array}$ **2.** $\begin{array}{r} 135 \\ \underline{\times\ 73} \end{array}$ **3.** $\begin{array}{r} 5{,}371 \\ \underline{\times\ \ \ 27} \end{array}$ **4.** $\begin{array}{r} 3{,}266 \\ \underline{\times\ \ \ 14} \end{array}$

5. $\begin{array}{r} 512 \\ \underline{\times\ 73} \end{array}$ **6.** $\begin{array}{r} 936 \\ \underline{\times\ 78} \end{array}$ **7.** $\begin{array}{r} 7{,}386 \\ \underline{\times\ \ \ 41} \end{array}$ **8.** $\begin{array}{r} 7{,}923 \\ \underline{\times\ \ \ 26} \end{array}$

Name ______________________

Practice
6-6

Multiplying Greater Numbers by 2-Digit Numbers

1. 263×17

2. 534×86

3. $3,357 \times 32$

4. 237×53

5. 855×54

6. $9,362 \times 71$

7. 421×45 ____________

8. 357×74 ____________

9. 64×848 ____________

10. $93 \times 4,247$ ____________

11. $9,989 \times 57$ ____________

12. $81 \times 2,777$ ____________

13. Algebra Find the value of $78 \times n$ when $n = 3,237$. ____________

14. Laura addresses 127 envelopes every week. Each envelope contains 4 pieces of paper. How many envelopes does Laura address in one year? Remember that there are 52 weeks in a year.

____

15. There are 36 large fish tanks at a zoo. Each tank holds 215 gallons of water. How many gallons of water would it take to fill all the tanks?

A 7,740 **B** 7,613 **C** 7,610 **D** 251

16. Writing to Explain Is the product of 686 and 50 greater than or less than 30,000? Explain.

____

____

Name ____________________

Reteaching **6-7**

Problem Solving: Two-Question Problems

Read and Understand

Problem 1: Gina gave 3 sheets of paper to each of the 12 students in her class. How many sheets of paper did she give out?

Problem 2: Each sheet of paper had 3 paperclips attached to it. How many paperclips did she give out?

Answer Problem 1 first.

⊢? Sheets of paper⊣

12	12	12

12 students × 3 sheets of paper = 36 sheets of paper
Gina gave out 36 sheets of paper.

Plan and Solve

Use the answer from Problem 1 to solve Problem 2.

⊢? Paper clips⊣

36	36	36

36 sheets of paper × 3 paperclips = 118 paperclips
Gina gave out 118 paperclips.

Solve. Use the answer from Problem 1 to solve Problem 2.

1. **Problem 1:** April made 16 baskets and glued 5 flowers on each one. How many flowers did she use altogether?

   Problem 2: Each flower April used had 8 petals. How many petals were there on all the flowers she used?

   ____

2. **Problem 1:** Jorge washed cars for four hours on Saturday. In the first hour, he washed 2 cars. In the second hour, he washed 1 car. In the third hour, he washed 3 cars. How many cars did he wash all together in the first three hours?

   Problem 2: Jorge washed the same number of cars in the fourth hour as he did in the first three hours combined. How many cars did he wash all together in four hours?

   ____

Name ______________________

Practice
6-7

Problem Solving: Two-Question Problems

Use the answer from the first problem to solve the second problem.

1. **Problem 1:** Francisco reads 75 pages every week for a summer reading program. There are about 4 weeks in a month. How many pages can Francisco read in a month?

   ____

   Problem 2: How many pages will Francisco read in the three months of summer?

   ____

2. **Problem 1:** Mr. Dunn drives 15 miles every day to work. Mr. Dunn works five days a week. How many miles does he drive?

   ____

   Problem 2: Mr. Dunn estimates he uses 3 gallons of gas over the course of a week. How many miles per gallon does his car get?

   ____

3. A company buys printer paper in a box which contains 8 packages. Each package of paper costs 3 dollars. Which number sentence shows how much 12 boxes will cost?

   A $8 + 3 \times 12$ **B** $24 \div 12$ **C** $24 + 12$ **D** 24×12

4. **Writing to Explain** There are 12 plots in a community garden. Each plot is the same size. What information would you need to know if you wanted to know how much area can be farmed in the community garden? Explain.

   ____

   ____

   ____

Name ____________________

Reteaching
7-1

Using Mental Math to Divide

When dividing numbers that end in zero, you can use basic division facts, as well as patterns, to help you divide mentally. For example:

	Find 210 ÷ 7.	Find 4,200 ÷ 6.
What You **Think**	First, find the basic fact. **210** ÷ **7** = **21** ÷ **7** = **21** tens ÷ **7** = 3 tens or 30	Find the basic fact. **4,2**00 ÷ **6** = **42** ÷ **6** = **42** hundreds ÷ **6** = 7 hundreds or 700
What You **Write**	210 ÷ 7 = 30	4,200 ÷ 6 = 700

Divide. Use mental math.

1. 250 ÷ 5 = ____________ **2.** 7,200 ÷ 9 = ____________

3. 200 ÷ 4 = ____________ **4.** 28,000 ÷ 7 = ____________

5. 810 ÷ 9 = ____________ **6.** 50,000 ÷ 5 = ____________

7. **Number Sense** What basic fact would you use to help solve 450,000 ÷ 9?

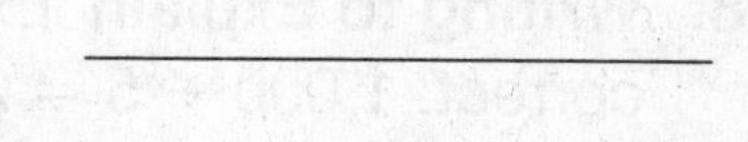

8. In 1 week there are 7 days. How many weeks are in 210 days?

9. How many weeks are there in 420 days? ____________

Name ____________________

Practice

7-1

Using Mental Math to Divide

Divide. Use mental math.

1. 250 ÷ 5 = ________

2. 1,400 ÷ 2 = ________

3. 300 ÷ 5 = ________

4. 1,600 ÷ 4 = ________

5. 240 ÷ 8 = ________

6. 36,000 ÷ 4 = ________

7. 16,000 ÷ 2 = ________

8. 270 ÷ 3 = ________

9. 4,200 ÷ 7 = ________

10. 640 ÷ 8 = ________

11. 2,000 ÷ 5 = ________

12. 320 ÷ 8 = ________

13. 12,000 ÷ 2 = ________

14. 1,600 ÷ 8 = ________

A fourth grade performed a play based on the story of Cinderella. There was one chair for each person present.

15. On Friday, 140 people came to the play. The chairs in the auditorium were arranged in 7 equal rows. How many chairs were in each row? ________

16. There were 8 equal rows set up for Saturday's performance. There were 240 people at the play on Saturday. How many chairs were in each row? ________

17. Which is the quotient of 56,000 ÷ 8?

A 400 **B** 4,000 **C** 700 **D** 7,000

18. **Writing to Explain** Explain why the following answer is not correct: 1,000 ÷ 5 = <u>2,000</u>.

____

____

____

Name ______________________________

Reteaching
7-2

Estimating Quotients

Estimate 460 ÷ 9.

You can use compatible numbers.

Ask yourself: What is a number close to 460 that could be easily divided by 9? Try 450.

450 ÷ 9 = 50

So, 460 ÷ 9 is about 50.

You can also estimate by thinking about multiplication.

Ask yourself: Nine times what number is about 460?

9 × 5 = 45, so 9 × 50 = 450.

So, 460 ÷ 9 is about 50.

50 is a good estimation for this problem.

Estimate each quotient.

1. 165 ÷ 4 ______________________

2. 35 ÷ 4 ______________________

3. 715 ÷ 9 ______________________

4. 490 ÷ 8 ______________________

5. 512 ÷ 5 ______________________

6. 652 ÷ 8 ______________________

7. 790 ÷ 9 ______________________

8. 200 ÷ 7 ______________________

9. 311 ÷ 6 ______________________

10. **Number Sense** Complete by filling in the circle with < or >. Without dividing, explain how you know which quotient is greater.
315 ÷ 5 ◯ 347 ÷ 5

____

____

Name ______________________

Practice
7-2

Estimating Quotients

Estimate each quotient.

1. $82 \div 4$ ______

2. $580 \div 3$ ______

3. $96 \div 5$ ______

4. $811 \div 2$ ______

5. $194 \div 6$ ______

6. $207 \div 7$ ______

7. $282 \div 4$ ______

8. $479 \div 8$ ______

9. Jacqui is writing a book. If she needs to write 87 pages in 9 days, about how many pages will she write each day? ______

10. Wade wants to give 412 of his marbles to 10 of his friends. If he gives each friend the same number of marbles, about how many will each friend receive? ______

11. Which is the best estimate for $502 \div 6$?

A 60 **B** 70 **C** 80 **D** 90

12. Writing to Explain You are using division to determine how much whole wheat flour to use in a bread recipe. Is an estimated answer good enough?

______

______

Name ______________________________

Reteaching
7-3

Dividing with Remainders

When you divide, you can think of putting items into groups. For example:

$$60 \div 6 = 10$$

60 items — 6 groups — 10 items in each group

Sometimes there are items left over. In division, the number of leftover items is called the ***remainder***. For example:

$$62 \div 6 = 10\text{ R2} \longrightarrow \text{2 items left over}$$

62 items — 6 groups — 10 items in each group

Divide. You may use counters or pictures to help.

1. $4\overline{)34}$ **2.** $8\overline{)65}$ **3.** $9\overline{)75}$

4. $6\overline{)28}$ **5.** $5\overline{)14}$ **6.** $9\overline{)37}$

7. Number Sense In division, why should the remainder not be greater than the divisor?

____

Name ______________________________

Practice
7-3

Dividing with Remainders

Divide. You may use counters or pictures to help.

1. $4\overline{)27}$ **2.** $6\overline{)32}$ **3.** $7\overline{)17}$ **4.** $9\overline{)29}$

5. $8\overline{)27}$ **6.** $3\overline{)27}$ **7.** $5\overline{)28}$ **8.** $4\overline{)35}$

9. $2\overline{)19}$ **10.** $7\overline{)30}$ **11.** $3\overline{)17}$ **12.** $9\overline{)16}$

If you arrange these items into equal rows, tell how many will be in each row and how many will be left over.

13. 26 shells into 3 rows ______________________

14. 19 pennies into 5 rows ______________________

15. 17 balloons into 7 rows ______________________

16. **Reasonableness** Ms. Nikkel wants to divide her class of 23 students into 4 equal teams. Is this reasonable? Why or why not?

____

____

17. Which is the remainder for the quotient of 79 ÷ 8?

A 7 **B** 6 **C** 5 **D** 4

18. **Writing to Explain** Pencils are sold in packages of 5. Explain why you need 6 packages in order to have enough for 27 students.

____

____

Name ____________________

Connecting Models and Symbols

You can use models to help you solve division problems.
The models below help you find 78 ÷ 5.
Find 78 ÷ 5.
Estimate 80 ÷ 5 = 16.

First divide the tens.

```
  1
5)78
 -5    5 tens
```

There is one ten in each group of 5 and 2 tens left over.

Now, change the left over tens into the ones.

```
  1
5)78
 -5    5 tens
  28   28 ones
```

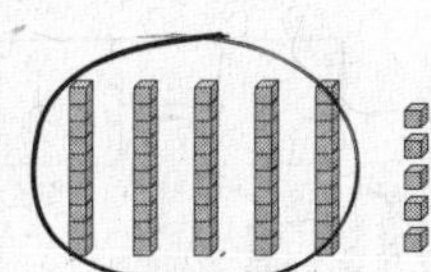

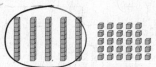

2 tens blocks and 8 ones blocks are equal to 28 ones blocks.

Now, divide the ones.

```
  15
5)78
 -5    5 tens
  28   28 ones
 -25
   3
```

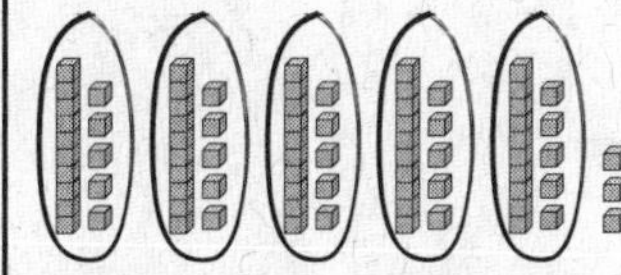

Each of the 5 groups has 1 ten and 5 ones.

Now, write the remainder.

```
  15 R3
5)78
 -5    5 tens
  28   28 ones
 -25
   3   remainder
```

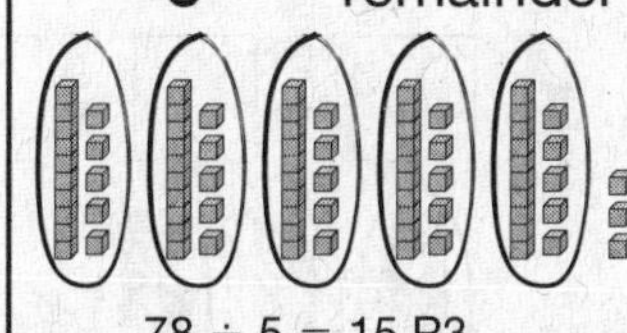

78 ÷ 5 = 15 R3

Use the models below to help you fill in the boxes.

1. 66 ÷ ☐ = ☐ R2

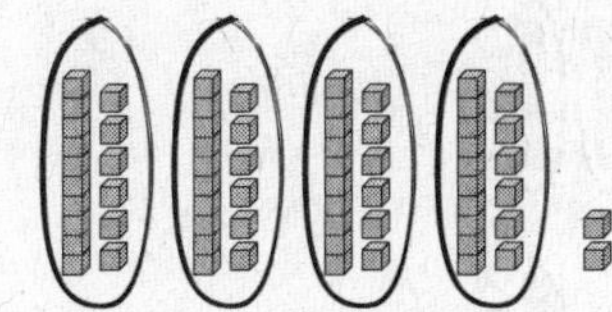

2. 97 ÷ 4 = ☐ R ☐

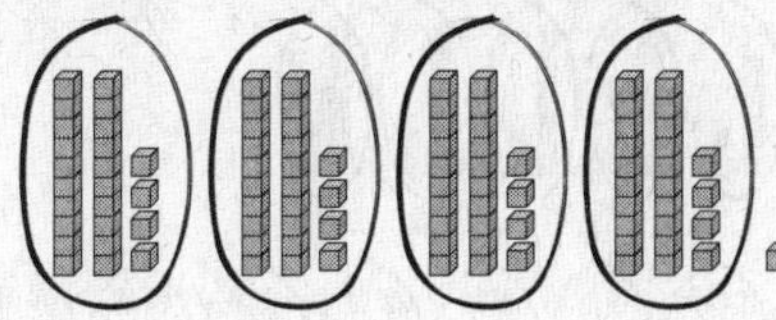

3. ☐ ÷ 7 = ☐ R6

4. 76 ÷ ☐ = ☐ R ☐

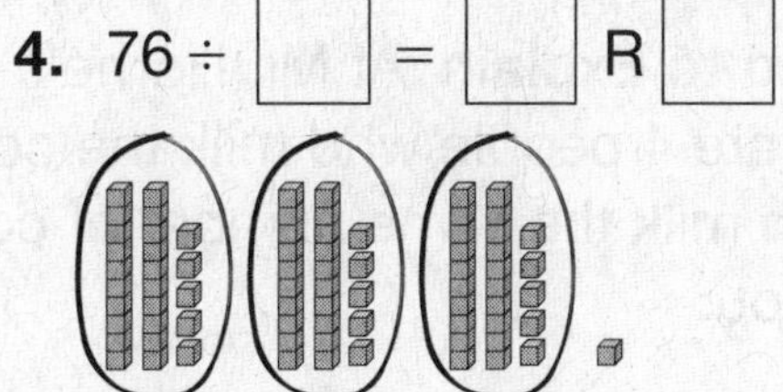

Name ______________________

Practice
7-4

Connecting Models and Symbols

Draw pictures to tell how many are in each group and how many are leftover.

1. 57 CDs in 8 organizers

____

2. 62 stickers on 5 rolls

____

3. 44 plants in 6 rows

____

4. 37 chairs for 9 tables

____

In **5** through **8**, use the model to complete each division sentence.

5. 27 ÷ ☐ = ☐ R3

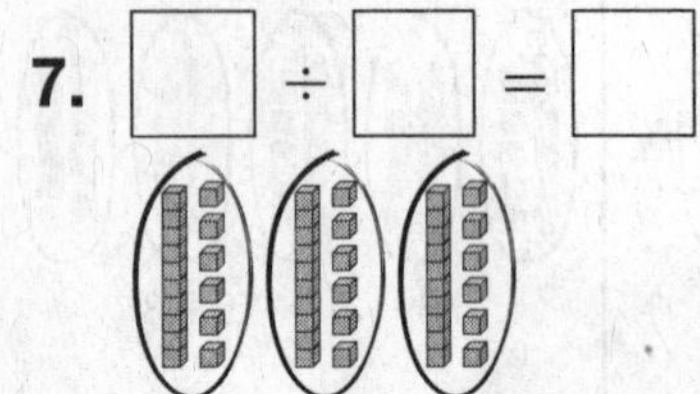

6. ☐ ÷ 9 = ☐

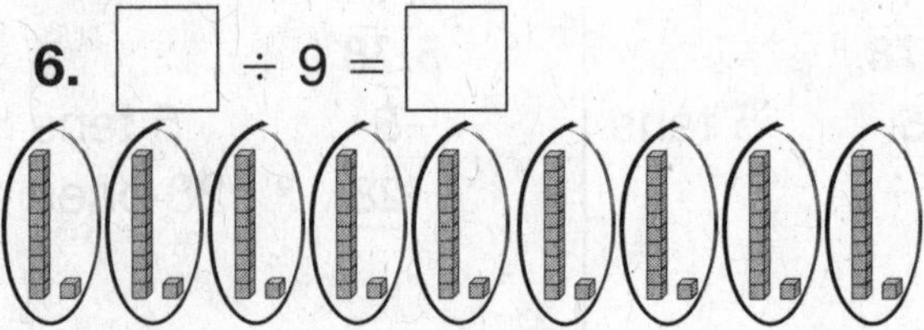

7. ☐ ÷ ☐ = ☐

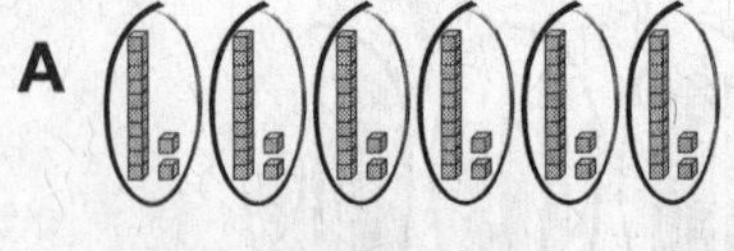

8. ☐ ÷ ☐ = ☐ R ☐

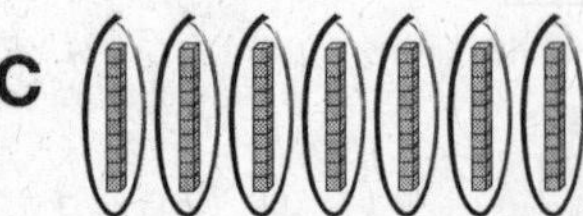

9. Ken has 72 marbles. He decides to share them with his friends so they can play a game. Which of the following models shows Ken sharing his marbles?

A 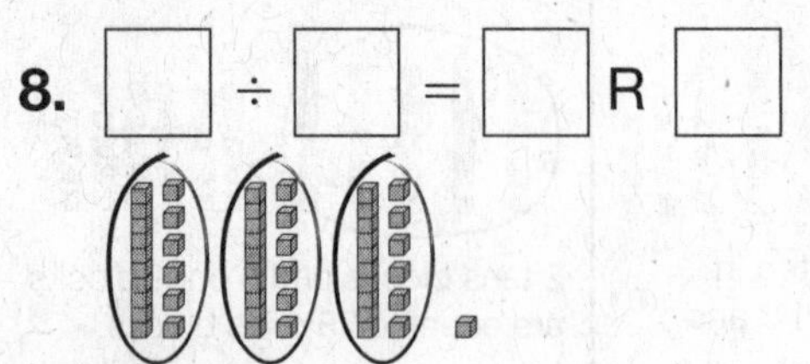

C

B 

D 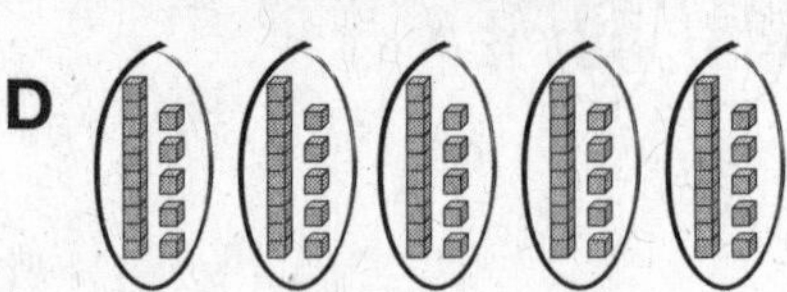

10. Writing to Explain At Mr. Horne's farm there are 53 cows. There are 4 people who milk the cows each day. Does each person milk the same number of cows? Use a model to help you.

____

____

Name ______________________________

Reteaching
7-5

Dividing 2-Digit by 1-Digit Numbers

You can find 2-digit quotients by breaking apart the problem and dividing tens, then ones.

Find 85 ÷ 5.
Estimate: 100 ÷ 5 = 20.

```
   17
5)85
 -5
  35
 -35
   0
```

Check: 17 × 5 = 85.
The answer checks.

Find 55 ÷ 3.
Estimate: 60 ÷ 3 = 20.

```
   18 R1
3)55
 -3
  25
 -24
   1
```

Check: 18 × 3 = 54.
54 + 1 = 55
The answer checks.

Find 83 ÷ 7.
Estimate: 84 ÷ 7 = 12.

```
   11 R6
7)83
 -7
  13
 - 7
   6
```

Check: 11 × 7 = 77.
77 + 6 = 83
The answer checks.

1. 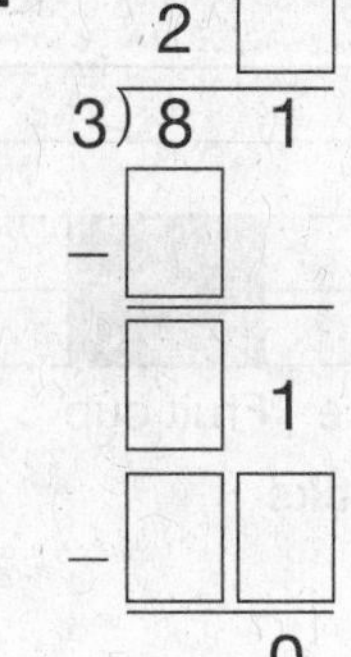

2. 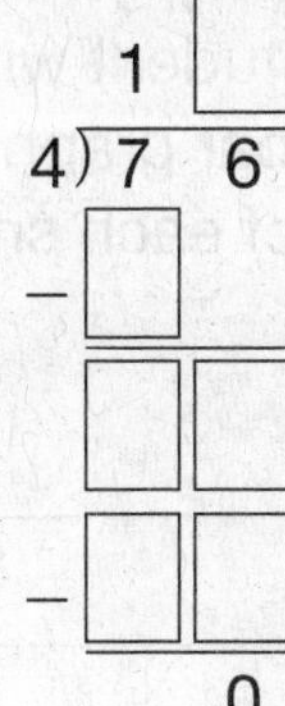

3. 3)91 **4.** 4)86 **5.** 2)75

Name ____________________

Practice
7-5

Dividing 2-Digit by 1-Digit Numbers

1. 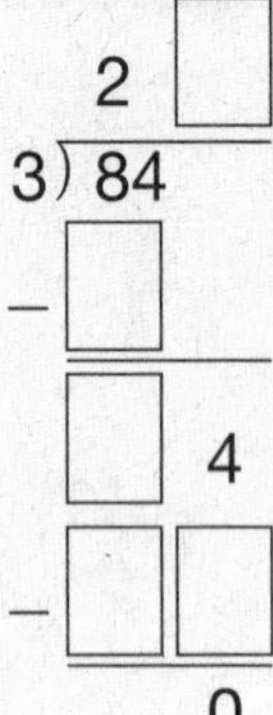

2. 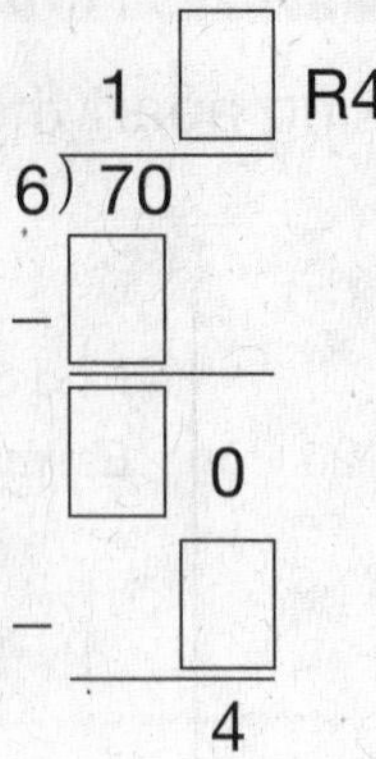

3. 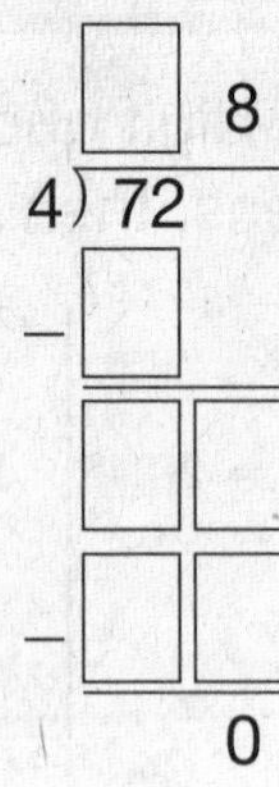

4. 2)72 **5.** 5)86 **6.** 7)94 **7.** 3)39

8. 8)99 **9.** 5)87 **10.** 2)96 **11.** 3)43

Mrs. Thomas is planning to provide snacks for 96 fourth graders when they go on a field trip to the aquarium. Each student will receive 1 of each snack. Using the bar graph to the right, how many packages of each snack does Mrs. Thomas need?

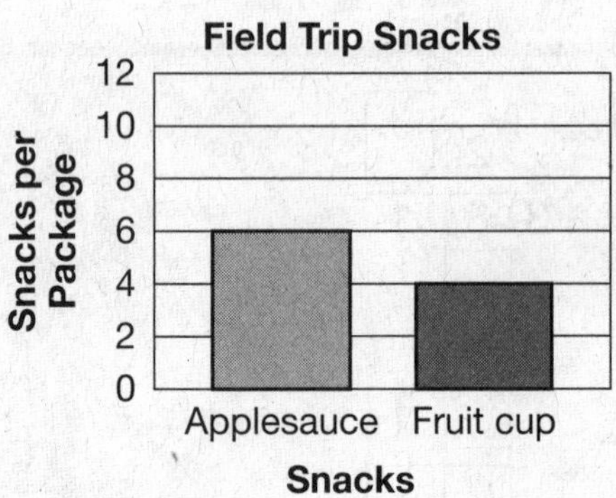

12. fruit cups ____________

13. applesauce ____________

14. Which is the remainder of 27 ÷ 4?

A 1 **B** 2 **C** 3 **D** 4

15. Writing to Explain Explain how to find the number of leftover pencils if Wendy wants to share 37 pencils with 9 people.

____

____

____

Name ______________________

Dividing 3-Digit by 1-Digit Numbers

You can find 3-digit quotients by breaking apart the problem.

Find 528 ÷ 4.
Estimate:
500 ÷ 4 = 125.

```
   132
 4)528
 - 4
   12
 - 12
    8
 -  8
    0
```

Check: 132 × 4 = 528.
The answer checks.

Find 575 ÷ 5.
Estimate:
600 ÷ 5 = 120.

```
   115
 5)575
 - 5
    7
  - 5
   25
 - 25
    0
```

Check: 115 × 5 = 575.
The answer checks.

Find 725 ÷ 3.
Estimate:
750 ÷ 3 = 250.

```
   241 R2
 3)725
 - 6
   12
 - 12
    5
 -  3
    2
```

Check: 241 × 3 = 723.
723 + 2 = 725
The answer checks.

Fill in the boxes in the problems below.

1.
```
   315R□
 2)631
 -□
   □
 - 2
 - 11
  □0
   □
```

2.
```
   □□□ R2
 6)788
 - 6
   1□
 - 1□
    □
  - 6
    □
```

3. 3)462 **4.** 5)640 **5.** 9)919

Name ____________________

Practice
7-6

Dividing 3-Digit by 1-Digit Numbers

In **1** through **8**, use place-value blocks to help you divide.

1. $4\overline{)412}$ **2.** $6\overline{)936}$ **3.** $7\overline{)798}$ **4.** $7\overline{)806}$

5. $3\overline{)420}$ **6.** $5\overline{)619}$ **7.** $7\overline{)842}$ **8.** $8\overline{)856}$

9. A train can hold 136 people in rows of 4 seats each. How many 4-seat rows are there? ____________

10. A song has 540 beats. If the song is 3 minutes long, how many beats per minute does the song have? ____________

11. **Geometry** A pizza has 360 degrees. If the pizza is divided into 8 equal slices, how many degrees does each slice measure? ____________

12. Harvey has 516 stamps in his collection. He has 6 stamp books. How many stamps are in each book? ____________

13. Zeeshan has collected 812 autographs. Each autograph is either from a baseball star, a football star, a movie star, or a rock star. He has an equal number of autographs for each group. How many autographs does he have in each group? ____________

14. Nicole has 189 teabags. There are 4 different flavors of tea. What information do you need to find how many teabags Nicole has of each flavor?

A The number of flavors.

B The number of teabags.

C If a teabag can be divided into fourths.

D If there are an equal number of teabags for each flavor.

15. An ant has 6 legs. There are 870 legs in Jose's ant farm. How many ants are there in his ant farm?

A 14 R5 **B** 145 **C** 864 **D** 5,220

16. **Writing to Explain** Jeff has 171 DVDs. He has 3 shelves that can each store 55 DVDs. Does he need to buy another shelf?

____

Name ______________________________

Deciding Where to Start Dividing

Sometimes there are not enough hundreds to divide by.
Sometimes you have to break up the hundreds into 10 tens.

Find 325 ÷ 5.
Estimate 300 ÷ 5 = 60.

Try to divide the hundreds.

$$\begin{array}{r} 0 \\ 5\overline{)325} \\ -\underline{0} \end{array}$$

5 does not divide into 3. The 3 hundreds now have to be changed to 30 tens.

Divide the tens.

$$\begin{array}{rl} 6 & \\ 5\overline{)325} & \\ -\underline{30} & \text{30 tens} \\ 2 & \end{array}$$

With 32 tens, 6 tens can each go into 1 of 5 groups. The 2 leftover tens now have to be changed to 20 ones.

Now divide the ones.

$$\begin{array}{rl} 65 & \\ 5\overline{)325} & \\ -\underline{30} & \text{30 tens} \\ 25 & \\ -\underline{25} & \text{2 tens and} \\ 0 & \text{5 ones; no remainder} \end{array}$$

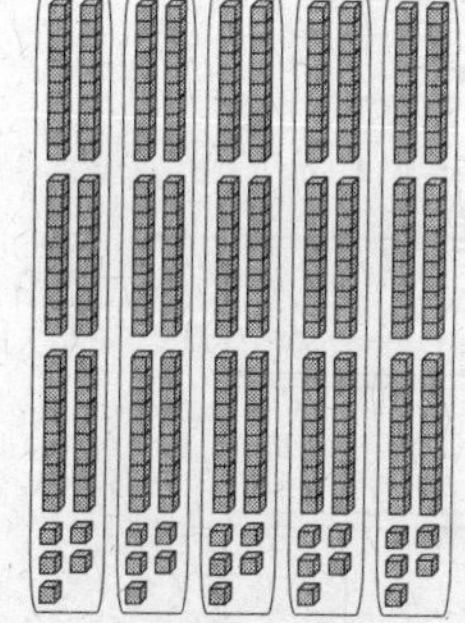

Each of the five groups has 6 tens and 5 ones.

Find the missing values in the problems below.

1.
$$\begin{array}{r} 8\ \ 3\text{R}\square \\ 4\overline{)3\ \ 3\ \ 4} \\ -\underline{\square\ \square} \\ \square\ \square \\ -\underline{1\ \ 2} \\ \square \end{array}$$

2.
$$\begin{array}{r} \square\ \square\ \text{R4} \\ 6\overline{)1\ \ 4\ \ 8} \\ -\underline{\square\ \square} \\ \square \\ -\underline{\square\ \ 4} \\ \square \end{array}$$

3. $5\overline{)125}$

4. $8\overline{)418}$

Name ______________________

Practice
7-7

Deciding Where to Start Dividing

Complete each calculation.

1.

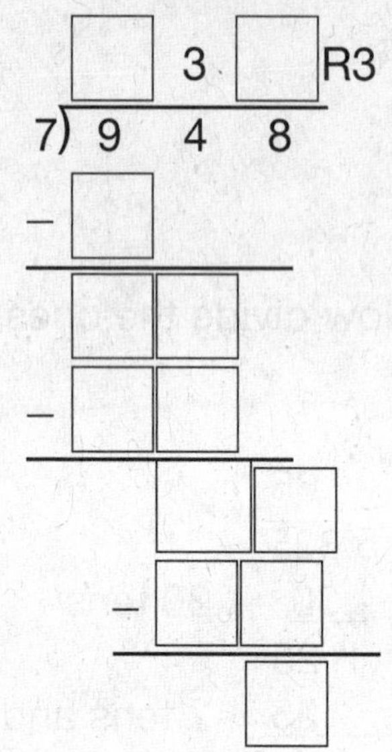

2.

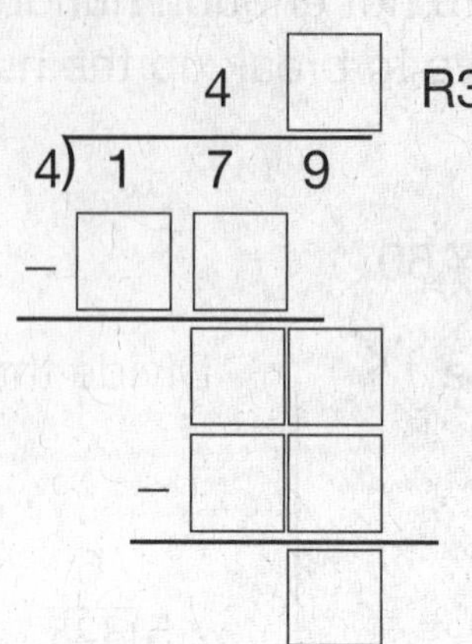

3.

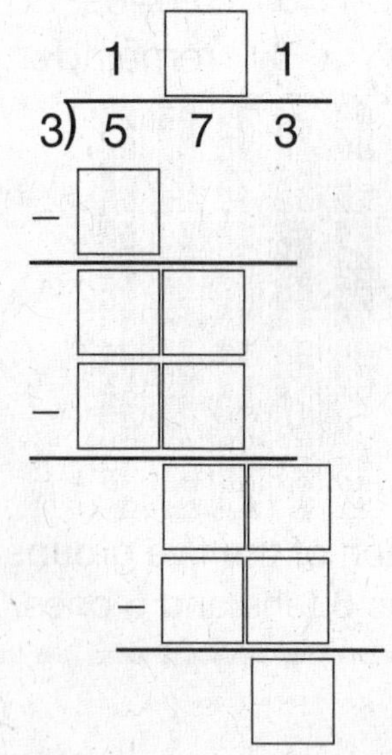

4.

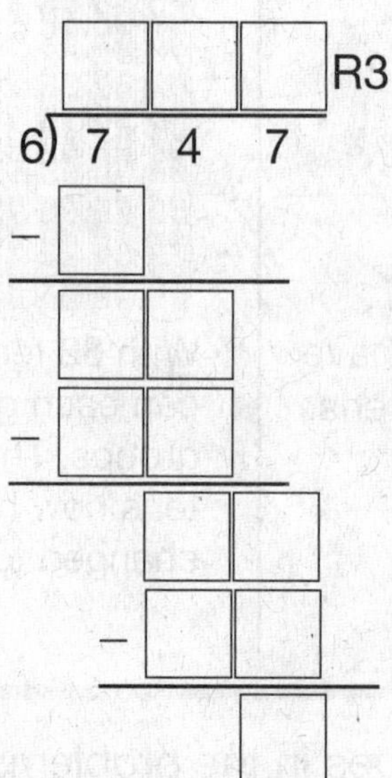

5. $2\overline{)587}$

6. $8\overline{)747}$

7. $9\overline{)411}$

8. $7\overline{)698}$

9. Gerald distributes 582 brochures to 3 businesses each week. How many brochures does each business get?

A 159 **B** 174 **C** 194 **D** 264

10. Writing to Explain Write and solve a word problem for 456 ÷ 6.

____

____

Name ______________________________

Reteaching **7-8**

Zeros in the Quotient

Find 956 ÷ 9.

First estimate: 900 ÷ 9 = 100.

Step 1	Step 2	Step 3	Check
Divide the hundreds.	Bring down the tens and divide.	Bring down the ones and divide.	Multiply the quotient by the divisor and add the remainder.
$\begin{array}{r} 1 \\ 9\overline{)956} \\ -9 \\ \hline 0 \end{array}$ Multiply. Compare. 0 < 9	$\begin{array}{r} 10 \\ 9\overline{)956} \\ -9 \\ \hline 05 \\ -0 \\ \hline 5 \end{array}$ Multiply. Subtract. Compare. 5 < 9	$\begin{array}{r} 106 \text{ R2} \\ 9\overline{)956} \\ -9 \\ \hline 05 \\ -0 \\ \hline 56 \\ -54 \\ \hline 2 \end{array}$ Multiply. Subtract. Compare. 2 < 9	$\begin{array}{r} \scriptstyle 5 \\ 106 \\ \times\ 9 \\ \hline 954 \end{array}$ $\begin{array}{r} 954 \\ +\ 2 \\ \hline 956 \end{array}$
	5 can't be divided by 9. Place a zero in the quotient.		The answer checks.

Divide. Then, check your answers.

1. $7\overline{)742}$ **2.** $5\overline{)520}$ **3.** $2\overline{)813}$ **4.** $4\overline{)808}$

5. Number Sense Could 540 ÷ 3 be 18? Why or why not?

____

____

____

____

Name ____________________

Practice 7-8

Zeros in the Quotient

Divide. Then, check your answer.

1. $3\overline{)921}$ **2.** $4\overline{)834}$ **3.** $5\overline{)549}$ **4.** $2\overline{)611}$

5. $6\overline{)627}$ **6.** $8\overline{)824}$ **7.** $7\overline{)762}$ **8.** $5\overline{)535}$

9. $4\overline{)810}$ **10.** $6\overline{)121}$ **11.** $7\overline{)712}$ **12.** $9\overline{)936}$

13. Number Sense When Donald divided 636 by 6, his quotient was 16. What common mistake did he make?

____

The fourth graders in Clifton's classroom used computer games to practice their math skills. Each student's score was the same in each round.

14. Clifton scored 918 points in 9 rounds of math facts. How many points did he score in each round? ________

15. Brionne scored 654 points in 6 rounds. How many points did she score in each round? ________

16. Which is the quotient of 617 ÷ 3?

A 203 R2 **B** 205 **C** 205 R1 **D** 205 R2

17. Writing to Explain In Patricia's class, 7 students need to share 714 building blocks to make a building model. Each student needs an equal number of blocks. Patricia thinks each student should have 100 blocks. Is this the best plan? Explain.

____

____

Name ______________________

Reteaching 7-9

Factors

When multiplying two numbers, you know that both numbers are factors of the product.

Example 1

Find the factors of 24.

Factors Product

$1 \times 24 = 24$
$2 \times 12 = 24$
$3 \times 8 = 24$
$4 \times 6 = 24$

Factors of 24:
1, 2, 3, 4, 6, 8, 12, and 24

Example 2

What numbers can you multiply together to get 16? Find the factors of 16.

What two numbers multiply together to equal 16?

$1 \times 16 = 16$
$2 \times 8 = 16$
$4 \times 4 = 16$
$8 \times 2 = 16$
$16 \times 1 = 16$

Factors of 16: 1, 2, 4, 8, and 16

List all the factors of each number.

1. 18 ______ **2.** 21 ______ **3.** 11 ______

4. 14 ______ **5.** 23 ______ **6.** 33 ______

7. Number Sense Look at the following multiplication sentences: 2×14 and 3×7. Are these numbers all factors of the same product? Explain your answer.

____

____

____

____

Name ______________________

Practice 7-9

Factors

For **1** through **12**, find all the factors of each number.

1. 54 ______ ______

2. 17 ______ ______

3. 28 ______ ______

4. 31 ______ ______

5. 44 ______ ______

6. 47 ______ ______

7. 77 ______ ______

8. 71 ______ ______

9. 65 ______ ______

10. 23 ______ ______

11. 57 ______ ______

12. 24 ______ ______

13. Karl's mother buys 60 party favors to give out as gifts during Karl's birthday party. Which number of guests will NOT let her divide the party favors evenly among the guests?

A 12 **B** 15 **C** 20 **D** 25

14. Writing to Explain Mrs. Fisher has 91 watches on display at her store. She says she can arrange them into rows and columns without any watches leftover. Mr. Fisher says that she can only make 1 row with all 91 watches. Who is right and why?

____

____

____

Name ______________________________

Reteaching

7-10

Prime and Composite Numbers

A **composite number** is a whole number greater than 1 that has more than two different factors. 15 has four different factors, 1, 3, 5, and 15, so 15 is a composite number.

A **prime number** is a whole number greater than 1 that has exactly two factors, itself and 1. 17 has exactly two factors, 1 and 17, so 17 is a prime number.

Example 1

Is 7 a prime or composite number?

Find all the factors of 7.

Factors of 7: 1,7

1 and 7 divide evenly into 7.

7 is a prime number because it only has two factors, 1 and itself.

Example 2

Is 6 a prime or composite number?

Find all the factors of 6.

Factors of 6: 1, 2, 3, 6

1, 2, 3, and 6 divide evenly into 6.

6 is a composite number because it has more than two factors.

Then tell if the number is prime or composite.

1. 5 ____________

2. 12 ____________

3. 18 ____________

4. 15 ____________

5. 37 ____________

6. 43 ____________

Name ______________________

Prime and Composite Numbers

In **1** through **12**, write whether each number is prime or composite.

1. 81 ________ **2.** 43 ________ **3.** 572 ________ **4.** 63 ________

5. 53 ________ **6.** 87 ________ **7.** 3 ________ **8.** 27 ________

9. 88 ________ **10.** 19 ________ **11.** 69 ________ **12.** 79 ________

13. 3,235 ________ **14.** 1,212 ________ **15.** 57 ________ **16.** 17 ________

17. Mr. Gerry's class has 19 students, Ms. Vernon's class has 21 students, and Mr. Singh's class has 23 students. Whose class has a composite number of students?

____

18. Every prime number larger than 10 has a digit in the ones place that is included in which set of numbers below?

A 1, 3, 7, 9

B 1, 3, 5, 9

C 0, 2, 4, 5, 6, 8

D 1, 3, 7

19. Writing to Explain Marla says that every number in the nineties is composite. Jackie says that one number in the nineties is prime. Who is correct? Explain your answer.

____

____

____

____

Name ______________________________

Reteaching **7-11**

Problem Solving: Multiple-Step Problems

Lawn Cutting Chad and his brother Brad cut lawns in their neighborhood to make money. They charge $20 per lawn. One weekend, Brad cut 4 lawns, and Chad cut 3 lawns. How much money did they earn altogether?

Solution One

Hidden Question: How many lawns did they mow altogether?

Chad cut 3 lawns, Brad cut 4 lawns.

$3 + 4 = 7$

They cut 7 lawns.

Question in the Problem: How much money did they earn altogether?

7 lawns × $20 = $140

Chad and Brad earned $140.

Solution Two

Hidden Question 1: How much money did Chad get for cutting lawns?

3 × $20 = $60

Hidden Question 2: How much money did Brad get for cutting lawns?

4 × $20 = $80

Question in the Problem: How much money did they earn altogether?

$60 + $80 = $140

Chad and Brad earned $140.

Write and answer the hidden question or questions. Then solve the problem. Write your answer in complete sentences.

1. Keisha sold 8 ribbons. Then she sold 6 pins. The ribbons sold for $3; the pins sold for $2. How much money did Keisha make?

____

____

____

____

____

____

____

Name ______________________

Problem Solving: Multiple-Step Problems

Write and answer the hidden question or questions. Then solve the problem. Write your answer in a complete sentence.

County Fair Admission	
Adults	$5.00
Students	$3.00
Children	$2.00

1. Mario and his family went to the county fair. They bought 2 adult passes and 3 children's passes. What was the total cost for the family?

2. A bus has 12 rows with 1 seat in each row on one side and 12 rows with 2 seats in each row on the other side. How many seats does the bus have altogether?

3. Writing to Explain Write a problem about going to the laundromat that has a hidden question. A single load of laundry costs $2 and a double load costs $4. Solve your problem.

Name ______________________________

Circles

A **circle** is a closed curve that is made up of points that are the same distance from the center.

The **radius** is a line segment that connects the center to any point on the circle.

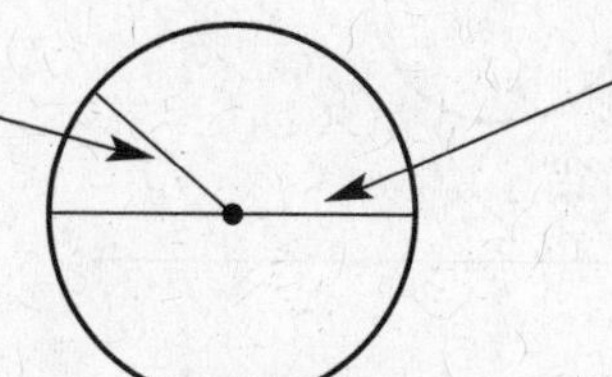

The **diameter** is a line segment that goes through the center and connects two points on a circle. The diameter is twice as long as the radius.

Find the radius or the diameter of each circle below.

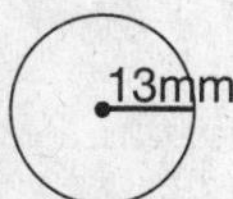

radius: 13 mm

diameter: 13 mm × 2 = 26 mm

diameter: 70 in.

radius: 70 in. ÷ 2 = 35 in.

Write the radius or diameter of each circle.

1.

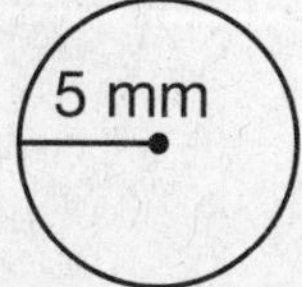

d = ____________

2.

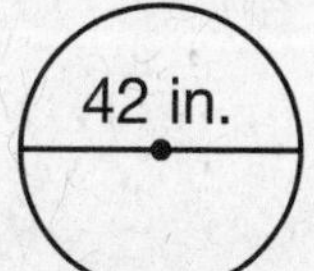

r = ____________

3.

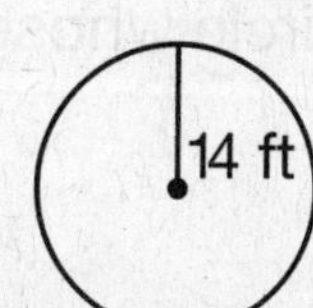

d = ____________

4.

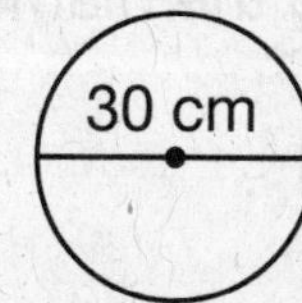

r = ____________

Name ______________________________

Circles

Write the part of each circle indicated by the arrow.

1. 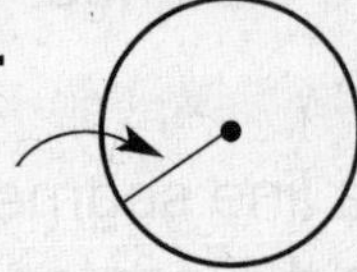
____

2. 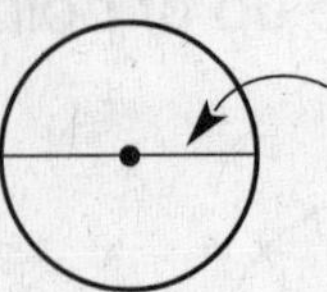
____

3. 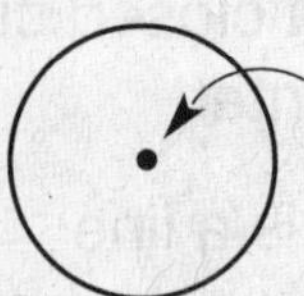
____

Use the circle at the right to complete Exercise 4.

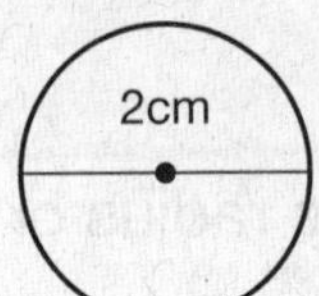

4. radius ____________ diameter ____________

5. How many times the radius is the diameter? ____________

Write the radius or diameter of each circle.

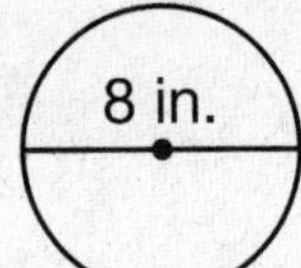

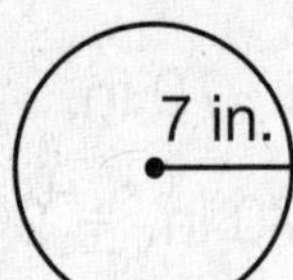

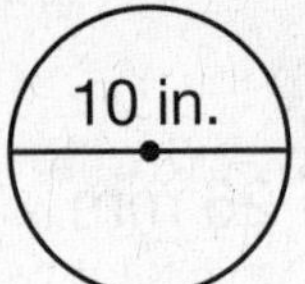

6. $r =$ ____________ 7. $d =$ ____________ 8. $r =$ ____________ 9. $d =$ ____________

10. Find the diameter of a circle whose radius is 2.

A 1 **B** 2 **C** 4 **D** 6

11. **Writing to Explain** What is the difference between a diameter and a radius?

____

____

____

____

Name ____________________

Solids

Solid figures have three dimensions: length, width, and height. Many solids have edges, faces, and vertices.

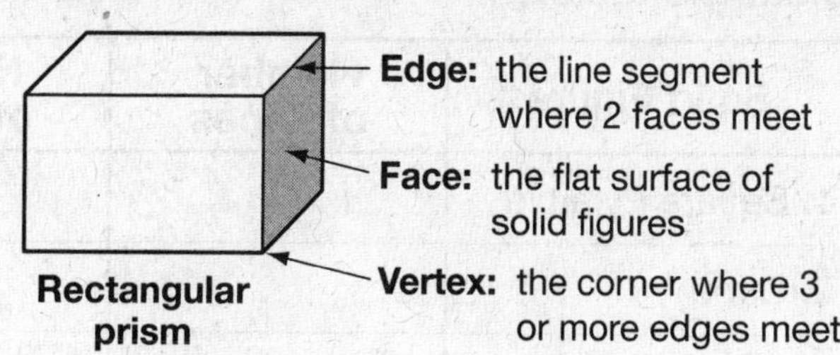

Spheres, cylinders, and cones have curved surfaces. Other solids have all flat surfaces.

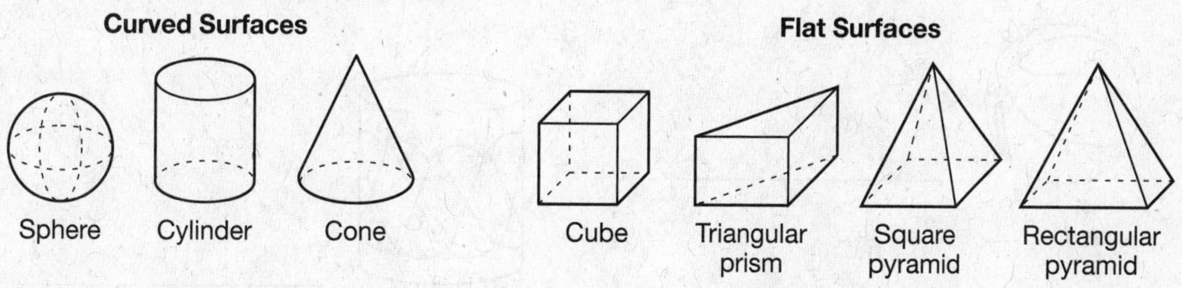

Complete the table.

	Solid Figure	Number of Faces	Number of Edges	Number of Vertices	Shape(s) of Faces
1.	Rectangular prism				
2.	Cube				
3.	Triangular prism				
4.	Square pyramid				

5. **Reasoning** Compare rectangular pyramids and rectangular prisms. How are they alike?

____

____

Name ____________________

Practice

8-7

Solids

Complete the table.

Solid Figure	Number of Faces	Number of Edges	Number of Vertices
1. Square Pyramid			
2. Cube			
3. Triangular Prism			

Identify the solid that best describes each object.

4.

____

5.

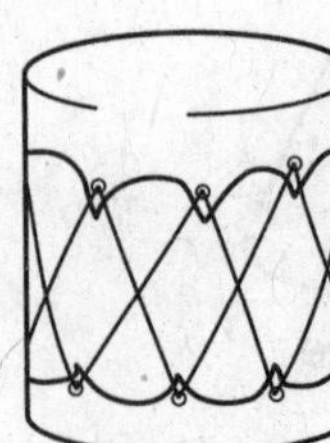

____

6.

____

7. How many total faces does a rectangular prism have? ____________

8. Which solid does the figure represent?

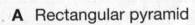

A Rectangular pyramid

B Cylinder

C Rectangular prism

D Square pyramid

9. Writing to Explain Explain the difference between a plane figure and a solid figure.

____

____

____

____

Name ______________________________

Views of Solids: Nets

You can make models of solid figures by using patterns called **nets**.

Here is a net for a cylinder.

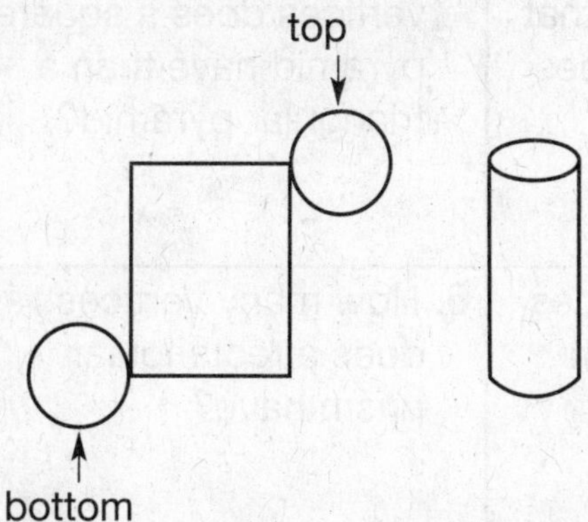

You can see the circles for the top and the bottom and the rectangle that makes up the side.

Here is a net for a rectangular prism. The dashed line segments show you where to fold. The solid line segments show you where to cut.

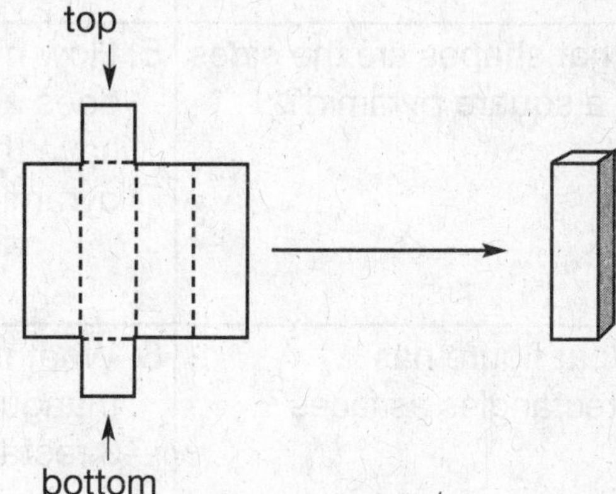

You can see 4 rectangles for the sides of the prism and the 2 squares for the top and bottom.

Circle the correct letter of the net for each solid.

1. Cone 

A  **B** 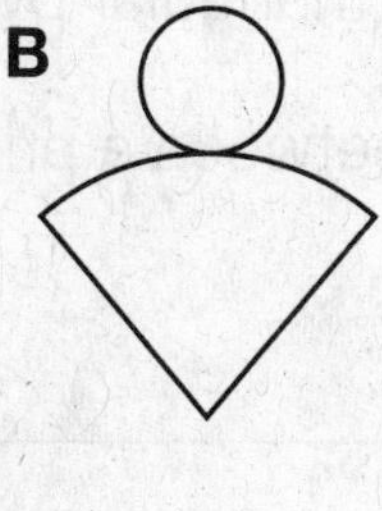

2. Cube

A 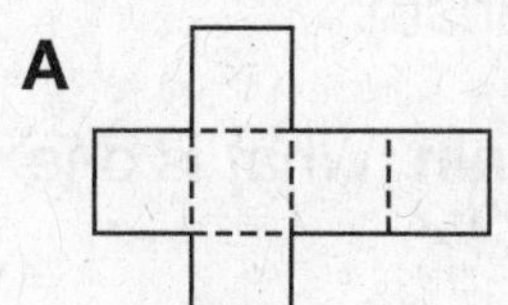 **B** 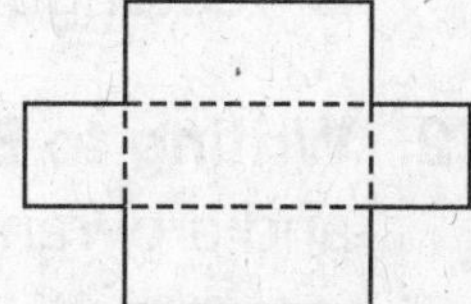

Name ________________________________

Practice
8-8

Views of Solids: Nets

Solve.

1. What are the shapes of the faces of a triangular prism?	**2.** What shape does a triangular prism have that a rectangular prism does not have?	**3.** How many more vertices does a square pyramid have than a triangular pyramid?
4. What shapes are the sides of a square pyramid?	**5.** How many more vertices does a triangular prism have than a triangular pyramid?	**6.** How many vertices does a rectangular prism have?
7. What figure has 6 rectangles as faces?	**8.** What figure has 2 triangular faces and 3 rectangular faces?	**9.** How many more vertices does a rectangular prism have than a rectangular pyramid?

10. Julie made a coin bank in the shape of a rectangular prism. She wants to paint each face a different color. How may colors will she need?

____

11. Which solid figure has the most vertices?

A triangular prism
B rectangular prism
C rectangular pyramid
D triangular pyramid

12. **Writing to Explain** What is one difference between a prism and a pyramid?

____

____

____

____

Name ______________________________

Views of Solids: Perspective

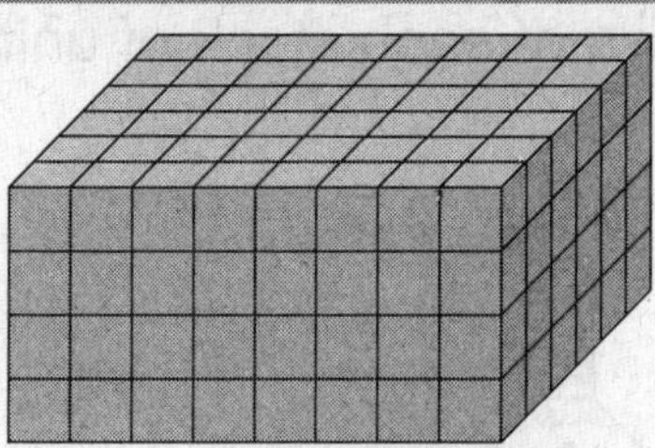

4 high by 8 wide by 6 deep

Front view:	Side view:	Top or bottom view:
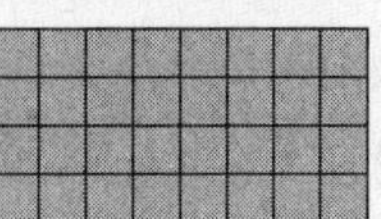	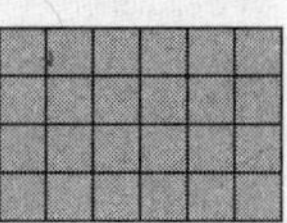	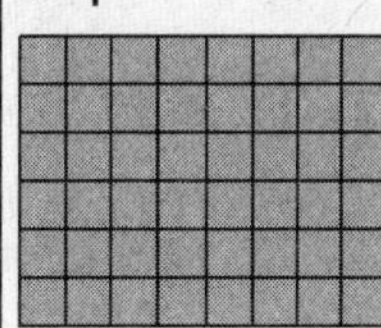
The front view of the solid is 32 cubes.	The side view of the solid is 24 cubes.	The top view and the bottom view are the same, 48 cubes.

Draw front, right, and top views of each stack of unit blocks.

1. 

front

2. 

front

3. 

front

Name ______________________

Views of Solids: Perspective

For **1** through **4**, draw front, right, and top views of each stack of unit blocks.

1. 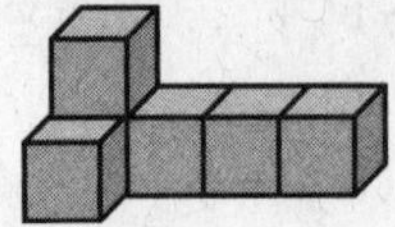

front

2. 

front

3. 

front

4. 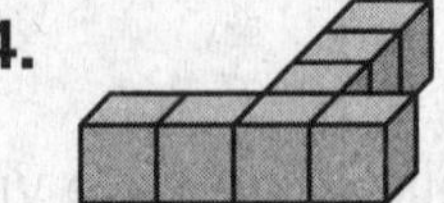

front

For **5** through **7**, draw the perspective of the figure.

5. The side view of a cube

6. The top view of a rectangular prism

7. The side view of a rectangular prism

8. Which view is shown for this solid?

solid

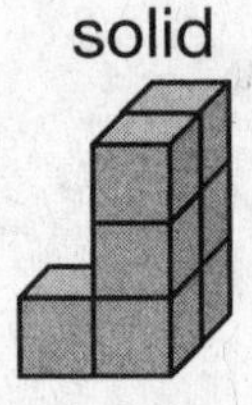

view

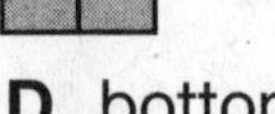

A front **B** top **C** side **D** bottom

9. Writing to Explain What is the difference between the shape of a side view of a rectangular pyramid and a top-down view of a rectangular pyramid?

____

____

Name ____________________

Reteaching **8-10**

Problem Solving: Make and Test Generalizations

When you make a generalization, you make a broad statement about something that a group has in common. A generalization helps you find patterns. When you make a generalization, it is important to test it to be sure it is correct.

Example: $1 \times 24 = 24$ $1 \times 93 = 93$ $1 \times 126 = 126$

Generalization: A number multiplied by 1 is itself.

Test: If I multiply a different number by 1, it is also equal to itself. For example, $1 \times 2 = 2$; $1 \times 3 = 3$; $1 \times 4 = 4$, etc.; any number multiplied by 1 is itself.
My generalization is correct.

In some cases, it is possible to find more than one correct generalization:

Example: Jessica found a red pencil, 3 red pens, and 2 red markers in her backpack.

Generalization: The things Jessica found are all writing instruments.

Generalization #2: The things Jessica found are all red.

Test: I can write with a pencil, a pen, and a marker. Also, the pencil, the pens, and the marker are all red. My generalizations are correct.

1. Randy has 2 tennis balls, 6 marbles, and 1 orange in his desk drawer. What generalization can you make about these things?

____

2. This week, Sandy was out sick on Monday and Tuesday. Last week, Jared was out sick on Thursday and Friday. The week before, Elisa was out sick on Wednesday and Thursday. What generalization can you make about these three students' absences? Can you make a second generalization?

____

3. Write down the multiples of 15, 20, and 25. What generalization can you make about all multiples of 5?

____

Name ______________________

Practice

8-10

Problem Solving: Make and Test Generalizations

For **1** through **3**, use the images to make a generalization and test your answer.

1.

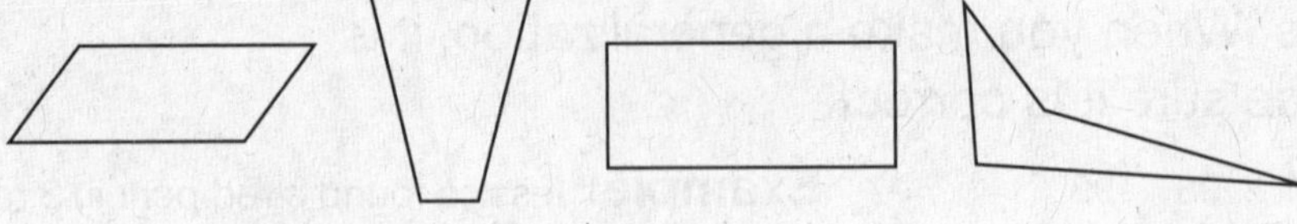

____

____

2.

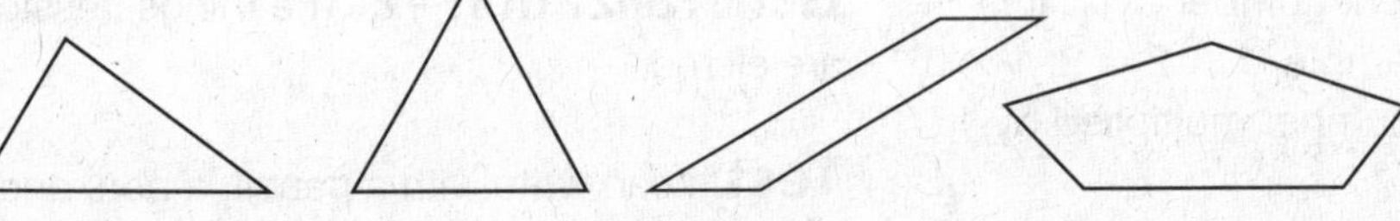

____

3.

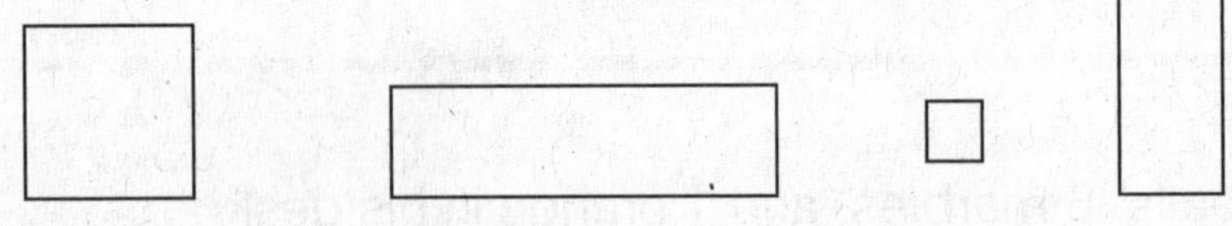

____

____

4. Which answer below is a good generalization about all rectangular prisms?

A All rectangular prisms have same sized faces

B All rectangular prisms have 12 edges

C All rectangular prisms are cubes

D All rectangular prisms have 1 net

5. Writing to Explain Try to draw a triangle with 2 right or obtuse angles. What generalizations can you make about the angles of a triangle? Explain.

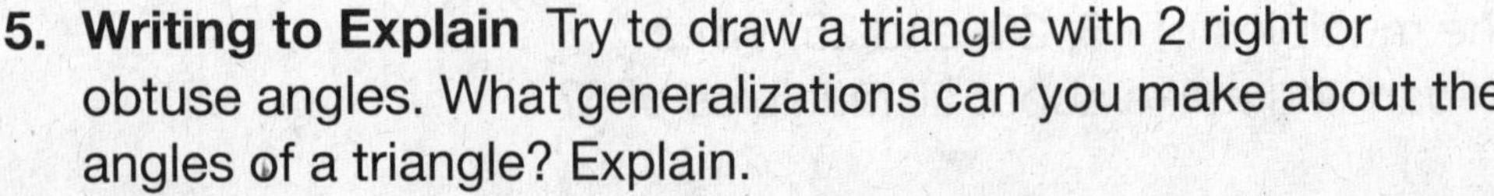

____

____

Name ______________________

Regions and Sets

The top number, the numerator, tells the number of equal parts described. The bottom number, the denominator, tells how many equal parts there are in all.

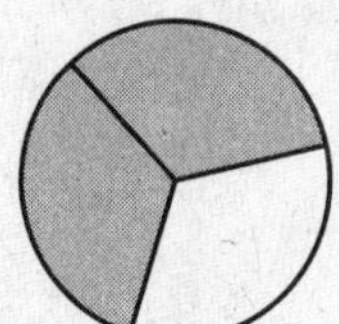

$\frac{2}{3}$ ← Numerator: 2 parts are shaded.
← Denominator: There are 3 parts total.

$\frac{2}{3}$ of the circle is shaded.

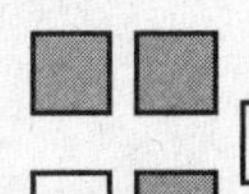

$\frac{3}{5}$ ← Numerator: 3 parts are shaded.
← Denominator: There are 5 parts total.

$\frac{3}{5}$ of the set is shaded.

Write a fraction for the part of the region that is shaded.

1. 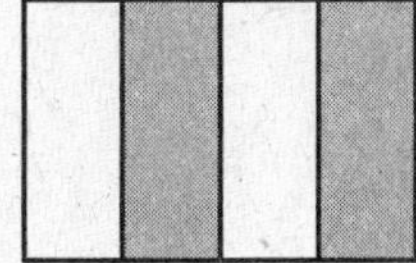 ______

2. 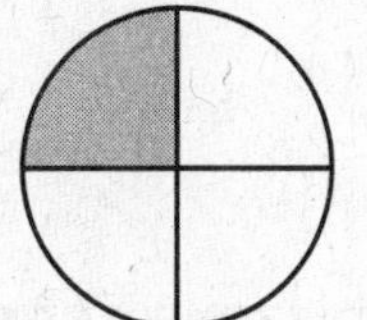 ______

3.  ______

4. 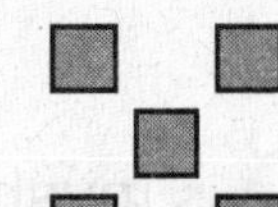 ______

Shade in the models to show each fraction.

5. $\frac{5}{15}$

6. $\frac{7}{9}$

7. Reasoning Tara says that $\frac{1}{2}$ of a salad is always the same amount. Lynn says that it could be different amounts, depending on how large the salad is. Who is correct? Why?

____

____

____

____

Name ______________________

Practice 9-1

Regions and Sets

Write a fraction for the part of the region below that is shaded.

1.  ______

2. 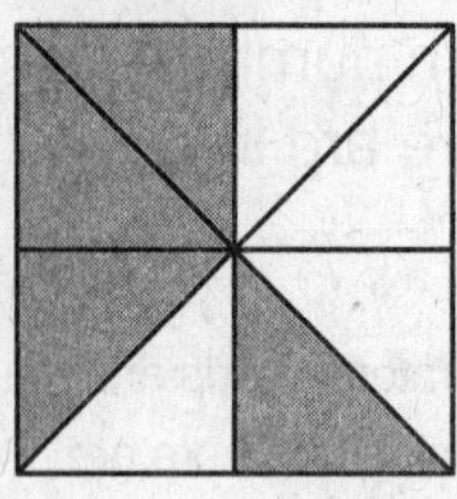 ______

Shade in the models to show each fraction.

3. $\frac{2}{4}$ 

4. $\frac{7}{10}$  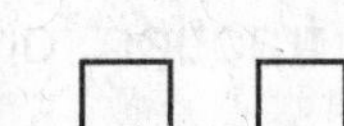

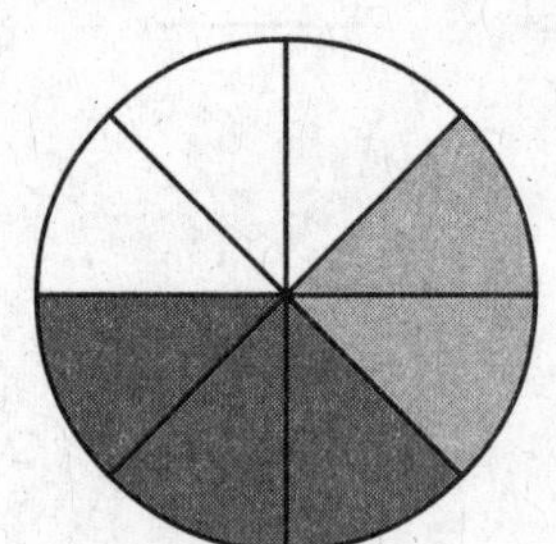

5. What fraction of the pizza is cheese?

____

6. What fraction of the pizza is mushroom?

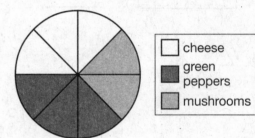

____

7. **Number Sense** Is $\frac{1}{4}$ of 12 greater than $\frac{1}{4}$ of 8? Explain your answer.

____

____

8. A set has 12 squares. Which is the number of squares in $\frac{1}{3}$ of the set?

A 3 **B** 4 **C** 6 **D** 9

9. **Writing to Explain** Explain why $\frac{1}{2}$ of Region A is not larger than $\frac{1}{2}$ of Region B.

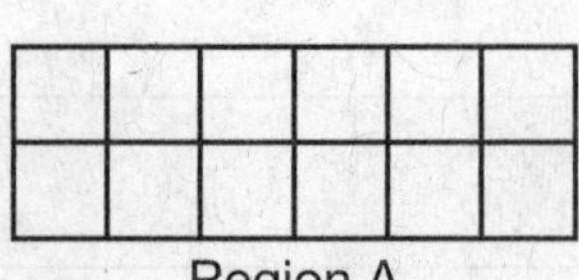
Region A

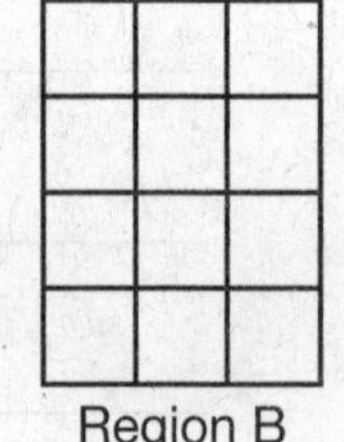
Region B

____

____

Name ______________________

Fractions and Division

To show how you can share items, you can divide to find a fraction of the total.

Four people shared two submarine sandwiches equally.

What fraction of the sandwiches did each person receive?

Divide each sandwich into 4 equal parts.

Each part is $1 \div 4$ or $\frac{1}{4}$.

Each person received one equal slice from each sandwich for a total of 2 slices.

There are 8 slices altogether, so each person received $\frac{2}{8}$ or $\frac{1}{4}$ of the shared sandwiches.

Tell what fraction each person gets when they share equally.

1. Six friends divide 2 apples.

____

____

2. Two friends pay for a $6 gift.

____

____

3. Eight runners run an equal part in a 5-mile relay.

____

____

4. Five rabbits share 4 carrots equally.

____

____

5. Five people share 2 cans of paint.

____

____

6. Two children share 2 small boxes of cereal.

____

____

Name ___________________

Fractions and Division

What fraction does each person get when they share equally?

1. Eight friends share 3 bags of toys. ___________

2. Five people share 2 jugs of water. ___________

Five friends are sharing supplies on a camping trip. Tell what fraction each person gets when they share equally.

3. Two boxes of trail mix. ___________

4. Three packages of water purifying tablets. ___________

5. **Reasoning** Four people each bought 2 bottles of Vermont maple syrup. Each person plans to share their bottles with 3 friends. How much does each person get? ___________

6. Which model represents 6 people sharing 1 five-foot sub?

A

C

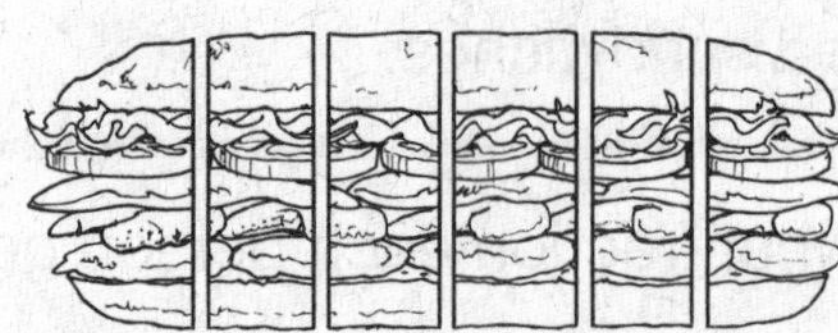

B

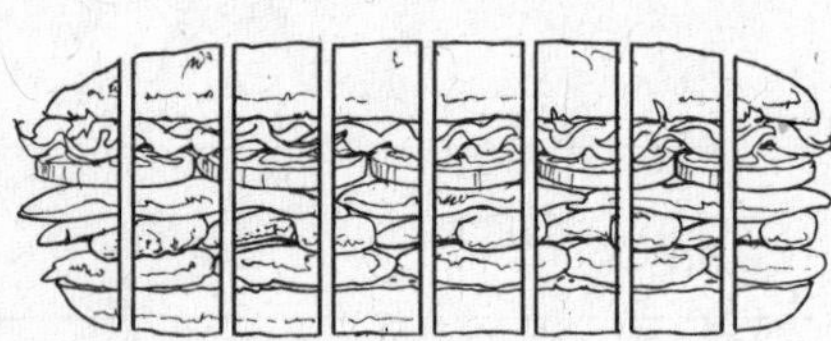

D

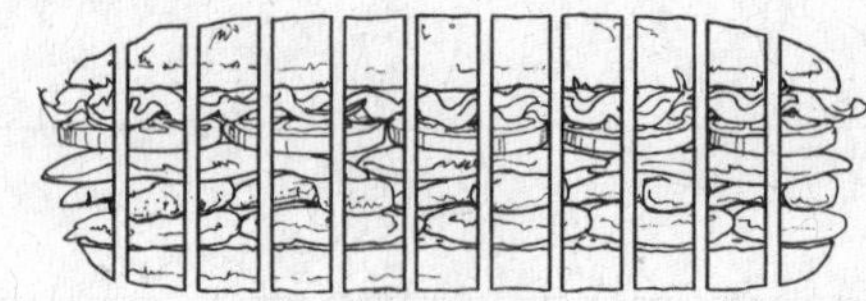

7. **Writing to Explain** Several friends are taking turns flying a kite. Each friend flies the kite for the same amount of time. They spend 6 hours flying the kite altogether. Explain what information you need to find how long each friend flew the kite for.

____

____

Name ______________________

Equivalent Fractions

If two fractions name the same amount, they are called **equivalent fractions**.

Are $\frac{1}{2}$ and $\frac{3}{6}$ equivalent fractions?

Multiply the numerator and denominator by the same number.

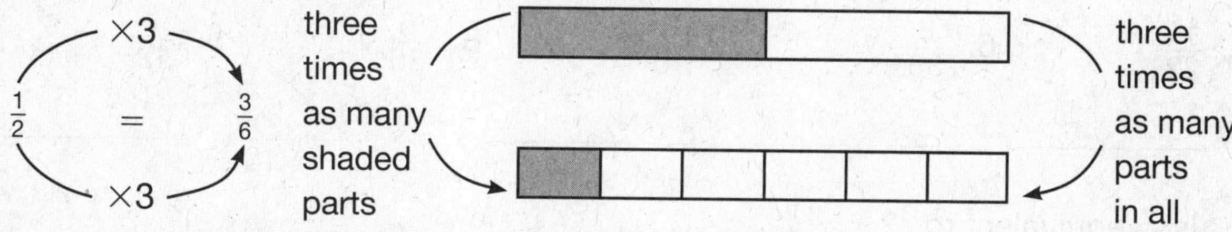

Use division to write a fraction that is equivalent to $\frac{6}{24}$.

Think of a number that is a factor of both 6 and 24. 3 is a factor of 6 and 24. Divide the numerator and the denominator by 3.

$$\frac{6}{24} \overset{\div 3}{=} \frac{2}{8} \overset{\div 2}{=} \frac{1}{4}$$

$\frac{2}{8}$ and $\frac{1}{4}$ are both equivalent to $\frac{6}{24}$.

Find the missing number.

1. $\frac{1}{4} = \frac{\square}{8}$ ____
2. $\frac{15}{20} = \frac{\square}{4}$ ____
3. $\frac{2}{7} = \frac{\square}{21}$ ____
4. $\frac{9}{27} = \frac{\square}{3}$ ____

Multiply to find an equivalent fraction.

5. $\frac{3}{10}$ ____
6. $\frac{1}{2}$ ____
7. $\frac{5}{6}$ ____
8. $\frac{3}{4}$ ____

Divide to find an equivalent fraction.

9. $\frac{10}{15}$ ____
10. $\frac{9}{24}$ ____
11. $\frac{21}{28}$ ____
12. $\frac{25}{35}$ ____
13. $\frac{8}{20}$ ____
14. $\frac{9}{18}$ ____
15. $\frac{8}{18}$ ____
16. $\frac{15}{40}$ ____

Name ______________________

Practice

9-3

Equivalent Fractions

Find the missing number.

1. $\frac{1}{2} = \frac{\square}{12}$ ________

2. $\frac{6}{10} = \frac{\square}{5}$ ________

3. $\frac{4}{16} = \frac{\square}{4}$ ________

4. $2\frac{4}{20} = 2\frac{\square}{40}$ ________

Multiply or divide to find an equivalent fraction.

5. $\frac{11}{22}$ ________

6. $\frac{6}{36}$ ________

7. $\frac{9}{10}$ ________

8. $\frac{5}{35}$ ________

9. $\frac{7}{12}$ ________

10. Is $\frac{2}{14}$ equivalent to $\frac{3}{7}$? ________

11. In Mark's collection of antique bottles, $\frac{4}{9}$ of the bottles are dark green. Write three equivalent fractions for $\frac{4}{9}$.

____

12. Write a pair of equivalent fractions for the picture above.

____

13. At the air show, $\frac{1}{3}$ of the airplanes were gliders. Which fraction is not an equivalent fraction for $\frac{1}{3}$?

A $\frac{5}{15}$ B $\frac{7}{21}$ C $\frac{6}{24}$ D $\frac{9}{27}$

14. **Writing to Explain** In Missy's sports-cards collection, $\frac{5}{7}$ of the cards are baseball. In Frank's collection, $\frac{12}{36}$ are baseball. Frank says they have the same fraction of baseball cards. Is he correct?

____

____

Name ___________________

Fractions in Simplest Form

Use division to write a fraction that is equivalent to $\frac{6}{24}$.

Think of a number that is a factor of both 6 and 24. 3 is a factor of 6 and 24. Divide the numerator and the denominator by 3. If you continue to divide until 1 is the only factor of both the numerator and denominator, you will find the fraction in **simplest form**.

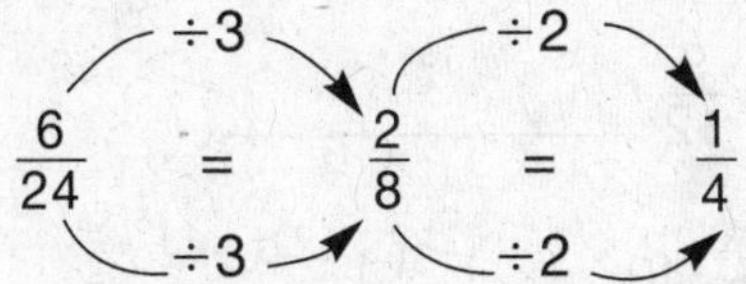

$\frac{2}{8}$ and $\frac{1}{4}$ are both equivalent to $\frac{6}{24}$.

Only $\frac{1}{4}$ is in simplest form.

Find the missing number.

1. $\frac{2}{8} = \frac{\square}{4}$ ____ **2.** $\frac{15}{20} = \frac{\square}{4}$ ____ **3.** $\frac{7}{21} = \frac{\square}{3}$ ____ **4.** $\frac{9}{27} = \frac{\square}{3}$ ____

Write each fraction in simplest form.

5. $\frac{6}{10}$ ____ **6.** $\frac{4}{10}$ ____ **7.** $\frac{25}{30}$ ____ **8.** $\frac{24}{32}$ ____

9. $\frac{10}{15}$ ____ **10.** $\frac{9}{24}$ ____ **11.** $\frac{21}{28}$ ____ **12.** $\frac{25}{35}$ ____

13. $\frac{8}{20}$ ____ **14.** $\frac{9}{18}$ ____ **15.** $\frac{8}{18}$ ____ **16.** $\frac{15}{40}$ ____

17. $\frac{2}{18}$ ____ **18.** $\frac{6}{24}$ ____ **19.** $\frac{32}{34}$ ____ **20.** $\frac{12}{26}$ ____

Name ______________________

Practice
9-4

Fractions in Simplest Form

For 1 through 18, write each fraction in simplest form. If it is in simplest form, write "simplest form."

1. $\frac{13}{14}$ ________ **2.** $\frac{7}{8}$ ________ **3.** $\frac{1}{23}$ ________

4. $\frac{15}{20}$ ________ **5.** $\frac{2}{18}$ ________ **6.** $\frac{6}{30}$ ________

7. $\frac{5}{18}$ ________ **8.** $\frac{13}{26}$ ________ **9.** $\frac{9}{12}$ ________

10. $\frac{7}{21}$ ________ **11.** $\frac{7}{10}$ ________ **12.** $\frac{40}{50}$ ________

13. $\frac{18}{36}$ ________ **14.** $\frac{25}{35}$ ________ **15.** $\frac{12}{14}$ ________

16. $\frac{8}{9}$ ________ **17.** $\frac{60}{80}$ ________ **18.** $\frac{2}{8}$ ________

19. Sheldon has scored $\frac{6}{18}$ of the points in a basketball game. How can you use division to simplify the fraction of the points he scored? What is $\frac{6}{18}$ in simplest form?

____

____

____

20. What is the simplest form of the fraction $\frac{40}{80}$?

A $\frac{4}{8}$ **B** $\frac{1}{4}$ **C** $\frac{2}{4}$ **D** $\frac{1}{2}$

21. **Writing to Explain** If the numerator of a fraction is a prime number, can the fraction be simplified? Why or why not?

____

____

____

Name ______________________

Reteaching **9-5**

Improper Fractions and Mixed Numbers

You can use fraction strips to write a mixed number as an improper fraction.

$3\frac{1}{2}$ of the strips below are shaded.

$\frac{1}{2}$	$\frac{1}{2}$
$\frac{1}{2}$	$\frac{1}{2}$
$\frac{1}{2}$	$\frac{1}{2}$
$\frac{1}{2}$	$\frac{1}{2}$

Into how many parts is each strip divided? 2. This is your denominator.

Count the shaded halves. There are 7. This is your numerator.

$3\frac{1}{2}$ is the same as the improper fraction $\frac{7}{2}$.

You can also use fraction strips to write an improper number as a mixed fraction.

$\frac{8}{3}$ of the strips below are shaded.

$\frac{1}{3}$	$\frac{1}{3}$	$\frac{1}{3}$
$\frac{1}{3}$	$\frac{1}{3}$	$\frac{1}{3}$
$\frac{1}{3}$	$\frac{1}{3}$	$\frac{1}{3}$

How many strips are completely shaded? 2. This is your whole number.

What fraction of the third strip is shaded? $\frac{2}{3}$. This is your fraction.

$\frac{8}{3}$ is the same as the mixed number $2\frac{2}{3}$.

Write each mixed number as an improper fraction.

1. $2\frac{1}{3}$ ________ **2.** $4\frac{1}{5}$ ________ **3.** $2\frac{3}{4}$ ________ **4.** $5\frac{2}{6}$ ________

Write each improper fraction as a mixed number or a whole number.

5. $\frac{13}{12}$ ________ **6.** $\frac{50}{10}$ ________ **7.** $\frac{23}{10}$ ________ **8.** $\frac{17}{15}$ ________

9. Writing to Explain Is $\frac{45}{5}$ equal to a whole number or a mixed number? Explain how you know.

____

____

____

____

Name ______________________

Practice 9-5

Improper Fractions and Mixed Numbers

Write each mixed number as an improper fraction.

1. $3\frac{2}{5}$ __________ **2.** $6\frac{1}{4}$ __________ **3.** $2\frac{1}{12}$ __________ **4.** $2\frac{7}{9}$ __________

Write each improper fraction as a mixed number or whole number. Write each in simplest form.

5. $\frac{12}{5}$ __________ **6.** $\frac{27}{9}$ __________ **7.** $\frac{32}{3}$ __________ **8.** $\frac{20}{12}$ __________

9. Number Sense Matt had to write $3\frac{8}{24}$ as an improper fraction. Write how you would tell Matt the easiest way to do so.

____

____

____

____

10. Jill has $\frac{11}{8}$ oz of trail mix. Write the weight of Jill's trail mix as a mixed number. __________

11. Nick has $1\frac{3}{4}$ gal of milk. Write the amount of milk Nick has as an improper fraction. __________

12. Which is NOT an improper fraction equal to 8?

A $\frac{24}{3}$ **B** $\frac{49}{7}$ **C** $\frac{56}{7}$ **D** $\frac{64}{8}$

13. Writing to Explain Write three different improper fractions that equal $4\frac{2}{3}$. (Hint: find equivalent fractions.)

____

____

Name ______________________________

Comparing Fractions

Leanne wanted to compare $\frac{4}{6}$ and $\frac{3}{4}$. She used fraction strips to help.

				$\frac{1}{6}$	$\frac{1}{6}$	$\frac{4}{6}$
			$\frac{1}{4}$			$\frac{3}{4}$

She compared the amounts that were shaded in each picture. Because the amount shaded in $\frac{3}{4}$ is more than the amount shaded in $\frac{4}{6}$, she knows that $\frac{3}{4}$ is greater than $\frac{4}{6}$.

So, $\frac{3}{4} > \frac{4}{6}$.

Write > or < for each ◯. Use fraction strips or benchmark fractions to help.

1. $\frac{5}{6}$ ◯ $\frac{2}{3}$ **2.** $\frac{1}{5}$ ◯ $\frac{2}{8}$ **3.** $\frac{9}{10}$ ◯ $\frac{6}{8}$ **4.** $\frac{3}{4}$ ◯ $\frac{1}{4}$

5. $\frac{8}{9}$ ◯ $\frac{5}{10}$ **6.** $\frac{2}{5}$ ◯ $\frac{2}{6}$ **7.** $\frac{6}{9}$ ◯ $\frac{7}{9}$ **8.** $\frac{2}{10}$ ◯ $\frac{3}{5}$

The same number of students attended school all week.

Day	Fraction of students buying lunch
Monday	$\frac{1}{2}$
Tuesday	$\frac{2}{5}$
Wednesday	$\frac{3}{4}$
Thursday	$\frac{5}{8}$
Friday	$\frac{4}{6}$

9. Did more students buy lunch on Tuesday or on Wednesday? ______________

10. Did more students buy lunch on Thursday or on Friday? ______________

Name ______________________

Practice **9-6**

Comparing Fractions

Write > or < for each ◯. You may use fraction strips to help.

1. $\frac{1}{2}$ ◯ $\frac{3}{13}$ **2.** $\frac{8}{9}$ ◯ $\frac{5}{9}$ **3.** $\frac{3}{8}$ ◯ $\frac{11}{22}$

4. $\frac{3}{3}$ ◯ $\frac{7}{8}$ **5.** $\frac{3}{5}$ ◯ $\frac{1}{3}$ **6.** $\frac{1}{4}$ ◯ $\frac{2}{4}$

7. $\frac{5}{6}$ ◯ $\frac{5}{8}$ **8.** $\frac{7}{12}$ ◯ $\frac{4}{5}$ **9.** $\frac{3}{7}$ ◯ $\frac{6}{7}$

10. Number Sense Explain how you know that $\frac{21}{30}$ is greater than $\frac{2}{3}$.

____

____

____

11. Tina completed $\frac{2}{3}$ of her homework before dinner. George completed $\frac{4}{7}$ of his homework before dinner. Who completed a greater fraction of homework? ______________

12. Jackson played a video game for $\frac{1}{6}$ hr. Hailey played a video game for $\frac{1}{3}$ hr. Who played the video game for a greater amount of time? ______________

13. Which fraction is greater than $\frac{3}{4}$?

A $\frac{5}{9}$ **B** $\frac{17}{24}$ **C** $\frac{15}{20}$ **D** $\frac{7}{9}$

14. Writing to Explain James says that $\frac{5}{5}$ is greater than $\frac{99}{100}$. Is he correct? Explain.

____

____

____

____

Name ______________________

Ordering Fractions

How can you order fractions?

Order $\frac{2}{3}$, $\frac{1}{6}$, $\frac{7}{12}$ from least to greatest.

$\frac{1}{3}$	$\frac{1}{3}$	$\frac{1}{3}$

$\frac{1}{6}$	$\frac{1}{6}$	$\frac{1}{6}$	$\frac{1}{6}$	$\frac{1}{6}$	$\frac{1}{6}$

$\frac{1}{12}$	$\frac{1}{12}$	$\frac{1}{12}$	$\frac{1}{12}$	$\frac{1}{12}$	$\frac{1}{12}$	$\frac{1}{12}$	$\frac{1}{12}$	$\frac{1}{12}$	$\frac{1}{12}$	$\frac{1}{12}$	$\frac{1}{12}$

Find equivalent fractions with a common denominator.

$\frac{1}{12}$	$\frac{1}{12}$	$\frac{1}{12}$	$\frac{1}{12}$	$\frac{1}{12}$	$\frac{1}{12}$	$\frac{1}{12}$	$\frac{1}{12}$
$\frac{1}{12}$	$\frac{1}{12}$						
$\frac{1}{12}$	$\frac{1}{12}$	$\frac{1}{12}$	$\frac{1}{12}$	$\frac{1}{12}$	$\frac{1}{12}$	$\frac{1}{12}$	

Compare the numerators.
Order the fractions from least to greatest.
$\frac{2}{12} < \frac{7}{12} < \frac{8}{12}$.

Order the fractions from least to greatest.

1. $\frac{7}{10}$, $\frac{9}{20}$, $\frac{4}{5}$ ______________________

$\frac{1}{10}$	$\frac{1}{10}$	$\frac{1}{10}$	$\frac{1}{10}$	$\frac{1}{10}$	$\frac{1}{10}$	$\frac{1}{10}$

$\frac{1}{20}$	$\frac{1}{20}$	$\frac{1}{20}$	$\frac{1}{20}$	$\frac{1}{20}$	$\frac{1}{20}$	$\frac{1}{20}$	$\frac{1}{20}$	$\frac{1}{20}$

$\frac{1}{5}$	$\frac{1}{5}$	$\frac{1}{5}$	$\frac{1}{5}$

2. $\frac{3}{8}$, $\frac{1}{3}$, $\frac{5}{24}$ ______________________

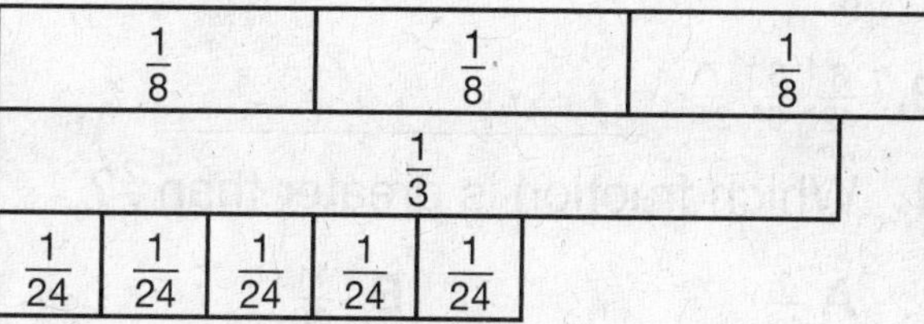

Find equivalent fractions with a common denominator and order from least to greatest.

3. $\frac{1}{2}$, $\frac{4}{9}$, $\frac{4}{18}$ ______________________

4. $\frac{3}{4}$, $\frac{2}{3}$, $\frac{7}{8}$ ______________________

5. $\frac{3}{10}$, $\frac{4}{30}$, $\frac{4}{5}$ ______________________

6. $\frac{1}{2}$, $\frac{3}{10}$, $\frac{4}{5}$ ______________________

7. $\frac{3}{42}$, $\frac{5}{6}$, $\frac{7}{21}$ ______________________

8. $\frac{9}{14}$, $\frac{1}{2}$, $\frac{6}{7}$ ______________________

Name ____________________

Ordering Fractions

Order the fractions from least to greatest.

1. $\frac{1}{9}, \frac{7}{8}, \frac{5}{6}$ ____________________

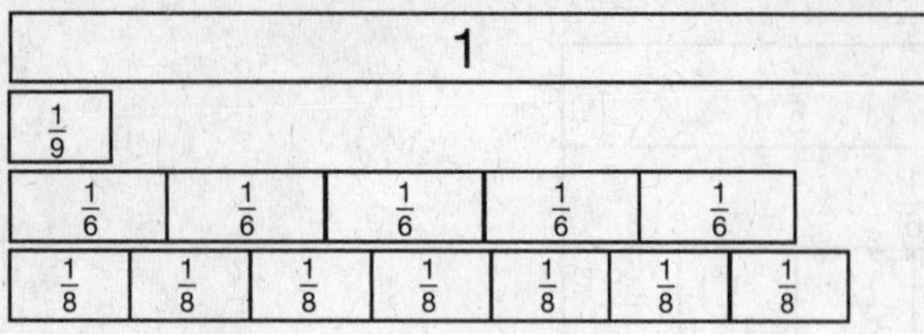

2. $\frac{1}{2}, \frac{7}{12}, \frac{4}{10}$ ____________________

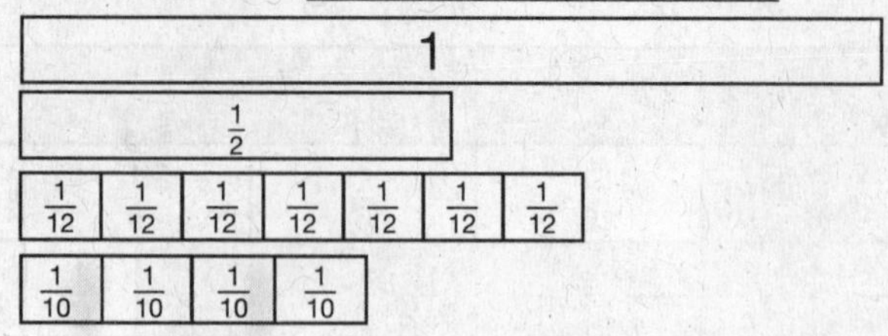

3. $\frac{3}{9}, \frac{1}{4}, \frac{5}{12}$ ____________________

1

$\frac{1}{4}$

$\frac{1}{9}$ $\frac{1}{9}$ $\frac{1}{9}$

$\frac{1}{12}$ $\frac{1}{12}$ $\frac{1}{12}$ $\frac{1}{12}$ $\frac{1}{12}$

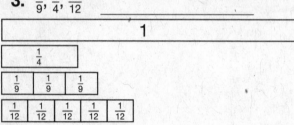

4. $\frac{4}{15}, \frac{2}{5}, \frac{1}{3}$ ____________________

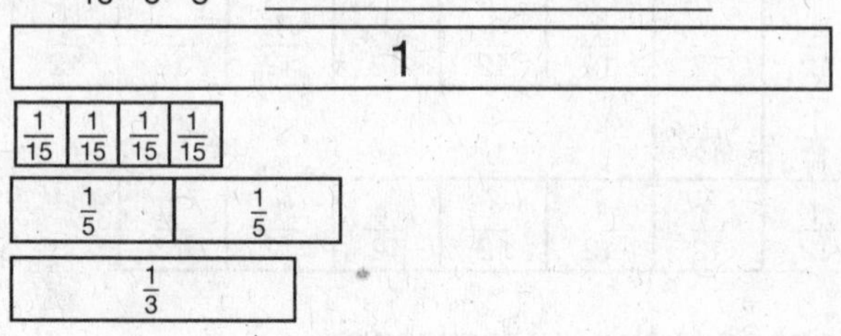

Find equivalent fractions with a common denominator and order from least to greatest.

5. $\frac{2}{3}, \frac{1}{2}, \frac{5}{12}$ ____________________

6. $\frac{3}{8}, \frac{1}{3}, \frac{3}{4}$ ____________________

7. $\frac{3}{7}, \frac{1}{9}, \frac{2}{3}$ ____________________

8. $\frac{7}{12}, \frac{2}{6}, \frac{7}{8}$ ____________________

9. $\frac{3}{42}, \frac{5}{6}, \frac{7}{21}$ ____________________

10. $\frac{9}{15}, \frac{1}{3}, \frac{2}{5}$ ____________________

11. Which fraction is greater than $\frac{2}{3}$?

A $\frac{1}{12}$ **B** $\frac{11}{36}$ **C** $\frac{5}{16}$ **D** $\frac{11}{15}$

12. **Writing to Explain** Explain how you know that $\frac{15}{30}$ is greater than $\frac{1}{3}$ but less than $\frac{2}{3}$?

____

____

____

____

Name ______________________________

Reteaching
9-8

Problem Solving: Writing to Explain

Gina and her brother Don made homemade pasta with their mother. Gina made $\frac{1}{4}$ of a pan of pasta. Don made $\frac{3}{8}$ of a pan. Which person made more pasta?

Writing to Explain

- Write your explanation in steps to make it clear.
- Tell what the numbers mean in your explanation.
- Tell why you took certain steps.

Example

- Because $\frac{1}{4}$ and $\frac{3}{8}$ have different denominators, I multiplied the numerator and denominator of $\frac{1}{4}$ by 2 to get $\frac{2}{8}$.
- Then I could compare the numerators of $\frac{2}{8}$ and $\frac{3}{8}$. Because $\frac{3}{8}$ is greater than $\frac{2}{8}$ I knew that Don made more pasta.

1. Humans usually have 20 baby teeth, which are replaced by 32 adult teeth. Raul said he has lost $\frac{6}{20}$ of his baby teeth. Write two fractions equivalent to this number. Explain how you came up with the fractions.

____

____

____

____

____

____

Name ______________________

Practice
9-8

Problem Solving: Writing to Explain

1. Mary has 23 marbles. $\frac{7}{23}$ of the marbles are yellow and $\frac{13}{23}$ of the marbles are blue. The rest of the marbles are green. How many marbles are green? Explain how you know.

2. Adam wants to compare the fractions $\frac{2}{5}$, $\frac{1}{6}$, and $\frac{1}{3}$. He wants to order them from least to greatest and rewrite them so they all have the same denominator. Explain how Adam can rewrite the fractions.

3. Adam used the three fractions to make a circle graph and colored each a different color. What fraction of the graph is not colored? Explain your answer.

Name ______________________________

Reteaching
10-1

Adding and Subtracting Fractions with Like Denominators

Example 1

$$\begin{array}{r} \frac{1}{9} \\ + \frac{2}{9} \\ \hline \end{array}$$

The denominators are the same, so you can add the numerators.

$\frac{3}{9} = \frac{1}{3}$ Rewrite $\frac{3}{9}$ as $\frac{1}{3}$

Example 2

$$\begin{array}{r} \frac{6}{18} \\ + \frac{6}{18} \\ \hline \end{array}$$

$\frac{12}{18} = \frac{6}{9} = \frac{2}{3}$

Write $\frac{12}{18}$ in simplest form.

$$\frac{12}{18} \overset{\div 6}{\underset{\div 6}{=}} \frac{2}{3}$$

Add or subtract fractions, and write answers in simplest form.

1. $\frac{1}{4} + \frac{1}{4}$ ______ **2.** $\frac{1}{3} + \frac{1}{3}$ ______ **3.** $\frac{5}{14} - \frac{3}{14}$ ______ **4.** $\frac{1}{11} + \frac{3}{11}$ ______ **5.** $\frac{17}{22} - \frac{5}{22}$ ______

6. $\begin{array}{r} \frac{1}{6} \\ + \frac{2}{6} \\ \hline \end{array}$ ______ **7.** $\begin{array}{r} \frac{9}{10} \\ - \frac{4}{10} \\ \hline \end{array}$ ______ **8.** $\begin{array}{r} \frac{11}{16} \\ - \frac{7}{16} \\ \hline \end{array}$ ______ **9.** $\begin{array}{r} \frac{3}{12} \\ + \frac{6}{12} \\ \hline \end{array}$ ______ **10.** $\begin{array}{r} \frac{1}{25} \\ + \frac{4}{25} \\ \hline \end{array}$ ______

11. At lunch, Alice ate $\frac{3}{8}$ of her sandwich. Later, for a snack, she ate another $\frac{3}{8}$ of the sandwich. How much of the sandwich did Alice eat?

____

Name ____________________

Practice **10-1**

Adding and Subtracting Fractions with Like Denominators

For **1** through **15**, add or subtract the fractions, and write the answer in simplest form. You may use fraction strips to help.

1. $\frac{1}{8} + \frac{3}{8}$

2. $\frac{8}{10} - \frac{1}{10}$

3. $\frac{1}{3} + \frac{1}{3}$

4. $\frac{7}{8} - \frac{3}{8}$

5. $\frac{1}{9} + \frac{4}{9}$

6. $\frac{8}{12} + \frac{2}{12}$

7. $\frac{9}{12} + \frac{2}{12}$

8. $\frac{3}{8} + \frac{2}{8}$

9. $\frac{5}{6} - \frac{1}{6}$

10. $\frac{5}{8} - \frac{2}{8}$

11. $\frac{7}{10} + \frac{1}{10}$

12. $\frac{9}{12} - \frac{4}{12}$

13. $\frac{1}{6} + \frac{2}{6}$

14. $\frac{6}{7} - \frac{5}{7}$

15. $\frac{1}{4} + \frac{1}{4}$

16. Jacob is making a stew. The stew calls for $\frac{3}{8}$ cup of rice. If he doubles the recipe how much rice will he need? Write your answer in simplest form.

____

17. A pizza was sliced into 10 pieces. Bill ate $\frac{2}{10}$ of the pizza. How much of the pizza was left?

A $\frac{1}{5}$ **B** $\frac{2}{5}$ **C** $\frac{4}{5}$ **D** 1

18. Writing to Explain Gerry folded $\frac{3}{8}$ of the pile of shirts. Molly folded $\frac{1}{8}$ of the pile of shirts. Together, did they fold more than half the shirts? Explain your answer.

____

____

Name ___________________________

Reteaching **10-2**

Add Fractions with Unlike Denominators

When you add fractions with unlike denominators, you need to change the fractions to equivalent fractions so they have a **common denominator**.

Example 1 Hassan used $\frac{1}{4}$ of a bag of black potting soil and $\frac{2}{3}$ of a bag of soil with clay in his container garden. How much soil did he use altogether? Find $\frac{1}{4} + \frac{2}{3}$.

Step 1 Rewrite the fractions using a common denominator. Think: What number has 4 and 3 as factors? 12

$$\frac{1 \times 3}{4 \times 3} = \frac{3}{12} \qquad + \qquad \frac{2 \times 4}{3 \times 4} = \frac{8}{12}$$

Step 2 Add the new fractions. Write the sum in simplest form.

$$\frac{1}{4} = \frac{3}{12}$$
$$+\frac{2}{3} = \frac{8}{12}$$
$$\frac{11}{12}$$

$\frac{11}{12}$ is already in simplest form.

Hassan used $\frac{11}{12}$ of a bag of soil altogether.

Example 2 When one denominator is a factor of the other denominator, you have to rewrite only one of the fractions. Find $\frac{2}{3} + \frac{2}{9}$.

Step 1 3 is a factor of 9, so rewrite $\frac{2}{3}$ with a denominator of 9.

$$\frac{2 \times 3}{3 \times 3} = \frac{6}{9}$$

Step 2 Add the new fractions.

$$\frac{2}{3} = \frac{6}{9}$$
$$+\frac{2}{9} = \frac{2}{9}$$
$$\frac{8}{9}$$

$\frac{8}{9}$ is already in simplest form.

Write the answers in simplest form.

1. $\frac{3}{5} + \frac{1}{10}$ ________ **2.** $\frac{1}{2} + \frac{1}{8}$ ________ **3.** $\frac{1}{6} + \frac{2}{3}$ ________ **4.** $\frac{7}{12} + \frac{1}{3}$ ________ **5.** $\frac{1}{3} + \frac{2}{9}$ ________

6. $\frac{3}{8} + \frac{1}{4}$ ________ **7.** $\frac{1}{4} + \frac{1}{6}$ ________ **8.** $\frac{2}{5} + \frac{1}{2}$ ________ **9.** $\frac{1}{3} + \frac{2}{5}$ ________ **10.** $\frac{1}{2} + \frac{3}{10}$ ________

Name ______________________

Practice
10-2

Adding Fractions with Unlike Denominators

Write the answers in simplest form.

1. $\frac{1}{6} + \frac{1}{3} =$ ________ **2.** $\frac{1}{5} + \frac{1}{10} =$ ________

3. $\frac{1}{4} + \frac{1}{2} =$ ________ **4.** $\frac{2}{3} + \frac{1}{6} =$ ________

5. $\frac{1}{4} + \frac{2}{5} =$ ________ **6.** $\frac{1}{4} + \frac{1}{6} =$ ________

7. $\frac{2}{5} + \frac{1}{6} =$ ________ **8.** $\frac{1}{4} + \frac{5}{8} =$ ________

9. $\frac{5}{12} + \frac{1}{4}$ **10.** $\frac{1}{5} + \frac{3}{10}$ **11.** $\frac{2}{5} + \frac{1}{2}$ **12.** $\frac{1}{12} + \frac{2}{3}$

________ ________ ________ ________

13. A recipe calls for $\frac{1}{4}$ cup of whole wheat flour and $\frac{1}{2}$ cup of white flour. How many cups of flour are needed in all? ________

14. Math Reasoning To trim a costume, you need $\frac{1}{2}$ yard of lace at the neck and $\frac{2}{6}$ yard to trim both of the wrists. How much lace is needed? ________

15. Algebra If $n = \frac{9}{14}$, then $n + \frac{2}{7} =$ ________

16. For the addition $\frac{1}{6} + \frac{2}{3}$, which sum is **NOT** correct?

A. $\frac{9}{12}$ **B.** $\frac{5}{6}$ **C.** $\frac{15}{18}$ **D.** $\frac{20}{24}$

17. Writing to Explain What common denominator would you use to add $\frac{1}{3}$, $\frac{1}{4}$, and $\frac{1}{12}$? Explain.

____

Name ______________________________

Reteaching **10-3**

Subtracting Fractions with Unlike Denominators

When you subtract fractions with unlike denominators, you need to change them to equivalent fractions that have a common denominator.

Sylvie wanted to pick $\frac{3}{4}$ of the flowers in her garden. Because it started to rain, she was able to pick only $\frac{1}{3}$ of the flowers. What fraction of the flowers are left for Sylvie to pick?

Find $\frac{3}{4} - \frac{1}{3}$.

Step 1 Rewrite the fractions using a common denominator. *Think:* What number has 4 and 3 as factors? 12

$\frac{3}{4} = \frac{3 \times 3}{4 \times 3} = \frac{9}{12}$ $\frac{1}{3} = \frac{1 \times 4}{3 \times 4} = \frac{4}{12}$

Step 2 Subtract the equivalent fractions. Write the difference in simplest form.

$$\frac{3}{4} = \frac{9}{12}$$
$$-\frac{1}{3} = \frac{4}{12}$$
$$\frac{5}{12}$$

$\frac{5}{12}$ is in simplest form.

Sylvie has $\frac{5}{12}$ of the flowers left to pick.

Write the answers in simplest form.

1. $\frac{1}{3} - \frac{2}{9}$ ________

2. $\frac{3}{5} - \frac{1}{10}$ ________

3. $\frac{1}{2} - \frac{1}{8}$ ________

4. $\frac{2}{3} - \frac{1}{6}$ ________

5. $\frac{7}{12} - \frac{1}{3}$ ________

6. $\frac{4}{5} - \frac{2}{10}$ ________

7. $\frac{7}{15} - \frac{2}{5}$ ________

8. $\frac{3}{4} - \frac{3}{16}$ ________

9. $\frac{5}{8} - \frac{1}{2}$ ________

10. $\frac{1}{2} - \frac{1}{5}$ ________

11. At the dance, Lyndi and Josh danced $\frac{3}{4}$ hour without stopping. This is $\frac{3}{8}$ hour more than Kecia and Les danced. How long did Kecia and Les dance? ________

Name ______________________

Practice 10-3

Subtracting Fractions with Unlike Denominators

Write the answers in simplest form.

1. $\frac{1}{2} - \frac{1}{8}$ ________

2. $\frac{7}{8} - \frac{1}{2}$ ________

3. $\frac{11}{15} - \frac{2}{5}$ ________

4. $\frac{8}{9} - \frac{1}{3}$ ________

5. $\frac{5}{6} - \frac{1}{4}$ ________

6. $\frac{3}{4} - \frac{2}{5}$ ________

7. $\frac{9}{16} - \frac{1}{8}$ ________

8. $\frac{9}{10} - \frac{3}{4}$ ________

9. $\frac{5}{8} - \frac{3}{16}$ ________

10. $\frac{5}{12} - \frac{1}{6}$ ________

11. $\frac{3}{4} - \frac{1}{6}$ ________

12. $\frac{7}{8} - \frac{1}{6}$ ________

13. There was $\frac{7}{8}$ of a pizza left at 1:00. Then Lou ate $\frac{1}{4}$ of the original pizza. How much was left then?

A $\frac{5}{8}$ **B** $\frac{6}{8}$ **C** $\frac{7}{8}$ **D** $\frac{3}{4}$

14. **Writing to Explain** In what way is subtracting fractions with unlike denominators like adding fractions with unlike denominators?

____

____

Name ______________________

Reteaching
10-4

Problem Solving: Draw a Picture and Write an Equation

Understand	Pippa filled $\frac{1}{8}$ of a jar with blue stones, $\frac{1}{4}$ of the jar with yellow stones, and $\frac{1}{2}$ of the jar with purple stones. How much of the vase is filled altogether? What do I know? Pippa filled $\frac{1}{8}$, $\frac{1}{4}$, and $\frac{1}{2}$ of the vase. What am I asked to find? How much of the vase is filled with stones altogether?
Plan	Find the common denominator between $\frac{1}{8}$, $\frac{1}{4}$, and $\frac{1}{2}$ so you can add the fractions. $\frac{1}{8} = \frac{1}{8}$ 8 is divisible by 2, 4, and 8, so 8 is the common denominator. $\frac{1}{4} = \frac{2}{8}$ $\frac{1}{2} = \frac{4}{8}$
Solve	Now add the fractions and simplify if you need to. $\frac{1}{8} + \frac{2}{8} + \frac{4}{8} = \frac{7}{8}$ Pippa filled the jar $\frac{7}{8}$ full of stones.
Look Back	I found the common denominator, changed the fractions to equivalent fractions, and added the numerators to find the answer.

Solve. Remember to simplify your answer.

1. Joel walked $\frac{2}{5}$ of a mile to the store, $\frac{3}{10}$ of a mile to the library, and $\frac{1}{20}$ of a mile to the post office. How far did he walk?

____

2. Number Sense Glenda wrote $\frac{1}{7}$ of her paper on Monday, $\frac{1}{14}$ of her paper on Tuesday, and $\frac{2}{28}$ of her paper on Wednesday. She said she wrote more than half of her paper. Is she correct? Why or why not?

____

____

Name ____________________

Practice
10-4

Problem Solving: Draw a Picture and Write an Equation

Solve each problem.

1. Jamie bought $\frac{5}{8}$ pound of wheat flour. He also bought $\frac{1}{4}$ pound of white flour. How much flour did he buy?

____

2. Katie is $\frac{3}{5}$ of the way to Brianna's house. Larry is $\frac{7}{10}$ of the way to Brianna's house. How much closer to Brianna's house is Larry?

____

3. Nina practiced the trumpet for $\frac{5}{9}$ hour. Santiago practiced the trumpet for $\frac{2}{3}$ hour. How many more hours did Santiago practice than Nina?

____

4. Joel caught $\frac{1}{3}$ pound fish. Sarah caught $\frac{5}{12}$ pound fish. Jessa caught $\frac{1}{6}$ pound fish. Which bar diagram shows how to find how many pounds of fish they caught?

A ? pounds in all

$\frac{2}{6}$	$\frac{2}{6}$	$\frac{1}{6}$

B ? pounds in all

$\frac{1}{3}$	$\frac{5}{12}$	$\frac{1}{6}$

C ? pounds in all

$\frac{3}{12}$	$\frac{5}{12}$	$\frac{6}{12}$

D ? pounds in all

$\frac{1}{12}$	$\frac{5}{12}$	$\frac{1}{12}$

5. Writing to Explain John added the numerators of several fractions with unlike denominators. What should John have done first?

____

____

Name ______________________

Decimal Place Value

A grid can be used to show tenths and hundredths. To show 0.3, you would shade 3 out of the 10 parts.

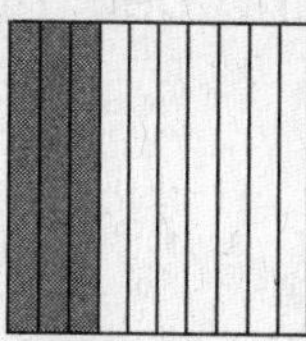
0.3
3 out of 10 parts are shaded.

To show 0.30, you would shade 30 out of the 100 parts.

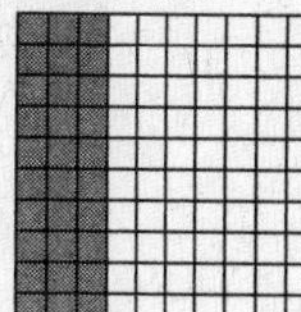
0.30
30 out of 100 parts are shaded.

One part of the hundredths grid can be compared to a penny, since one part of the grid is equal to 0.01 and a penny is equal to one hundredth of a dollar.

Tenths and hundredths are related. In the above examples, 3 tenths or 30 hundredths of the grids are shaded, or 0.3 and 0.30. These numbers are equal: 0.3 = 0.30.

Write the word form and decimal for each shaded part.

1. 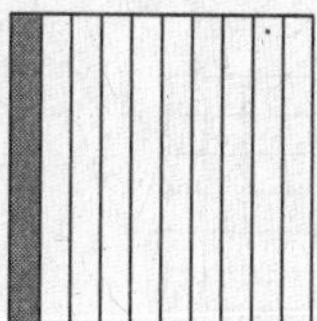

____

2. 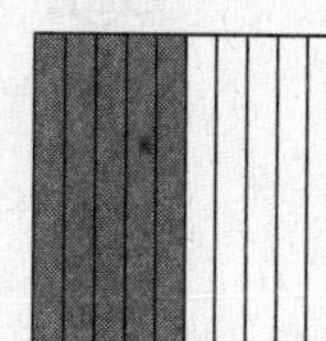

____

Shade each grid to show the decimal.

3. 0.57 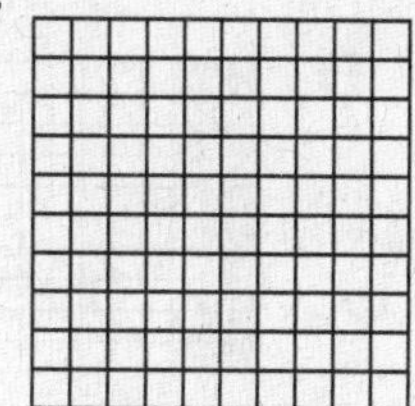

4. 0.4 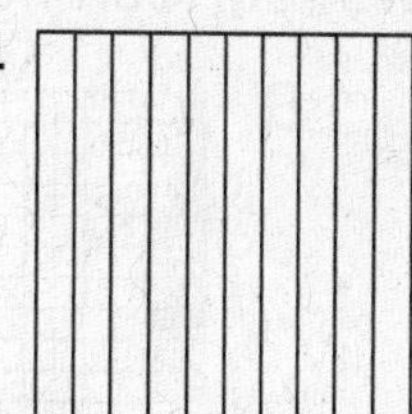

5. Number Sense Write three numbers between 2.02 and 2.2.

____

____

____

____

Name ______________________

Practice
11-1

Decimal Place Value

Write the word form and decimal for each shaded part.

1. 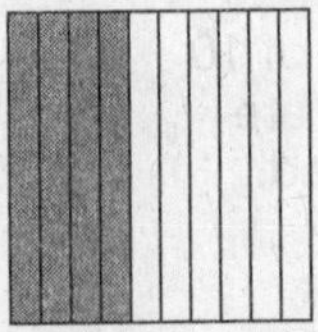 ______________________

2. 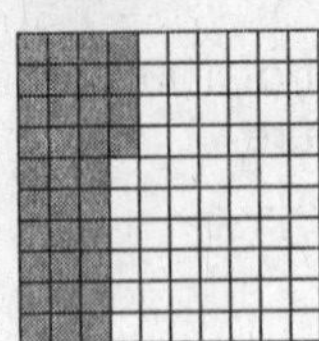 ______________________

For each fact, shade a grid to show the part of the population of each country that lives in cities.

3. In Jamaica, 0.5 of the people live in cities.

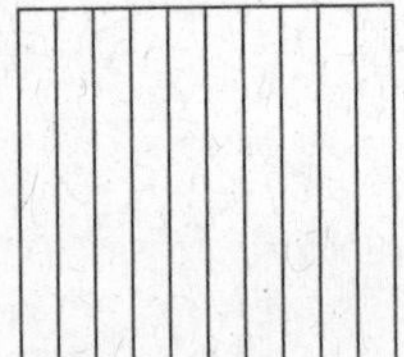

4. Only 0.11 of the population of Uganda live in cities.

5. In Norway, 0.72 of the people live in cities.

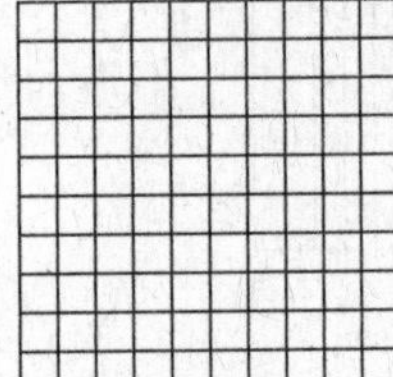

6. Which grid shows fourteen hundredths?

A 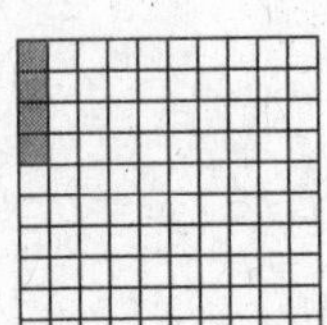

B 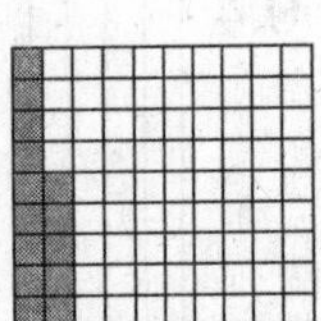

C 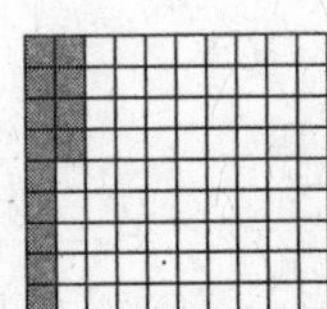

D 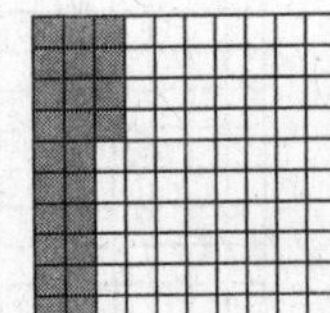

7. **Writing to Explain** Explain why one column in a hundredths grid is equal to one column in a tenths grid.

____

____

____

Name ___________________________

Comparing and Ordering Decimals

Compare 0.87 to 0.89.

First, begin at the left. Find the first place where the numbers are different.

0.87

0.89

The numbers are the same in the tenths places, so look to the next place.

The first place where the numbers are different is the hundredths place. Compare 7 hundredths to 9 hundredths.

0.07 < 0.09, so 0.87 < 0.89

Compare. Write >, <, or = for each ◯.

1. 0.36 ◯ 0.76
2. 5.1 ◯ 5.01
3. 1.2 ◯ 1.20
4. 6.55 ◯ 6.6
5. 0.62 ◯ 0.82
6. 4.71 ◯ 4.17

Order the numbers from least to greatest.

7. 1.36, 1.3, 1.63 ______________
8. 0.42, 3.74, 3.47 ______________
9. 6.46, 6.41, 4.6 ______________
10. 0.3, 0.13, 0.19, 0.31 ______________

11. **Number Sense** Which is greater, 8.0 or 0.8? Explain.

____

____

____

Name ______________________

Practice
11-2

Comparing and Ordering Decimals

Compare. Write >, <, or = for each ○.

1. 0.31 ○ 0.41 **2.** 1.9 ○ 0.95 **3.** 0.09 ○ 0.1

4. 2.70 ○ 2.7 **5.** 0.81 ○ 0.79 **6.** 2.12 ○ 2.21

Order the numbers from least to greatest.

7. 0.37, 0.41, 0.31 **8.** 1.16, 1.61, 6.11

______________ ______________

9. 7.9, 7.91, 7.09, 7.19 **10.** 1.45, 1.76, 1.47, 1.67

______________ ______________

Margaret has three cats. Sophie weighs 4.27 lb, Tigger weighs 6.25 lb, and Ghost weighs 4.7 lb.

11. Which cat has the greatest weight? ______________

12. Which cat weighs the least? ______________

13. Which group of numbers is ordered from least to greatest?

A 0.12, 1.51, 0.65

B 5.71, 5.4, 0.54

C 0.4, 0.09, 0.41

D 0.05, 0.51, 1.5

14. Darrin put the numbers 7.25, 7.52, 5.72, and 5.27 in order from greatest to least. Is his work correct? Explain.

____

____

Name ______________________________

Fractions and Decimals

Any fraction that has a denominator of 10 or 100 can be written as a decimal. Tenths and hundredths are written as digits to the right of the decimal point.

The shaded part is $\frac{2}{10}$ of the whole area.

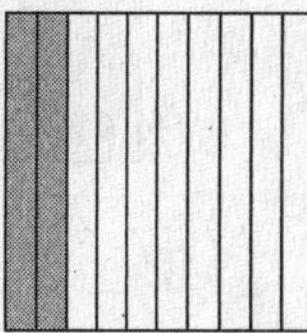

Write it as a decimal: 0.2

Say: two tenths.

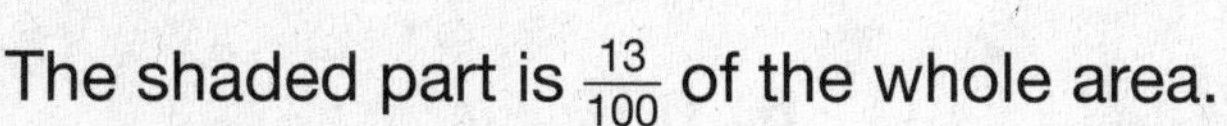

The shaded part is $\frac{13}{100}$ of the whole area.

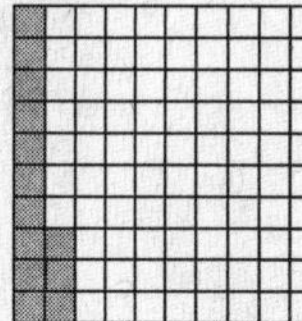

Write it as a decimal: 0.13

Say: thirteen hundredths

Write a fraction and a decimal to tell how much is shaded.

1. 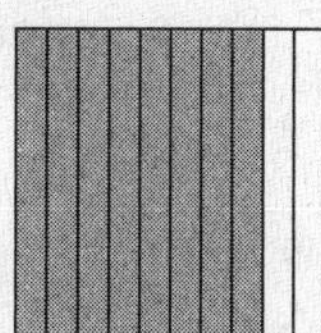

____

2. 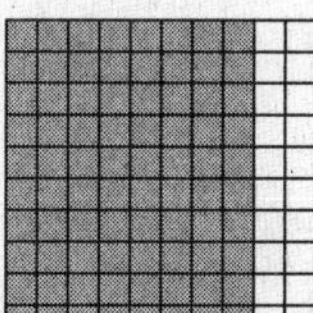

____

3. How are the two shaded grids alike? How are they different?

____

____

____

____

Write each fraction as a decimal.

4. $\frac{3}{10}$ ______________

5. $\frac{9}{10}$ ______________

6. $\frac{9}{100}$ ______________

7. $\frac{27}{100}$ ______________

Write each decimal as a fraction in its simplest form.

8. 0.40 ______________

9. 0.76 ______________

10. 4.8 ______________

11. 0.07 ______________

Name ______________________

Practice 11-3

Fractions and Decimals

Write a fraction and a decimal to show how much is shaded.

1. 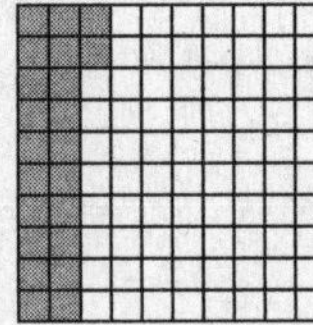

2. 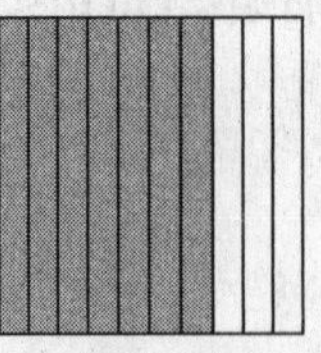

3. 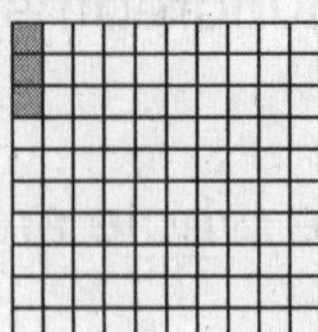

______ ______ ______

Draw a model that shows each decimal.

4. 0.16 **5.** 1.70 **6.** 0.78

Write each fraction as a decimal.

7. $\frac{1}{100}$ **8.** $9\frac{4}{10}$ **9.** $\frac{6}{10}$ **10.** $\frac{17}{100}$

______ ______ ______ ______

Write each decimal as a fraction in its simplest form.

11. 0.5 **12.** 0.70 **13.** 0.3 **14.** 3.60

______ ______ ______ ______

15. In the decimal models, how many strips equal 10 small squares?

A 70 strips **B** 10 strips **C** 7 strips **D** 1 strip

16. Writing to Explain Explain the steps you would take to write $3\frac{6}{10}$ as a decimal.

____

____

____

Name ______________________________

Fractions and Decimals on the Number Line

How do you locate fractions and decimals on a number line?

Show $\frac{1}{8}$ on a number line.

Draw a number line and label 0 and 1. Divide the distance from 0 to 1 into 8 equal lengths.

Label 0, $\frac{1}{8}$, $\frac{2}{8}$, $\frac{3}{8}$, $\frac{4}{8}$, $\frac{5}{8}$, $\frac{6}{8}$, $\frac{7}{8}$, and 1.

Draw a point at $\frac{1}{8}$.

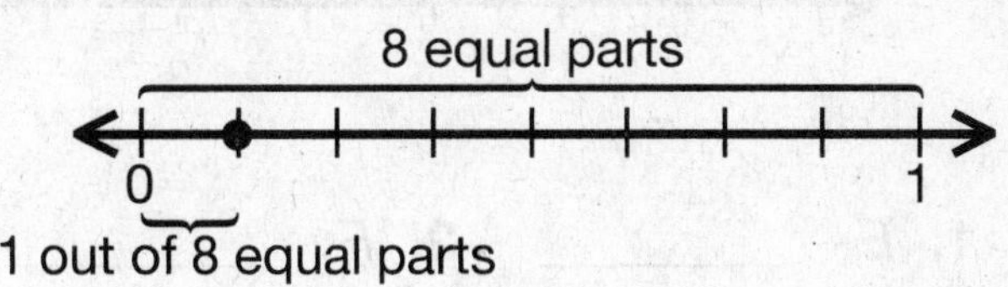

Show 0.3 on a number line.

Use the same number line. Divide the distance from 0 to 1 into 10 equal lengths.

Label 0.1, 0.2, 0.3, 0.4, and so on.

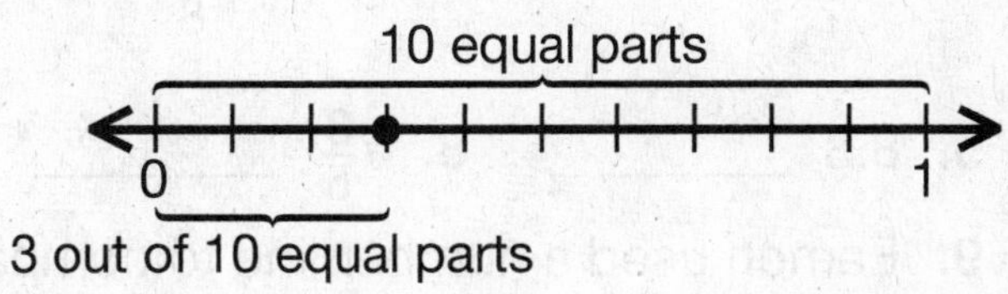

Use the number line to name the fraction or decimal that should be written at each point.

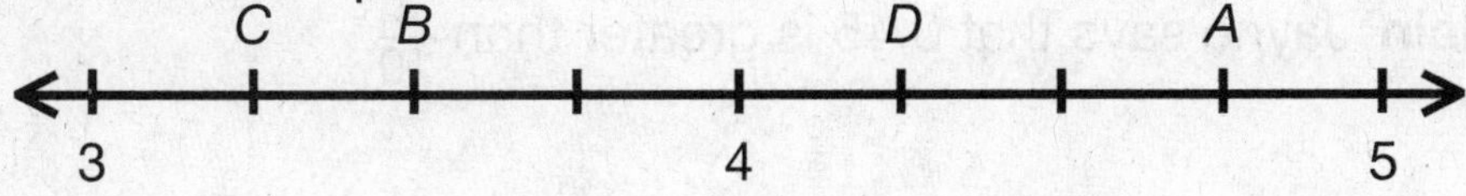

1. *A* ________ **2.** *B* ________ **3.** *C* ________ **4.** *D* ________

Identify the correct point on the number line for each fraction or decimal.

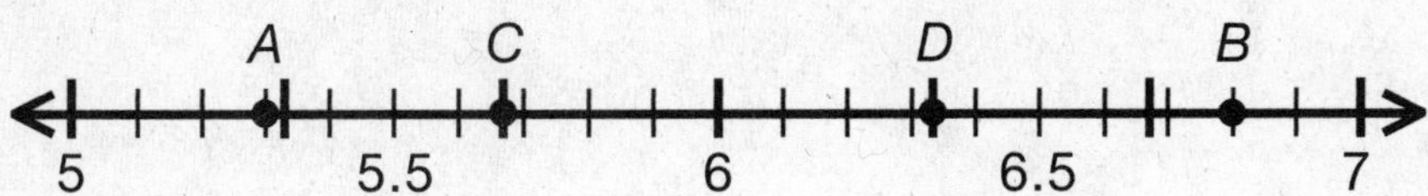

5. $6\frac{1}{3}$ ________ **6.** 5.3 ________ **7.** $5\frac{2}{3}$ ________ **8.** 6.8 ________

Name ______________________________

Practice 11-4

Fractions and Decimals on the Number Line

Use the number line to name the fraction or decimal that should be written at each point.

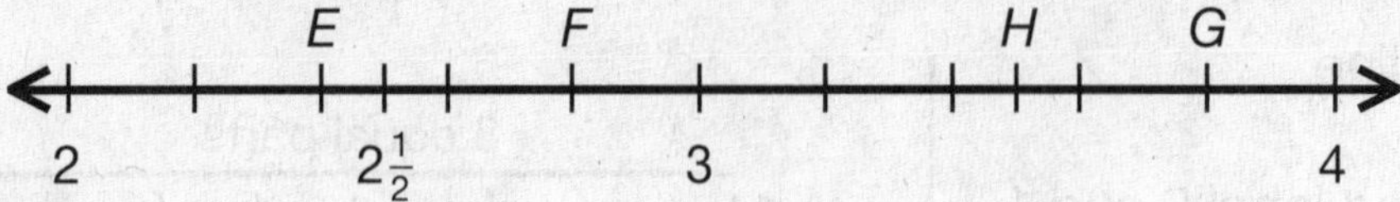

1. *E* ________ **2.** *F* ________ **3.** *G* ________ **4.** *H* ________

Identify the correct point on the number line for each fraction or decimal.

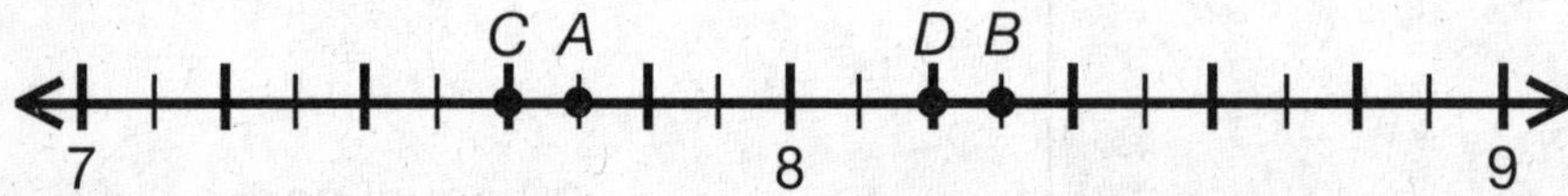

5. 8.3 ________ **6.** $7\frac{3}{5}$ ________ **7.** 7.7 ________ **8.** 8.2 ________

9. Eamon used a number line to compare two numbers, 0.48 and $\frac{3}{5}$. One number was less than $\frac{1}{2}$ and the other number was greater than $\frac{1}{2}$. Which number was less than $\frac{1}{2}$? ________

10. Which of the following choices is not correct?

A $0.43 < \frac{4}{5}$ **B** $\frac{2}{3} > 0.07$ **C** $\frac{1}{2} > 0.09$ **D** $\frac{1}{3} > 0.35$

11. Writing to Explain Jayne says that 0.45 is greater than $\frac{4}{10}$. Is she correct?

____

____

____

Name ____________________

Reteaching
11-5

Mixed Numbers and Decimals on the Number Line

Compare $2\frac{1}{2}$, 1.75, and $2\frac{9}{10}$ on a number line.

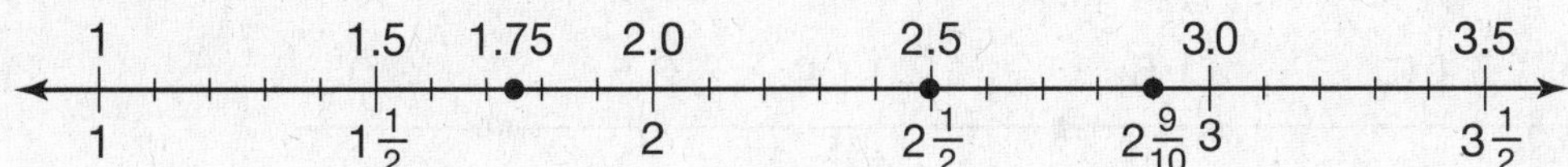

$2\frac{1}{2}$ is halfway between 2 and 3. 1.75 is halfway between 1.5 and 2.

$2\frac{9}{10}$ is just to the left of 3.0, or 3.

Remember that on a number line the numbers increase when moving from left to right.

Name the decimal that should be written at each point.

1. 5.0 5.7 6.0

2. 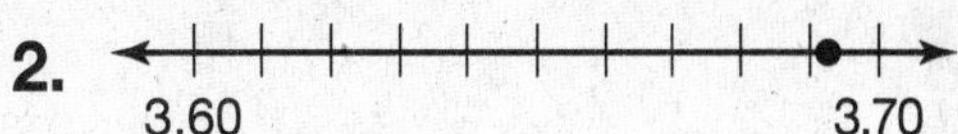

For Exercises **3–8**, use the two number lines below. What point shows the location of each number?

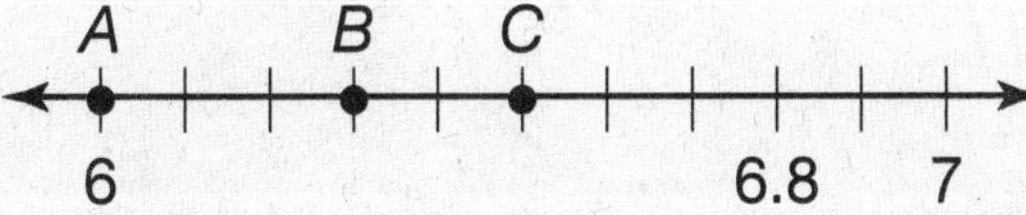

3. 6.3 ________ **4.** 6.5 ________ **5.** 6.0 ________

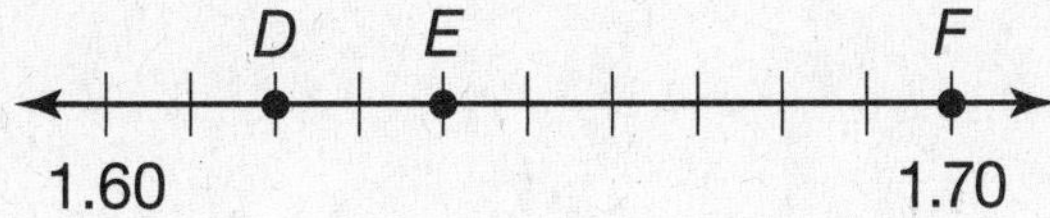

6. 1.64 ________ **7.** 1.70 ________ **8.** $1\frac{62}{100}$ ________

Show each set of numbers on a number line.

9. $\frac{1}{2}$, $1\frac{3}{4}$, 2.2

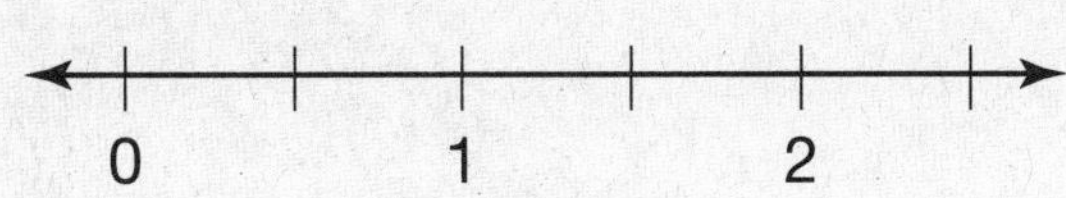

10. $2\frac{1}{4}$, 2.3, 0.4

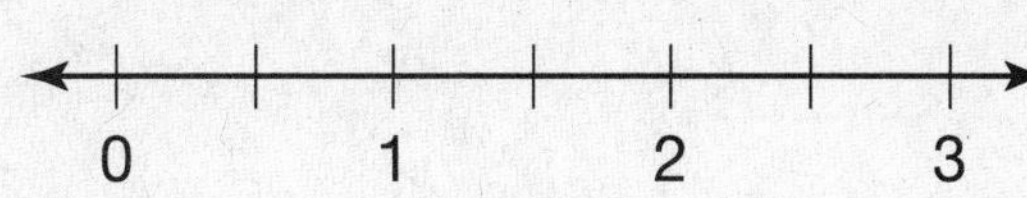

Name ______________________

Practice

11-5

Mixed Numbers and Decimals on the Number Line

Show each number on the number line.

1. $\frac{3}{10}$, $2\frac{3}{4}$, 2.8, 1.7

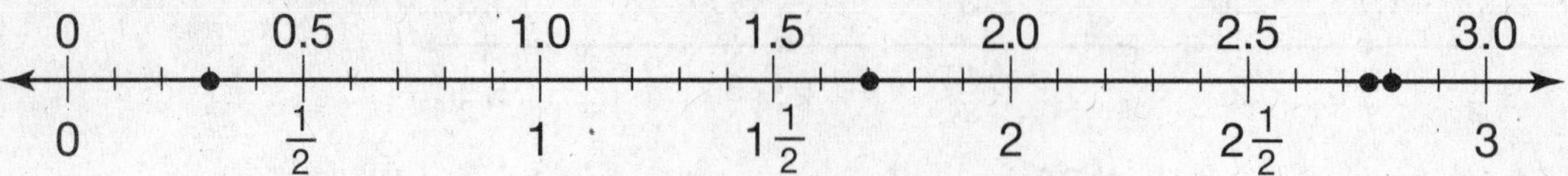

What point shows the location of each number?

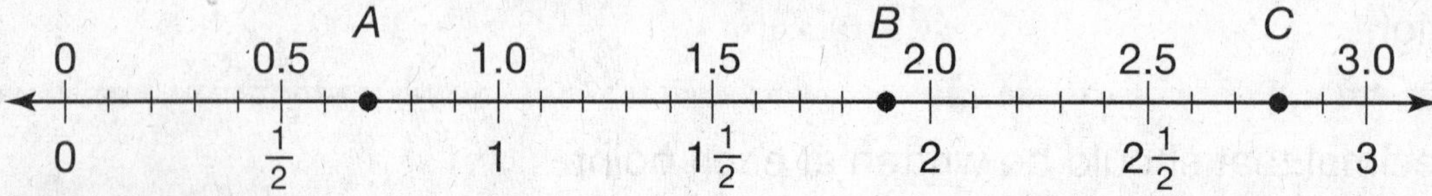

2. 1.9 ________

3. $\frac{7}{10}$ ________

4. $2\frac{8}{10}$ ________

5. Draw a number line to show the heights of each plant.

Plant Heights	
Seedling 1	$2\frac{3}{4}$ inches
Seedling 2	$3\frac{6}{10}$ inches
Seedling 3	2.8 inches
Seedling 4	3.4 inches

6. Which number is less than $3\frac{1}{2}$?

A 3.7 **B** 3.6 **C** 3.5 **D** 3.4

7. Writing to Explain Last year, Mike grew 2.9 inches. Emily grew $2\frac{1}{4}$ inches. Who grew more?

____

Name ______________________________

Problem Solving: Use Objects and Make a Table

Find an Equivalent Fraction Rita has 12 roses. She wants to keep $\frac{1}{2}$ for herself, and give $\frac{1}{2}$ to her sister Julie. What fraction equivalent to $\frac{1}{2}$ shows the number of roses each person will have?

Step 1: Set up your problem: $\frac{1}{2} = \frac{\boxed{?}}{12}$

Step 2: Make a table to help you visualize the fraction:

12 roses											
1	2	3	4	5	6	1	2	3	4	5	6
1 group of 6						1 group of 6					

1 group of 6 $= \frac{1}{2}$ of the roses. $\frac{1}{2} = \frac{\boxed{6}}{12}$

Each person will have 6 of the 12 roses. The fraction $\frac{6}{12}$ is equivalent to $\frac{1}{2}$.

Solve. Use objects, and make a table to help.

1. Phil has a box of 16 pencils. He wants to put $\frac{1}{4}$ of them into his desk drawer. Find a fraction equivalent to $\frac{1}{4}$ that shows how many pencils he puts into his drawer. ______

2. Jack has 18 slices of bread. He wants to put $\frac{1}{2}$ the slices into one bag, and $\frac{1}{2}$ the slices into another bag. Find a fraction equivalent to $\frac{1}{2}$ that tells you how many of the 18 slices he will put in each bag. ______

3. Rhonda borrowed 9 books from the library. She wants to read $\frac{1}{3}$ of them today. Find a fraction equivalent to $\frac{1}{3}$ that tells you how many books she will read today. ______

Name ______________________________

Practice **11-6**

Problem Solving: Use Objects and Make a Table

For **1** through **3**, use the table to the right.

1. Jade collected 45 seashells when she was at the beach. She wants to arrange them so there will be an equal number on each shelf. Complete the table to the right.

Number of shelves	Shells per shelf	Number of shells
	15	45
5		45
9		45

2. Does the table to the right show all possible ways Jade can put her seashells on shelves in equal numbers? If not, what are all the other ways?

____

____

3. Adam has a large piece of paper. After he folds it once he has 2 equal sized pieces. After he folds it twice he has 4 equal sized pieces. Use the table below to find out how many equal sized pieces he has after folding the paper 6 times.

Folds	0	1	2	3	4	5	6
Number of pieces	1	2	4				

4. On a computer game it takes Lance 20 minutes to beat a level and it takes Diane 15 minutes. If the game has 5 levels how many more minutes will it take Lance to beat the game? Use a table to help get your answer.

A 100 **B** 75 **C** 25 **D** 15

5. **Writing to Explain** If you know one possible combination of shelves and number of shells on a shelf, why do you already know another combination?

____

____

Name ____________________

Rounding Decimals

Round 84.62 to the nearest tenth.

Step 1 Look at the digit in the tenths place. 84.62

Step 2 Look at the digit to the right. 84.62

Step 3 If the digit to the right is less than 5, the rounding digit stays the same. If the digit is 5 or greater, add one to the rounding digit. Since 2 is less than 5, the underlined digit does not change.

Step 4 84.62 rounds to 84.6.

Round 28.91 to the nearest whole.

Step 1 Look at the digit in the ones place. 28.91

Step 2 Look at the digit to the right. 28.91

Step 3 Since 9 is greater than 5, add one to the underlined digit.

Step 4 28.91 rounds to 29.

Round each decimal to the nearest tenth.

1. 81.42 ______ **2.** 65.88 ______ **3.** 93.86 ______

4. 13.91 ______ **5.** 45.63 ______ **6.** 25.83 ______

7. 71.19 ______ **8.** 50.55 ______ **9.** 33.39 ______

Round each decimal to the nearest whole number.

10. 86.32 ______ **11.** 25.88 ______ **12.** 13.68 ______

13. 91.13 ______ **14.** 54.63 ______ **15.** 83.25 ______

16. 71.59 ______ **17.** 65.49 ______ **18.** 43.51 ______

19. Writing to Explain Do the decimals 32.32, 32.49, and 32.51 all round to the same whole number? Why or why not?

____

____

Name ______________________

Practice
12-1

Rounding Decimals

Round each decimal to the nearest whole number.

1 25.78 ______ 2. 17.26 ______ 3. 34.52 ______

4. 52.61 ______ 5. 73.49 ______ 6. 42.35 ______

7. 27.38 ______ 8. 46.52 ______ 9. 18.16 ______

Round each decimal to the nearest tenth.

10. 13.13 ______ 11. 49.45 ______ 12. 14.51 ______

13. 9.99 ______ 14. 2.70 ______ 15. 5.77 ______

16. 4.01 ______ 17. 0.50 ______ 18. 7.49 ______

19. When rounded to the nearest whole number, which decimals round to 9?

9.6 9.4 8.05 9.69 9.07 8.71 9.02 9.6 8.45

____

20. When rounded to the nearest tenth, which decimals round to 3.8?

3.61 3.06 3.79 2.55 3.77 3.84 3.80 3.68

____

21. **Math Reasoning** A swimmer's time in the 100-meter backstroke is 58 seconds when rounded to the nearest whole number. Name the fastest and slowest times possible, in decimals rounded to the hundredths place.

____

22. It is 3.6 miles from Steve's house to the skating rink. Estimate the distance from Steve's house to the skating rink.

A 3 miles **B** 4 miles **C** 5 miles **D** 6 miles

23. **Writing to Explain** Round 8.95 to the nearest tenth. Did the ones place change? Explain.

____

____

Name ______________________

Reteaching
12-2

Estimating Sums and Differences of Decimals

To estimate, you change numbers so they are easier to add and subtract.

Estimate 11.7 + 3.8.

Estimate by rounding to the nearest whole number.

11.7 + 3.8
↓ ↓
12 + 4 = 16

So, 11.7 + 3.8 is about 16.

Estimate 12.9 − 7.1.

Estimate by rounding to the nearest whole number.

12.9 − 7.1
↓ ↓
13 − 7 = 6

So, 12.9 − 7.1 is about 6.

Estimate each sum or difference.

1. 7.12 + 8.64 ________

2. 12.74 − 6.11 ________

3. 22.91 + 4.86 ________

4. 17.4 − 12.8 ________

5. 19.8 + 7.12 ________

6. 31.22 − 18.3 ________

7. 9.3 + 6.27

8. 8.4 − 3.1

9. 4.13 − 1.68

10. 0.31 + 0.74

11. 24.7 + 3.88

12. 51.99 + 11.11

13. 24.24 − 12.81

14. 0.79 + 1.88

15. Writing to Explain Explain why 20 is **NOT** a reasonable estimate for 33.71 − 17.25.

____

____

Name ______________________

Practice

12-2

Estimating Sums and Differences of Decimals

Estimate each sum or difference.

1. 1.45 + 0.6 ______
2. 8.91 + 1.16 ______
3. 7.09 − 5.11 ______
4. 6.59 − 3.84 ______
5. 8.54 + 9.01 ______
6. 6.11 − 0.15 ______
7. 18.05 + 0.85 ______
8. 11.45 − 0.9 ______
9. 8.65 − 5.1 ______
10. 9.50 + 6.8 ______

11. **Reasoning** Cheryl had $86.51. She bought 6 cases of fruit drink and had $50.67 left. About how much did Cheryl pay for each case of fruit drink?

____

12. Jean walked 19.87 mi last week, 17.15 mi the week before, and 18.92 mi this week. About how many miles has Jean walked in the 3 weeks?

____

13. William drives 14.81 mi to work each day. Kathy drives 2.6 mi to work each day. About how much farther does William drive each day?

____

14. Which is the best estimate for the sum of 22.36 + 19.6?

A 41 **B** 42 **C** 43 **D** 44

15. **Writing to Explain** Kayla needs $15.00 to buy a CD. She has $8.18 in her wallet, $3.19 in her pocket, and $5.42 in her piggy bank. Does Kayla have enough? Explain.

____

____

____

____

Name ______________________

Modeling Addition and Subtraction of Decimals

Adding decimals using a hundredths grid:

Add 0.32 + 0.17.

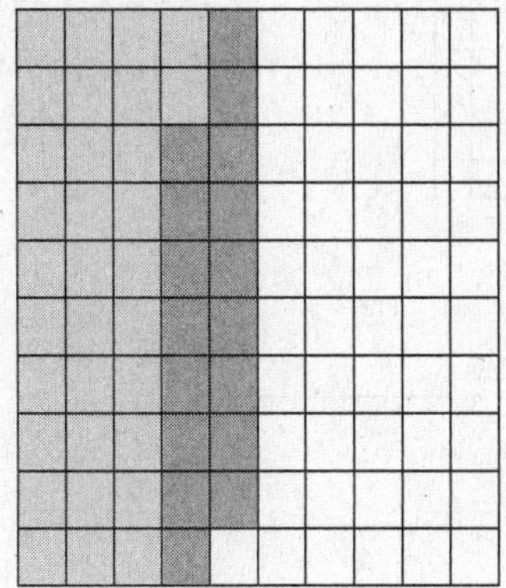

Step 1: Shade 32 squares to show 0.32.

Step 2: Use a different color. Shade 17 squares to show 0.17.

Step 3: Count all the squares that are shaded. How many hundredths are shaded in all? Write the decimal for the total shaded squares: 0.49.

So, 0.32 + 0.17 = 0.49.

Subtracting decimals using a hundredths grid:

Subtract 0.61 − 0.42.

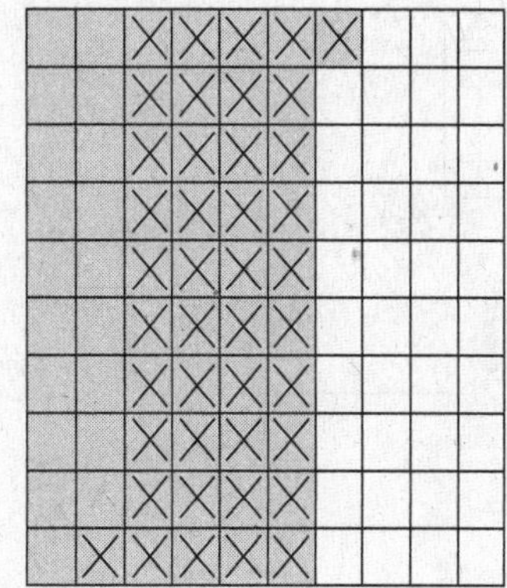

Step 1: Shade 61 squares to show 0.61.

Step 2: Cross out 42 squares to show 0.42.

Step 3: Count the squares that are shaded but not crossed out. Write the decimal: 0.19.

So, 0.61 − 0.42 = 0.19.

Add or subtract. You may use grids to help.

1. 0.22 + 0.35 = ____________

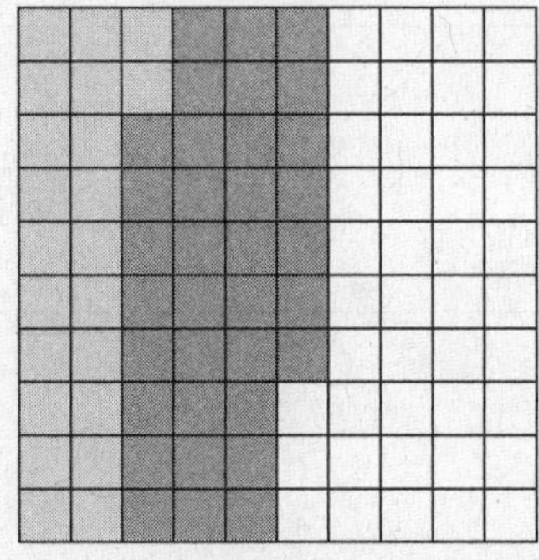

2. 0.52 − 0.41 = ____________

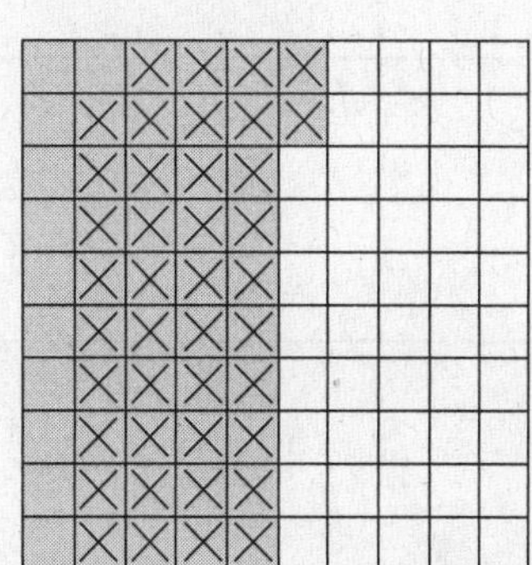

Name ____________________

Practice
12-3

Modeling Addition and Subtraction of Decimals

Add or subtract. You may use grids to help.

1. 0.12 + 0.56 = ________

2. 0.27 − 0.09 = ________

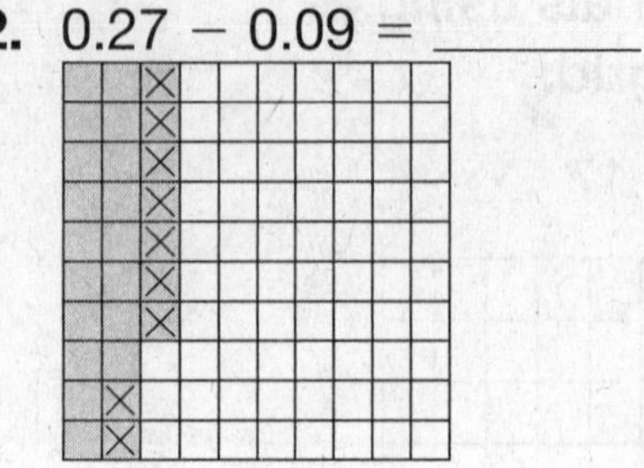

3. 0.86 + 0.54 = ________

4. 1.27 + 0.75 = ________

5. 0.93 − 0.25 = ________

6. 1.07 − 0.61 = ________

7. 1.13 − 1.02 = ________

8. 0.28 + 1.96 = ________

9. Number Sense Is the difference of 1.45 − 0.12 less than or greater than 1? ________

10. A bottle of nail polish holds 0.8 oz. A bottle of perfume holds 0.45 oz. How many more ounces does a bottle of nail polish hold? ________

11. Add 1.18 + 1.86.

A 2.04 **B** 2.94 **C** 3.04 **D** 3.14

12. Writing to Explain Explain how you can use a grid to subtract 1.65 − 0.98.

____

____

____

____

Name ______________________

Adding and Subtracting Decimals

Example 1 Find 1.35 + 2.4.

Step 1
Line up the decimal points. Write zeros as placeholders

```
  1.35
+ 2.40  ← Remember: 2.4 = 2.40
```

Step 2
Add hundredths. Regroup if necessary.

```
  1.35
+ 2.40
     5
```

Step 3
Add tenths. Regroup if necessary.

```
  1.35
+ 2.40
    75
```

Step 4
Add ones. Place the decimal point.

```
  1.35
+ 2.40
  3.75
```

Example 2 Find 6 + 1.75.

Step 1
Line up the decimal points.

```
  6
- 1.75
```

Step 2
Write zeros as place holders.

```
  6.**00**
- 1.75
```

Step 3
Subtract hundredths. Regroup if necessary.

```
     9
  5 10 10
  6. 0  0
- 1. 7  5
        5
```

Step 4
Subtract tenths and ones. Place the decimal point.

```
     9
  5 10 10
  6. 0  0
- 1. 7  5
  4. 2  5
```

Find each sum.

1. 0.3 + 2.8

2. 5.47 + 0.56

3. 5.7 + 4.38

4. 56.3 + 26.55

5. 73.27 + 1.06

6. 22.69 + 22.72

Find each difference.

7. 3.8 − 3.6

8. 4.78 − 0.57

9. 6.9 − 3.25

10. 36.35 − 24.7

11. 32 − 17.43

12. 62.22 − 29.35

13. **Number Sense** In 1957, rainfall in El Camino was 0.34 inches in the spring and 4.74 inches in the summer. How much more rain fell in the summer than in the spring?

____

Name ______________________________

Practice 12-4

Adding and Subtracting Decimals

For **1** through **18**, add or subtract.

1. 6.33 + 0.23	**2.** 37.41 − 16.43	**3.** 15.19 + 60.91
4. 2.67 + 0.45	**5.** 66.34 − 17.55	**6.** 68.33 − 7.52
7. 54.08 − 45.81	**8.** 32.8 + 0.46	**9.** 54.28 − 17.7
10. 44.37 + 0.99	**11.** 14.19 − 12.14	**12.** 17.4 − 17.13
13. 8.27 + 7.84	**14.** 46.78 − 4.8	**15.** 17.66 − 12.79
16. 81.82 + 5.24	**17.** 61.22 − 33.82	**18.** 4.98 + 72.94

19. Christina walked 44.2 meters. She then walked 19.82 meters more. How many meters did she walk?

____

20. Nelson has $18.82 in his left pocket. He has $14.33 in his right pocket. How much more money does he have in his left pocket?

A $4.44 **B** $4.49 **C** $4.51 **D** $4.59

21. **Writing to Explain** Explain why 4.2 + 0.2 is more than 4.2 + 0.12.

____

____

Name ____________________

Reteaching
12-5

Multiplying and Dividing with Decimals

Nelly has $6.00. Notebooks cost $1.50 each and she wants to buy 4 of them. Does she have enough money to buy them?

Multiply 4 by $1.50 to find out how much 4 notebooks will cost. 2 1.50 — 2 decimal places × 4 — +0 decimal places 6.00 — 2 decimal places	• Multiply the same way you do with whole numbers. • Find the number of decimal places in the product by combining the number of decimal places in the factors.
4 notebooks cost $6.00, so Nelly will have enough money to buy them.	

Jo has $9.75 and wants to buy toys for her 3 pets. How much can she spend on each pet?

Divide $9.75 by 3 to find out how much she can spend on each pet. $3.25 3)$9.75 — decimal point moves straight up −9 07 −06 15 +15 0	• Divide the same way you do with whole numbers. • Remember to write the $ symbol and the decimal point in the quotient.
Jo will have $3.25 to spend on each pet.	

Multiply or divide.

1. $4.23 × 3	**2.** 7)$2.31	**3.** $2.68 × 4	**4.** 5)$12.85
______	______	______	______

Name ______________________

Practice **12-5**

Multiplying and Dividing with Decimals

For 1 through 18, multiply or divide.

1. $2.43 × 5	2. 2)$8.84	3. $13.95 × 7
4. 6)$8.52	5. $44.29 × 6	6. 4)$7.44
7. 3)$5.34	8. $12.77 × 9	9. 9)$7.65
10. $2.41 × 6	11. 5)$3.85	12. 6)$8.88
13. $3.21 × 4	14. 4)$6.72	15. $32.40 × 3
16. 3)$3.99	17. $76.90 × 4	18. 2)$9.22

19. Beth bought 9 candles for $2.89 each. How much did she spend? __________

20. Joan bought 9 DVDs for $89.91. Each DVD cost the same amount. How much did a DVD cost?

A $9.99 **B** $9.32 **C** $8.99 **D** $8.42

21. Writing to Explain Which is greater, 0.9 × 2 or 0.9 + 2? Explain your answer.

____

____

____

Name ______________________

Reteaching **12-6**

Problem Solving: Try, Check, and Revise

Try, Check, and Revise	
Try	Sandwich $3.99, Soup $2.99, Salad $3.50, Drinks $1.50 Jackie spent $7.99 on lunch. She ordered three items from the menu. What did she order? Did she order a sandwich, a soup, and a drink? Try adding the three items.
Check	$3.99 $2.99 +$1.50 $8.48 That's too high. Try again.
Revise	Did she order soup, salad, and a drink? Try adding these items.
Check	$2.99 $3.50 +$1.50 $7.99 That's right. These three items total $7.99.

Use the price list to solve the following problems.

Dave's Fruit Market			
grapes $2.25/bag	bananas $1.99/bag	strawberries $3.40/box	watermelon $5.00

1. Wanda spent $11.99 at Dave's Fruit Market. She bought 2 of one thing and 1 of another thing. What did she buy?

____

2. Ted spent $7.64 at Dave's Fruit Market. He bought three different items. What did he buy?

____

____

3. **Number Sense** Scott bought two items at Dave's Fruit Market. The cashier told him that he owed $5.49. Why is the cashier incorrect? What did Scott purchase?

____

____

____

Name ______________________

Problem Solving: Try, Check, and Revise

Use the first try to help you make a second try. Finish solving the problem.

1. Mrs. Reid brought 32 orange and apple slices to her daughter's soccer practice. There were three times as many orange slices as there were apple slices. How many of each kind did she bring?

____

Use the table to answer questions **2** through **4**.

Zeke's Toy Store	
Toy	**Cost**
Car	$5.55
Boat	$8.99
Train	$9.50

2. Todd bought 2 items and spent $15.05. What did he buy?

____

3. Sarah bought 4 items and spent $30.10. What did she buy?

____

4. Erin bought 3 items and spent $26.97. What did she buy?

____

5. Greg has 5 coins in his pocket. The value of all 5 coins is $.57. Which coins does he have in his pocket?

   A 1 quarter, 2 dimes, and 2 pennies **B** 2 quarters, 1 nickel, and 2 pennies

   C 3 quarters and 2 pennies **D** 2 quarters, 1 dime, and 2 pennies

6. **Writing to Explain** Jack has $2.00. What information do you need to find which coins he has?

____

Name ____________________

Equal or Not Equal

Whenever you add, subtract, multiply, or divide two equal quantities by the same amount, the two resulting quantities will be equal to each other.

Equals added to equals are equal.	You know $4 + 5 = 9$. Therefore, $4 + 5 + 10 = 9 + 10$.
Equals subtracted from equals are equal.	You know $10 + 12 = 22$. Therefore, $(10 + 12) - 18 = 22 - 18$.
Equals mutiplied by equals are equal.	You know $2 \times 5 = 10$. Therefore, $2 \times 5 \times 3 = 10 \times 3$.
Equals divided by equals (except 0) are equal.	You know $10 + 11 = 21$. Therefore, $(10 + 11) \div 7 = 21 \div 7$.

Answer each question. Tell why or why not.

1. You know $48 \div 8 = 6$. Does $(48 \div 8) \times 9 = 6 \times 9$?

____

2. Given the equation $8 \times w = 152$, does $8 \times w \times 3 = 152 \div 3$?

____

____

3. You know $250 \div 5 = 50$. Does $(250 \div 5) \times 5 = 50 \times 5$?

____

____

4. Given the equation $12 \times x = 144$, does $(12 \times x) \div 4 = 144 \div 4$?

____

____

5. You know $23 + 32 = 55$. Does $(23 + 32) - 44 = 55 \div 44$?

____

____

Name ______________________

Equal or Not Equal

Answer each question. Tell why or why not.

You know:	Does:
1. $61 + 27 = 88$	$61 + 27 - 8 = 88 \times 8$?
2. $76 - 59 = 17$	$(76 - 59) + 12 = 17 - 12$?
3. $24 \times 6 = 144$	$(24 \times 6) - 72 = 144 - 72$?
Given the equation:	**Does:**
4. $15 \times w = 105$	$15 \times w + 51 = 105 + 51$
5. $57 + x = 202$	$57 + x - 13 = 202 - 13$
6. $w + 9 = 27$	$(w + 9) \times 4 = 27 + 4$

Circle the correct letter for each answer.

7. What could you do to the equation $40 \times y = 320$ to keep the sides equal?

A $(40 \times y) \times 2 = 320 \times 2$
B $(40 \times y) + 3 = 320 - 3$
C $(40 \times y) \div 8 = 320 - 8$
D $(40 \times y) + 12 = 320 + 18$

8. Writing to Explain If you start with an unbalanced scale and add the same amount to each side, what happens to the scale?

____

Name ____________________

Reteaching

13-2

Solving Addition and Subtraction Equations

Inverse operations are opposite operations that undo each other. Addition and subtraction have an inverse relationship.

1. Use inverse operations to find the value of *n* in the following equation.

$n + 5 = 8$

Since $n + 5$ is equal to 8, subtract 5 from both sides of the equation to find the value of *n*.

$$\begin{aligned} n + 5 &= 8 \\ -5 &\quad -5 \\ n &= 3 \end{aligned}$$

Use inverse operations to find the value of the variable in the following equations.

1. $j + 5 = 19$ ____________

2. $u + 7 = 15$ ____________

3. $p + 13 = 25$ ____________

4. $c - 6 = 9$ ____________

5. $a + 25 = 31$ ____________

6. $v - 18 = 2$ ____________

7. Number Sense Andrea has an equal number of apples in two baskets. There are $z + 16$ apples in one basket, and 23 apples in the other basket. How many apples should she remove from both baskets to find the value of *z*?

____

Name ______________________________

Practice
13-2

Solving Addition and Subtraction Equations

For **1** and **2**, solve for each ☐.

1. $w - 8 = 26$ $w - 8 + ☐ = 26 + ☐$ $w = ☐$	**2.** $r + 11 = 19$ $r + 11 - ☐ = 19 - ☐$ $r = ☐$

In **3** through **14**, solve each equation.

3. $k + 4 = 21$	**4.** $j - 7 = 6$	**5.** $q - 2 = 39$
6. $h + 350 = 450$	**7.** $b - 44 = 6$	**8.** $t + 52 = 61$
9. $e - 28 = 44$	**10.** $n + 63 = 108$	**11.** $p + 7 = 111$
12. $s + 25 = 64$	**13.** $c - 71 = 18$	**14.** $z - 13 = 13$

15. Ben walked 8 miles to a friend's house and 4 more miles to the park. Write and solve an equation to show how many miles Ben walked in all.

____

16. Carla made 27 gift baskets. She has given 8 away. Which equation shows how to find the number of gift baskets Carla has left?

A $8 + 27 = b$ **B** $b + 27 = 8$ **C** $8 + 27 = b$ **D** $27 - 8 = b$

17. Writing to Explain Roger knows how many keys a piano has. He knows that some of the keys are broken. How can he find the number of keys that work?

____

____

____

Name ____________________

Solving Multiplication and Division Equations

Example 1 Find the value of y in the following equation.	**Example 2** Henry had b pairs of socks and separated them into 3 separate drawers. He put 4 pairs of socks into each drawer. How many pairs of socks did Henry have?
$y \times 5 = 40$ Since y is multiplied by 5 to equal 40, use the opposite operation to find the value of y. Divide each side of the equation by 5. $y \times 5 \div \boxed{5} = 40 \div \boxed{5}$ $\times 5 \div 5$ cancel each other out. $y = 40 \div 5$ $y = 8$	You can write an equation for this problem. $b \div 3 = 4$ (total pairs) (drawers) (pairs per drawer) Since b is divided by 3 to equal 4, use the opposite operation to find the value of b. Multiply each side of the equation by 3. $b \div 3 \boxed{\times 3} = 4 \boxed{\times 3}$ $\div 3 \times 3$ cancel each other out. $b = 4 \times 3$ $b = 12$

Find the value of the variables in the following problems.

1. $j \div 9 = 2$ ____________

2. $u \times 6 = 18$ ____________

3. $p \times 5 = 25$ ____________

4. $c \div 7 = 4$ ____________

5. **Number Sense** What numbers belong in the blanks in the following equation? What is the value of a?
   $a \div 6 \times$ ____ $= 5 \times$ ____

   ____

Name ______________________

Practice

13-3

Solving Multiplication and Division Equations

Solve each equation.

1. $q \times 9 = 18$	**2.** $99 \div e = 33$	**3.** $k \times 4 = 48$
4. $y \div 8 = 9$	**5.** $7 \times w = 42$	**6.** $y \times 5 = 65$
7. $b \div 7 = 7$	**8.** $54 \div a = 6$	**9.** $u \div 3 = 18$
10. $2 \times t = 2$	**11.** $x \div 6 = 8$	**12.** $7 \times r = 21$
13. $m \div 8 = 7$	**14.** $v \times 8 = 96$	**15.** $e \times 4 = 68$

Solve.

16. Kyle spent 3 hours each day for 4 days making a song. Write and solve an equation to find the number of total hours Kyle spent making his song.

____

17. Liz played hockey for 28 hours last week. She played for an equal amount of time for 7 days. Write and solve an equation to find the number of hours Liz played hockey for each day.

____

18. Vincent worked 9 hours each day for 8 days. Write and solve an equation to find the total number of hours Vincent worked.

____

19. Veronica reads 9 pages in a book each day. The book is 216 pages long. Which equation shows how to find the number of days it will take Veronica to read the book?

A $b \div 9 = 216$ **B** $b \div 216 = 9$ **C** $9 \times 216 = b$ **D** $216 \div 9 = b$

20. Writing to Explain Alexandra has 18 yo-yos. She spent $9.00 to buy them all. She wrote the equation $18 \div 9 = y$ to find how many yo-yos she got for each dollar she spent. Sven has 9 yo-yos. He spent $18.00 to buy them all. He wrote the equation $18 \div 9 = y$. What does Sven's equation tell him?

____

Name ___________________________

Reteaching
13-4

Translating Words to Equations

Read	Example 1 Jackie bought 4 bags of balloons. In total, she has 84 balloons. How many balloons are in each bag?	Example 2 Erin bought 6 bags of beads. There were 9 beads in each bag. How many beads were there in all?
Plan	Write an equation to help you find the number of balloons per bag. $84 \div 4 = y$ (total) ÷ (bags) = (balloons per bag)	Write an equation to help you find the number of beads in all. $6 \times 9 = a$ (bags) × (beads) = (beads in all)
Solve	$84 \div 4 = 21$ $y = 21$ There are 21 balloons in each bag.	$6 \times 9 = 54$ $a = 54$ There are 54 beads in all.
Check	Multiply 21 (balloons per bag) by 4 (number of bags). $21 \times 4 = 84$ There are 84 balloons in total, so I know my answer is correct.	Divide 54 (beads in all) by 6 (bags). $54 \div 6 = 9$ There are 9 beads per bag, so I know my answer is correct. OR Divide 54 (beads in all) by 9 (beads per bag). $54 \div 9 = 6$ There are 6 bags, so I know my answer is correct.

Solve.

1. In a parking lot, there are 6 cars per row. There are 42 cars in all. What operation do you need to use to find the number of rows?

____

2. Luis has 6 bags of pears. There are 16 pears in each bag. Write an equation to find how many pears there are in all. Solve the equation.

____

3. Strategy Practice Gina bought boxes of pens. Each box had 8 pens. There were 48 pens in all. Write an equation to find the number of boxes of pens. Then, solve the equation and show how to check your answer.

____

Name ____________________

Practice 13-4

Translating Words to Equations

In **1** through **6**, circle the equation that matches the situation.

1. Jay bundles 5 strands of wire to make 1 cable. How many strands of wire are there in 7 cables? $1 \div 5 = w$ $5 \times 7 = w$	**2.** Jill has 9 CDs and bought 6 more. How many CDs does Jill have? $15 - 6 = c$ $9 + 6 = c$
3. There are 6 parking spots in 1 row. How many parking spots are there in 18 rows? $6 \times 18 = p$ $18 \div p = 6$	**4.** Eugene gave an equal number of his 48 crackers to 4 friends. How many crackers were in each group? $12 \times 4 = c$ $48 \div 4 = c$
5. In a school, there are 5 classes of 22 fourth graders. How many fourth graders are there? $5 \times f = 22$ $5 \times 22 = f$	**6.** Max and Sarah each have 9 water balloons. How many water balloons do they have? $9 + 9 = b$ $18 \div 2 = b$

21. Jeff bought 7 coins for his collection. He spent $49.00, and each coin cost the same amount. Write a multiplication equation to find the cost of each coin.

____

22. Karen has a box of 216 toothpicks. She gives her toothpicks away to 8 friends. Which equation shows how many toothpicks each friend got?

A $t \div 8 = 216$ **B** $216 \div 8 = t$ **C** $8 \times 216 = t$ **D** $216 - t = 8$

23. Writing to Explain Seth has 6 groups of 7 stamps. He multiplied the number of groups by the number of stamps to find the total number of stamps he has. Would he find the same amount if he multiplied the number of stamps by the number of groups?

____

Name ______________________________

Problem Solving: Work Backward

Read and Understand	Plan and Solve	Check
Four students shared some mangoes for lunch, but 2 mangoes were too ripe to eat. The students cut up 4 mangoes, which made up $\frac{1}{3}$ of the mangoes that were left. How many mangoes were there in all? You need to find the number of mangoes the students started with.	Start with the number of mangoes the students cut up. Then work backward to find the original number of mangoes. These were $\frac{1}{3}$ of the mangoes left after the 2 ripe ones were thrown away. 4 mangoes are $\frac{1}{3}$ of 12. So there must have been 12 mangoes left after the ripe ones were discarded. Add the 2 overripe mangoes to the 12. The students started out with 14 mangoes.	Work forward to check your work. Start with 14 mangoes. Subtract the 2 overripe ones to get 12. One third of the 12 mangoes left is 4 mangoes, which is the number of mangoes the students cut up.

Work backward to help you solve each exercise.

1. Phoebe played checkers with her sister. She won 4 times as many games as she lost. Phoebe won 12 games. If there were no ties, how many games did Phoebe play?

____

2. Kim ordered a super-sized submarine sandwich and had it cut into equal pieces. She and 3 friends ate the same number of pieces. $\frac{1}{4}$ of the sandwich was not eaten. For dinner that night, she ate 3 pieces, which were $\frac{1}{2}$ of the leftovers. How many pieces were there originally?

____

Name ______________________________

Practice
13-5

Problem Solving: Work Backward

Work backward to help you solve each exercise.

1. Jenny is training for a race. On Day 1, she ran 5 miles, which was $\frac{1}{3}$ the distance she ran on Day 3 and $\frac{1}{2}$ the distance she ran on Day 2. How many miles did she run over the 3-day period?

   ____

2. In June 1995, a sixth-grade class planted a tree in the scoolyard. The tree grew about 3 inches a year. If the tree was 38 inches high in June 2000, about how high was the tree when it was planted?

   ____

3. Sean is 4 months older than Tony. Heather is 6 months younger than Tony. If Sean's birthday is in April, in which months are Heather's and Tony's birthdays?

   ____

4. Joe made a frozen yogurt shake with 10 ounces of milk and some strawberry frozen yogurt. He used the mixture to fill three 5-ounce glasses and had 2 ounces left over. How much frozen yogurt did he use?

   ____

5. The debate club members sold raffle tickets to raise money for T-shirts. They sold 3 times as many raffle tickets on the weekend as they did during the week. On the weekend, they sold 246 tickets. How many raffle tickets did they sell during the week?

   ____

Name ______________________

Reteaching
14-1

Understanding Integers

Integers are positive and negative whole numbers, and 0.

Examples of positive and negative integers and their word descriptions:

Word Description	Positive or Negative?	Integer
1. 20 degrees Celsius	Positive number	$^{+}20$
2. 20 degrees below 0	Negative number	$^{-}20$
3. 18 feet above sea level	Positive number	$^{+}18$
4. 18 steps backward	Negative number	$^{-}18$
5. 13 feet below sea level	Negative number	$^{-}13$
6. 13 steps forward	Positive number	$^{+}13$

Write the integer for each word description.

1. 34 degrees Fahrenheit ______________

2. 1,800 feet below sea level ______________

3. $82 owed ______________

4. 44 floors above ground ______________

5. Jill climbed a mountain that was 1,500 feet high.
Write the number of feet she climbed as an integer.

____

6. Katie had 52 more pages of her book to read.
Write the number of pages she has to read as an integer.

____

7. Number Sense What is the opposite of the integer $^{+}5$?
Write word descriptions for each integer.

____

____

Name ______________________

Practice

14-1

Understanding Integers

For **1** through **10,** use the number line below. Write the integer for each point.

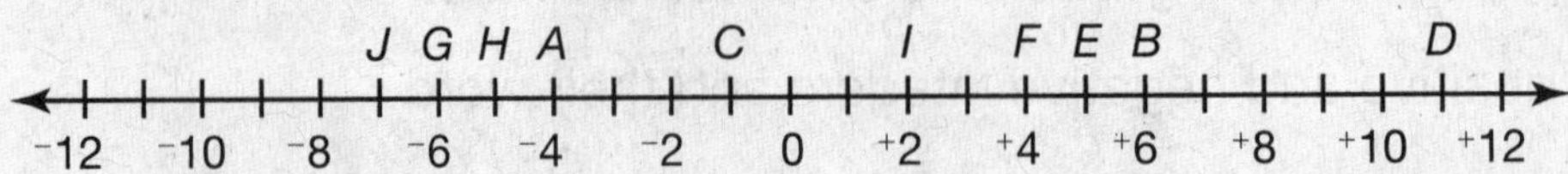

1. *A* _____ **2.** *B* _____ **3.** *C* _____ **4.** *D* _____ **5.** *E* _____

6. *F* _____ **7.** *G* _____ **8.** *H* _____ **9.** *I* _____ **10.** *J* _____

For **11** through **20,** use the number line below. Write the letter for each integer.

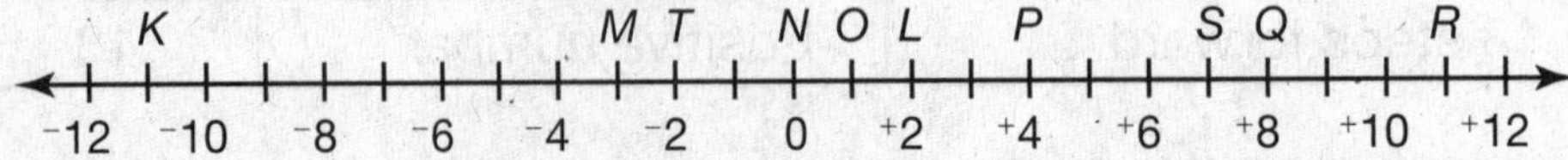

11. $^{+}8$ _____ **12.** 0 _____ **13.** $^{+}11$ _____ **14.** $^{+}4$ _____ **15.** $^{-}3$ _____

16. $^{+}1$ _____ **17.** $^{-}11$ _____ **18.** $^{+}7$ _____ **19.** $^{+}2$ _____ **20.** $^{-}2$ _____

21. Rita recorded the low temperature last night. It was seven degrees below zero. Express this temperature as an integer. _____

22. Which integers come between $^{-}2$ and 3 on a number line?

A $^{-}1$, 4, 0 **C** 2, $^{-}1$, 1

B 0, 5, $^{-}1$ **D** $^{-}2$, 2, 0

23. Writing to Explain Nate owes Michael $5.00. Nate expressed how much he owes as an integer. Michael expressed how much Nate owes him as an integer. What do the two integers have in common?

____

____

Name ______________________

Reteaching

14-2

Comparing Integers

Judy wrote down the temperature at 8 A.M. each day for one week.

Day	Temperature
Monday	$^{+}3$° Celsius
Tuesday	$^{+}7$° Celsius
Wednesday	$^{-}2$° Celsius
Thursday	$^{+}1$° Celsius
Friday	$^{-}3$° Celsius

Which number is greater, $^{-}3$ or $^{+}7$?

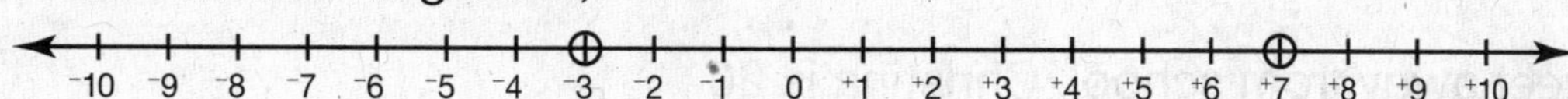

The value of numbers decreases as you move left down the number line.
The value of numbers increases as you move right up the number line.

$^{-}3$ is less than $^{+}7$.

Was the temperature lower on Wednesday or on Thursday?

The temperature was $^{-}2$° on Wednesday and $^{+}1$° on Thursday. $^{-}2$ is less than $^{+}1$, so the temperature was lower on Wednesday.

1. **Number Sense** How many units do you have to count from $^{-}1$ to get to 3 on a number line? Which direction do you move on the number line?

____

Compare. Fill in the blank with <, >, or =.

2. $^{-}9$ _____ $^{+}9$

3. $^{-}8$ _____ $^{+}2$

4. $^{+}5$ _____ $^{-}5$

5. $^{-}2$ _____ $^{+}1$

6. $^{-}6$ _____ $^{-}8$

7. $^{-}9$ _____ $^{-}7$

8. $^{+}7$ _____ $^{-}8$

9. $^{+}2$ _____ $^{-}1$

Name ______________________________

Practice
14-2

Comparing Integers

For **1** through **16**, write $>$, $<$, or $=$ for each. Use a number line to help.

1. $^-2$ ____ $^+1$ **2.** $^-11$ ____ $^+9$ **3.** $^-7$ ____ $^+8$ **4.** $^-19$ ____ $^-17$

5. $^+7$ ____ $^-8$ **6.** $^-1$ ____ $^-21$ **7.** $^-13$ ____ $^+18$ **8.** $^-19$ ____ $^+19$

9. $^+8$ ____ $^-13$ **10.** $^-2$ ____ $^-1$ **11.** $^+11$ ____ $^-2$ **12.** $^-7$ ____ $^+9$

13. $^-9$ ____ $^-12$ **14.** $^-4$ ____ $^-3$ **15.** $^-6$ ____ $^+3$ **16.** $^-8$ ____ $^-7$

17. Sonya owes Mark $5.00. Clair owes Mark $4.00. Who owes Mark more money? ____________

18. Fred is 18 feet away from school. Christina is 20 feet away from school. Who is closer to the school? ____________

19. Sarah is swimming. She is at 2 feet below sea level. Her friend Lucy is 4 feet below sea level. Who is the most below sea level? ____________

20. Kevin owes Irving $30.00. Which integer shows how much Kevin is in debt?

A $^-70$ **C** $^+30$

B $^-30$ **D** $^+70$

21. Writing to Explain Dylan says that when comparing numbers the number closest to zero on a number line is always the smallest. Is he correct?

____

____

Name ______________________

Ordering Integers

Order the integers from greatest to least: $^{+}8$, $^{-}4$, $^{+}1$, $^{-}7$, $^{+}7$.

Use a number line to locate each integer.

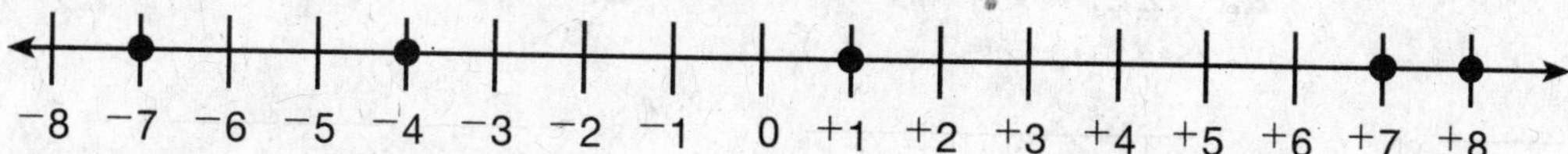

From greatest to least: $^{+}8$, $^{+}7$, $^{+}1$, $^{-}4$, $^{-}7$.

For **1** and **2**, write the integers in order from least to greatest. Use the number line below to help you.

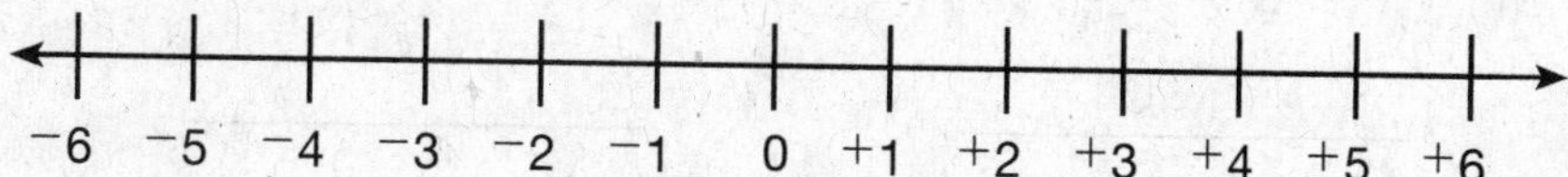

1. $^{-}4$, $^{+}3$, $^{-}1$

____

2. $^{+}2$, $^{+}3$, $^{-}5$

____

For **3** and **4**, write the integers in order from greatest to least. Use the number line below to help you.

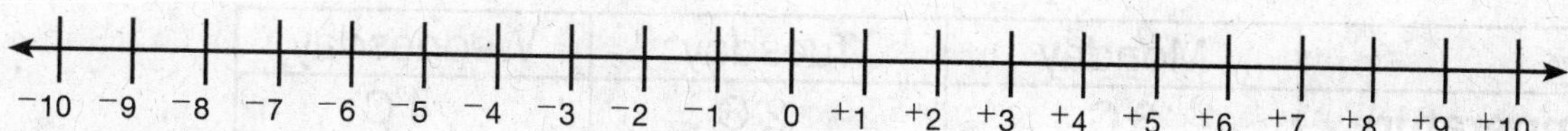

3. $^{+}8$, $^{-}7$, $^{-}9$

____

4. $^{-}10$, $^{+}5$, 0

____

Name ______________________

Practice 14-3

Ordering Integers

For **1** through **12**, write the numbers in order from least to greatest. You may use a number line to help.

1. +6, 0, −3 ______

2. −22, +11, −6 ______

3. −13, −15, +5 ______

4. −11, +5, −7 ______

5. +7, +8, −8 ______

6. −14, −16, −21 ______

7. +1, +2, −3 ______

8. −63, +64, −6 ______

9. −23, −99, +24 ______

10. −18, +13, −8 ______

11. +23, +45, −1 ______

12. −67, −87, −98 ______

13. Derek recorded the low temperature each day for 3 days. Order the temperature from greatest to least. ______

Day	Monday	Tuesday	Wednesday
Temperature	3°C	−2°C	−4°C

14. Rachael wrote the integers 3, −7, 9, −9, and −1 on pieces of paper. She then read them out loud in order from greatest to least. What was the third number she called out?

A −7 **B** −1 **C** 3 **D** 9

15. Writing to Explain Ted put several different integers in order from least to greatest. He then put the same integers in order from greatest to least. Both times the same number was third in order. Explain how this is possible.

______

______

______

Name ____________________

Reteaching **14-4**

Problem Solving: Draw a Picture

Read and Understand

Janie is in the fourth row of the marching band. There are 7 rows of musicians with 8 in each row. How many musicians are ahead of Janie? How many musicians are behind Janie?

You need to find how many are ahead of Janie and behind Janie.

Plan and Solve

You can **draw a picture** of the musicians: Write an A for each musician ahead of Janie, a B for each musician behind Janie, and a J for each musician in Janie's row.

```
A A A A A A A A ┐
A A A A A A A A ├ 3 × 8 = 24 musicians ahead of Janie
A A A A A A A A ┘
J J J J J J J J } 8 musicians in Janie's row
B B B B B B B B ┐
B B B B B B B B ├ 3 × 8 = 24 musicians behind Janie
B B B B B B B B ┘
```

Check

How many musicians are there in all? You can multiply $7 \times 8 = 56$ musicians or add $24 + 8 + 24 = 56$ musicians.

Draw a picture to solve each problem.

1. Ahmed has 12 seashells mounted in a row. The 6 shells in the center of the row are nautilus shells. How many shells are there on each side of the nautilus shells? ____________

2. Howard and Marla are in a marching band. Howard is in the fourth row and Marla is in the eighth row. There are 14 rows with 7 musicians per row. How many musicians are lined up between Howard's row and Marla's row? ____________

Name ____________________

Practice
14-4

Problem Solving: Draw a Picture

For problems **1** through **3**, use the graph to the right.

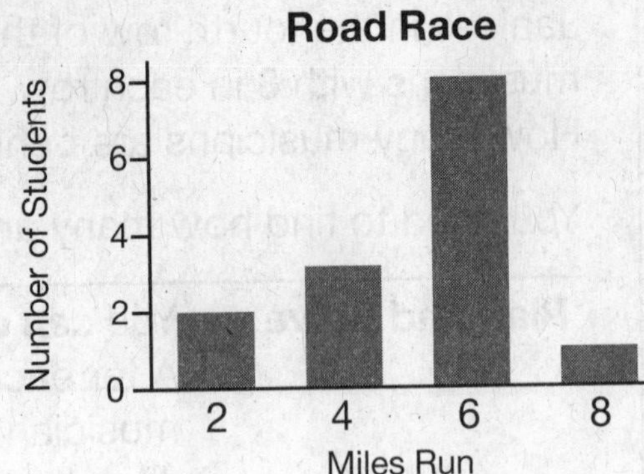

1. How many students ran the race?

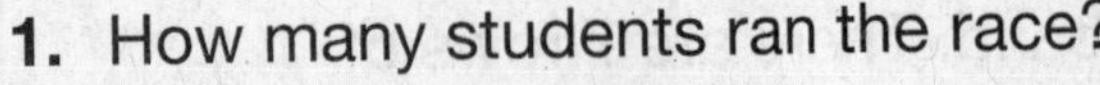

____

2. How many students ran more than 4 miles?

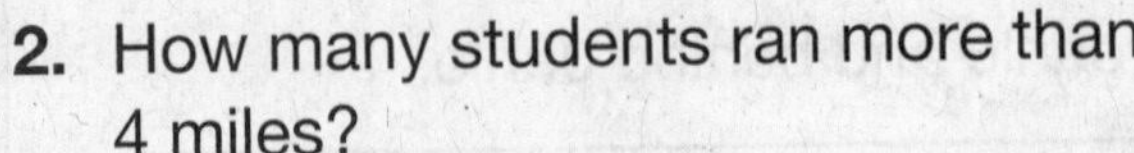

____

3. How many more students ran 6 miles than 4 miles?

____

4. The low temperature for one day in November was 18°F. The high temperature for that day was 19°F higher. What was the high temperature?

?°F	
18	19

____

5. Jenna spent $76.00 to buy 12 movie tickets for her birthday party. She bought 2 adult tickets. The rest were children's tickets. Which diagram shows how to find the number of children's tickets she bought?

A

76	
74	2

B

76	
12	66

C

12	
10	2

D

14	
12	2

6. **Writing to Explain** Ted has 8 autographed baseballs. All together the baseballs are worth $200.00. Explain why you do not have enough information to make a bar diagram to find the value of each baseball.

____

____

Name ______________________________

Customary Measures

Customary Units of Length, Weight, and Capacity

You can use customary units to measure length, weight, and capacity. You can use the chart to change a measurement from one unit to another.

Length

1 ft = 12 in.

1 yd = 3 ft

1 mi = 5,280 ft

Weight

1 lb = 16 oz

1 T = 2,000 lb

Capacity

1 tbsp = 3 tsp

1 fl oz = 2 tbsp

1 c = 8 fl oz

1 pt = 2 c

1 qt = 2 pt

1 gal = 4 qt

To change larger units to smaller units, multiply.

5 mi = ☐ ft

Think: 1 mi = 5,280 ft

5 × 5,280 = 26,400

5 mi = 26,400 feet

To change smaller units to larger units, divide.

72 fl oz = ☐ c

Think: 1 c = 8 fl oz

72 ÷ 8 = 9

72 fl oz = 9 cups

1. 4 ft. = ____ in

2. 12 pt = ____ qt

3. 2 gal = ____ qt

4. 6,000 lb = ____ T

5. 51 ft = ____ yd

6. 12 tbsp = ____ tsp

7. 3 yd = ____ ft

8. 2 T = ____ lb

9. 3 pt = ____ c

Name ______________________________

Practice
15-1

Customary Measures

Find each missing number.

1. 5 yd = ☐ ft ________

2. 2 mi = ☐ ft ________

3. 3 yd 1 ft = ☐ ft ________

4. 5 lb = ☐ oz ________

5. 2 T = ☐ lb ________

6. 3 lb 4 oz = ☐ oz ________

7. 6 qt = ☐ pt ________

8. 8 qt = ☐ gal ________

9. 48 fl oz = ☐ c ________

Compare. Write >, <, or = for each ◯.

10. 3 mi ◯ 12,320 ft

11. 60 in. ◯ 2 yd

12. 2,500 lb ◯ 2 T

13. 3 lb ◯ 48 oz

14. 1 qt ◯ 1 gal

15. 6 c ◯ 3 pt

Choose the most appropriate unit of measure for each.

16. the weight of a penny

____

17. the length of a closet shelf

____

18. A gold nugget weighs 2 pounds. If an ounce of gold is worth $300, how much is the nugget worth?

A $600 **B** $9,600 **C** $4,800 **D** $1,200

19. Writing to Explain Mary said that the best unit of measure to weigh her cat was ounces. Is she correct? Explain.

____

____

Name ____________________

Metric Measures

To change metric measurements from one unit to another, you can multiply or divide.

LENGTH
1 cm = 10 mm
1dm = 10 cm
1m = 100 cm
1 km = 1,000 m
MASS
1 kg = 1,000 g
CAPACITY
1 L = 1,000 mL

MULTIPLY to change larger units to smaller units.

How many mm are there in 3 cm?
You know that 1 cm = 10 mm
You want to find 3 × 10 mm
3 × 10 = 30 mm

DIVIDE to change smaller units to larger units.

How many kg are 6,000 g?
You know that 1,000 g = 1 kg.
You want to find 6,000 g ÷ 1,000 g.
6,000 g = 6 kg

Fill in the blank with the correct number.

1. 5 cm = ________ mm **2.** 30 cm = ________ dm **3.** 4,000 mL = ________ L

4. 8 kg = ________ g **5.** 9 dm = ________ cm **6.** 5 m = ________ cm

7. 7,000 m = ________ km **8.** 9 L = ________ mL **9.** 6,000 g = ________ kg

10. Number Sense Judy measured the length of her desk and found that it is 10 dm long. She said that her desk is 1 m long. Is she correct? Why or why not?

____

____

Name ______________________

Practice

15-2

Metric Measures

Find each missing number.

1. 6 m = ◯ cm ______

2. 8 km = ◯ m ______

3. 30 cm = ◯ dm ______

4. 8 km = ◯ m ______

5. 10,000 g = ◯ kg ______

6. 3 kg = ◯ g ______

7. 7,000 mL = ◯ L ______

8. 13 L = ◯ mL ______

9. 2,000 mL = ◯ L ______

Compare. Write >, <, or = for each ◯.

10. 25 km ◯ 20,000 m

11. 200 cm ◯ 3 m

12. 7,000 g ◯ 7 kg

13. 14,000 g ◯ 7 kg

14. 6 L ◯ 6,000 mL

15. 7,000 mL ◯ 4 L

Choose the most appropriate unit of measure for each.

16. mass of safety pin ______

17. water in an aquarium ______

18. length of a highway ______

19. width of your hand ______

20. The mass of a nickel is 5 grams. If you have 140 nickels in a box, how many grams of mass are in the box?

A 7,000 grams **B** 280 grams **C** 28 grams **D** 700 grams

21. Writing to Explain William wants to know how many kilograms a 1,000-gram cantaloupe weighs. He converts the measurement and says the melon is 1,000,000 kilograms. What did he do wrong?

____

____

Name ______________________________

Perimeter

You can use addition to find the perimeter of a figure.

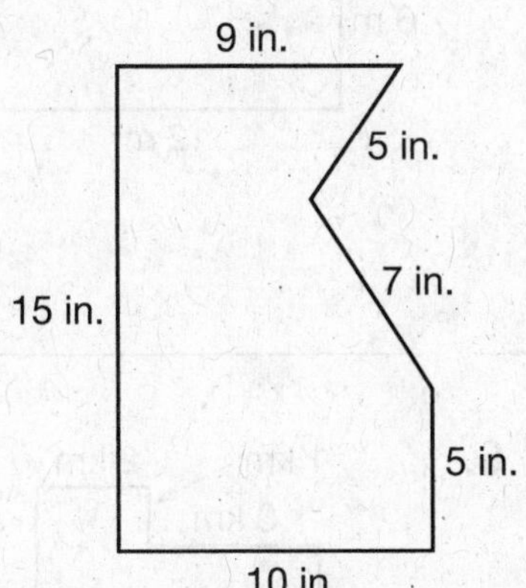

Add the lengths of the sides.

9 + 5 + 7 + 5 + 10 + 15 = 51 in.

Sometimes you can use a formula to find the perimeter.

11 m

3 m 3 m

11 m

$P = (2 \times l) + (2 \times w)$

l is the length and w is the width.

$P = (2 \times l) + (2 \times w)$

$P = (2 \times 11) + (2 \times 3)$

$P = 22 + 6$

$P = 28$ m

Find the perimeter of each figure.

1.

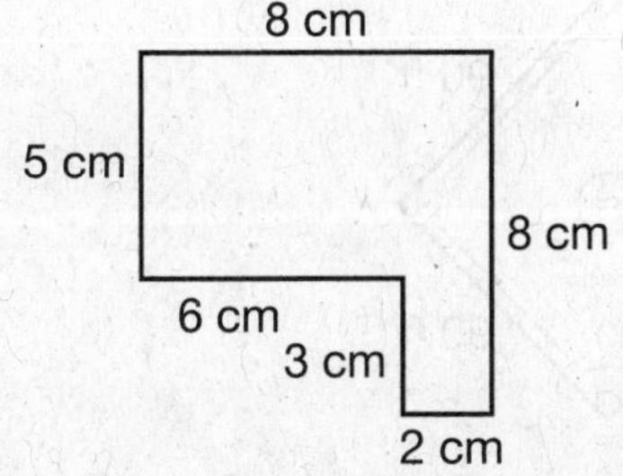

____

2.

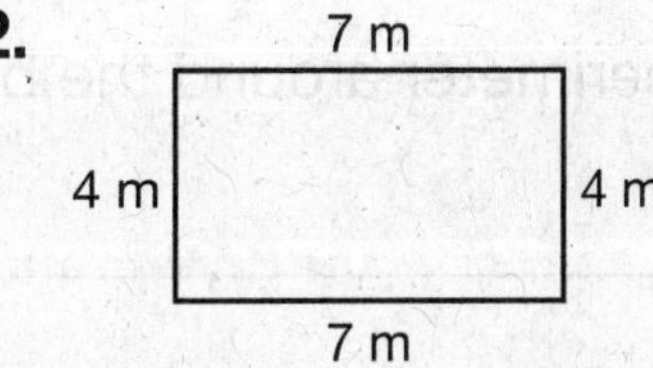

____

3.

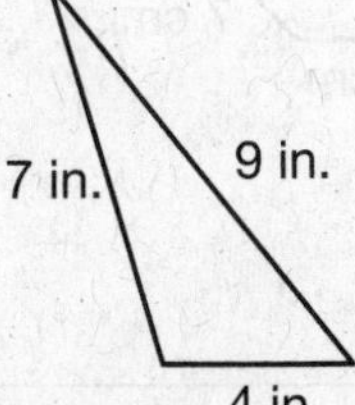

____

4.

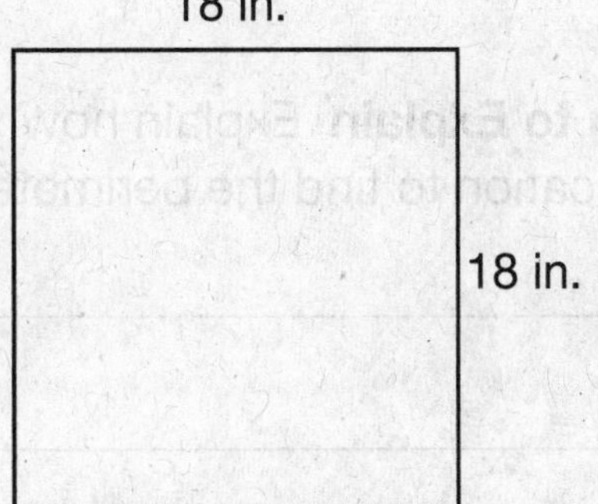

____

Name ________________________________

Practice
15-3

Perimeter

Find the perimeter of each figure.

1.

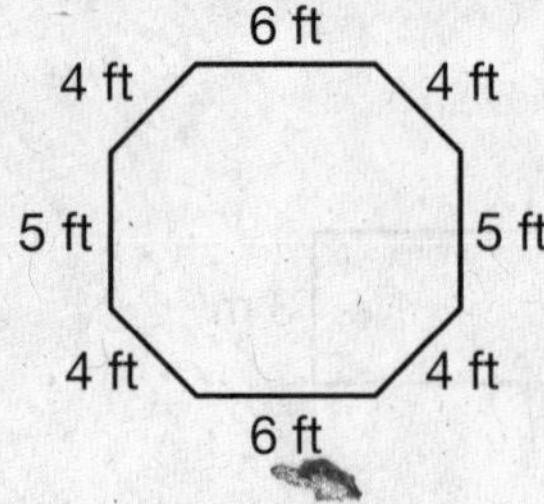

____

2.

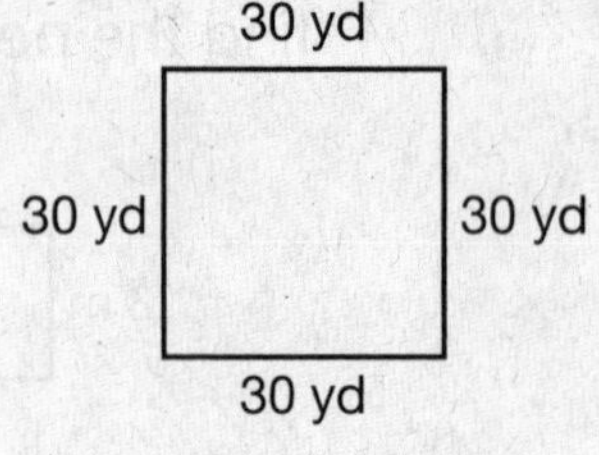

____

3.

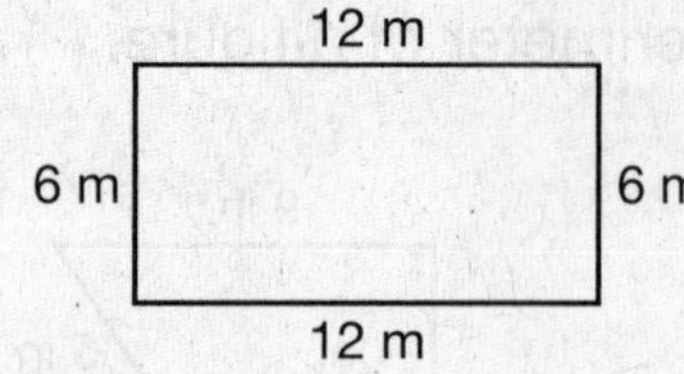

____

4.

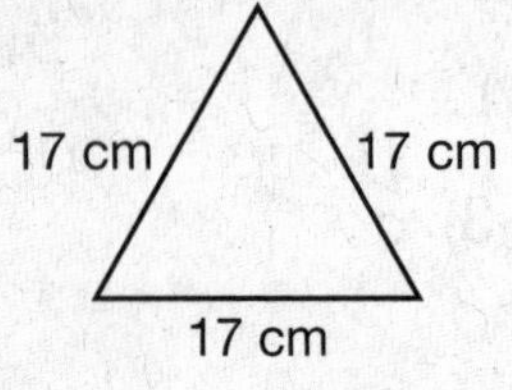

____

5.

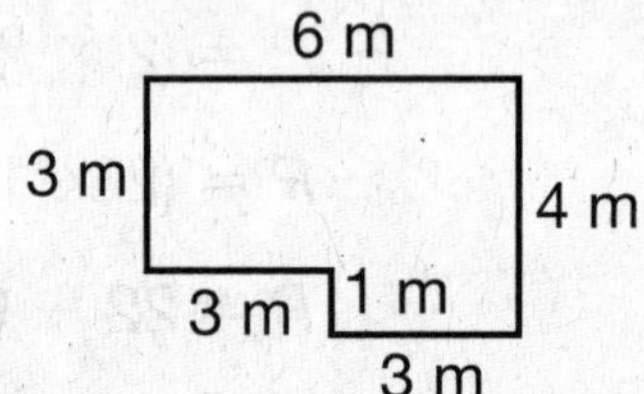

____

6.

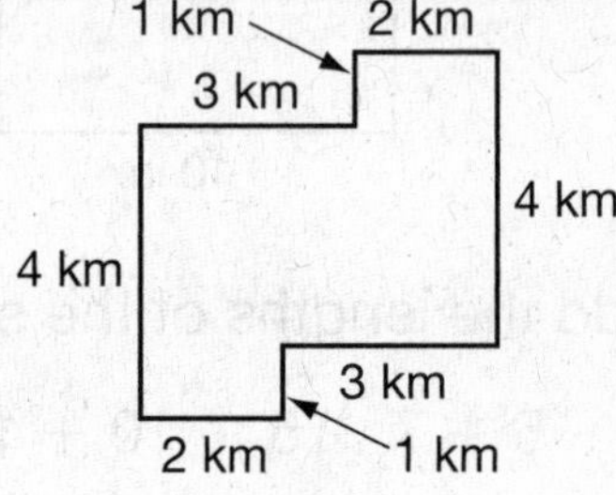

____

7. What is the perimeter around the bases?

____

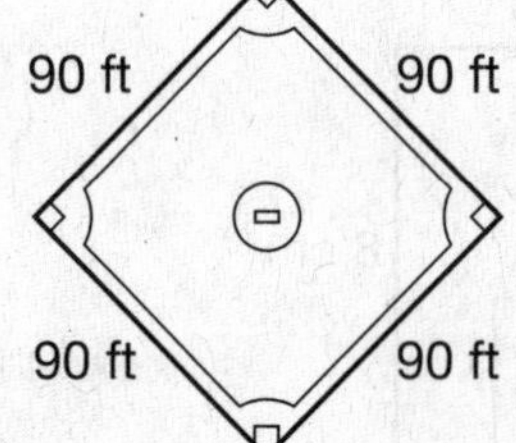

8. Which is the perimeter of this figure?

A 77 cm **B** 63 cm
C 56 cm **D** 28 cm

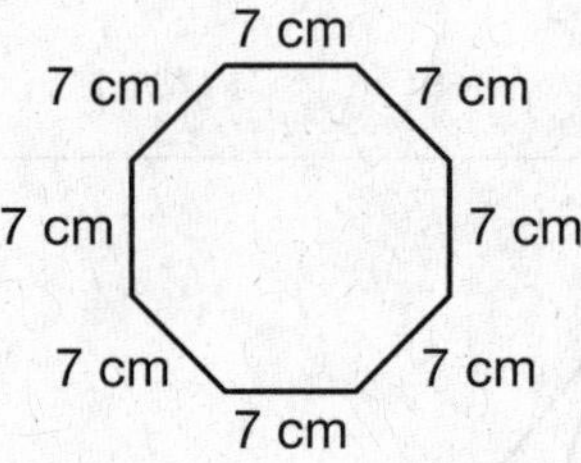

9. Writing to Explain Explain how you can use multiplication to find the perimeter of a square.

____

____

____

____

Name ______________________________

Area of Squares and Rectangles

What is the area of this figure?

Use the formula Area = length × width:

$A = 8 \times 5$

$A = 40$

The area is 40 square feet.

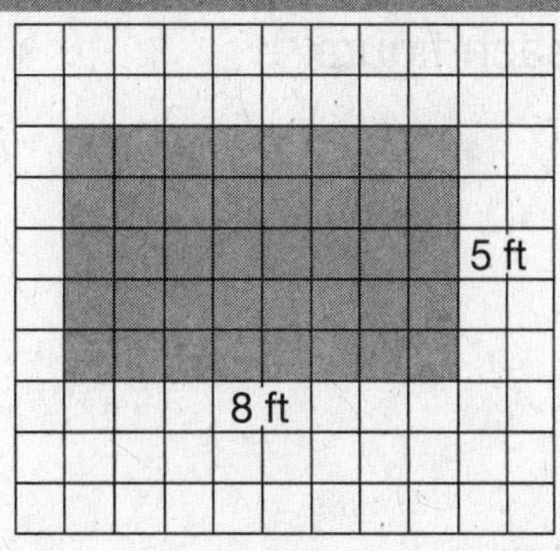

Find the area of each figure.

1.

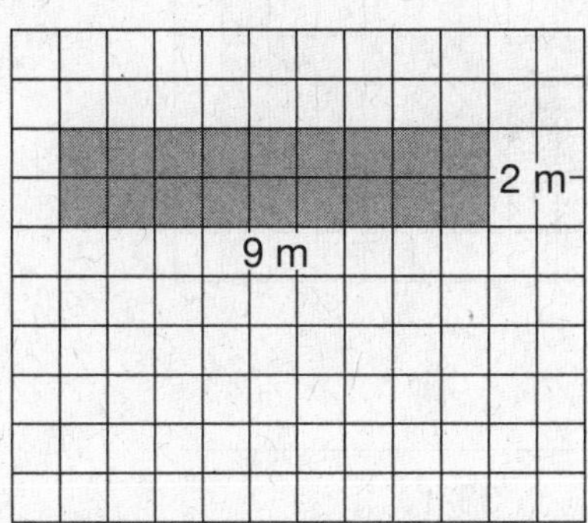

____

2.

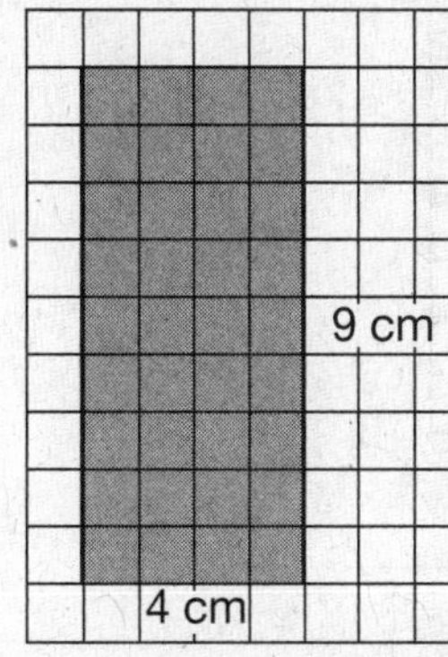

____

3.

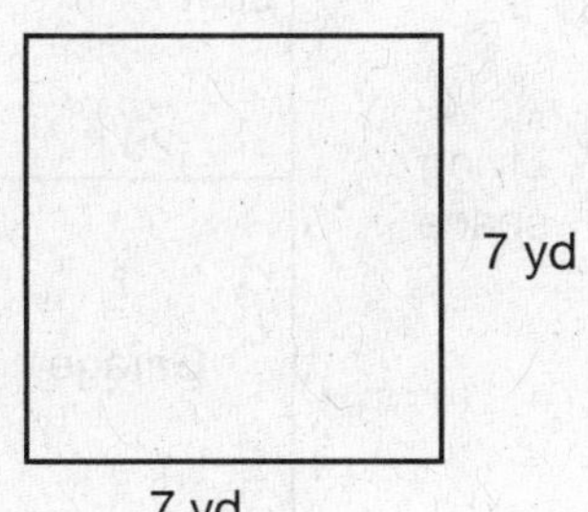

____

4.

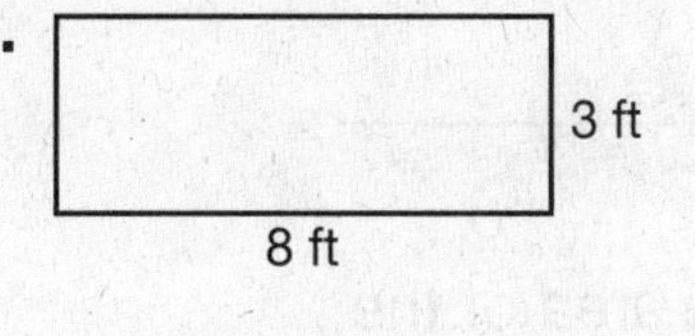

____

5. Reasoning The area of a rectangle is 56 square inches. The width of the rectangle is 7 in. What is the length? ______________

Name ____________________

Practice

15-4

Area of Squares and Rectangles

Find the area of each figure.

1. 5 in. / 5 in.

____

2. 5 ft / 9 ft

____

3.

____

4.

____

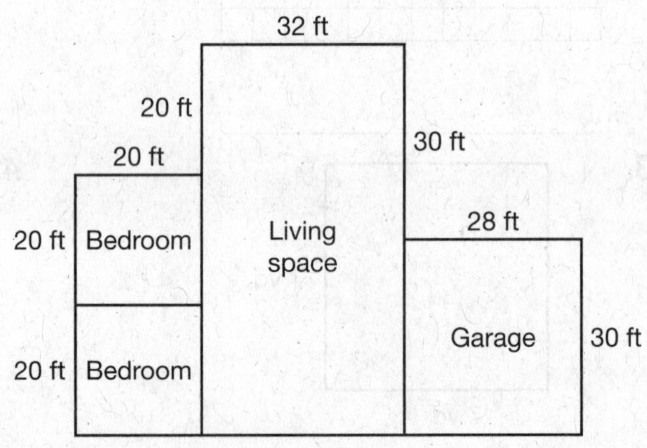

5. What is the area of one of the bedrooms?

____

6. What is the area of the garage?

____

7. Which is the area of a rectangle with a length of 26 cm and a width of 34 cm?

A 992 cm **B** 884 cm **C** 720 cm **D** 324 cm

8. Writing to Explain Explain how you would find the length of one side of a square if the area is 36 square units.

____

Name ____________________

Reteaching 15-5

Area of Irregular Shapes

To estimate the area of an irregular shape, you can add squares on a grid, or you can subtract squares from a larger area.

Adding Squares

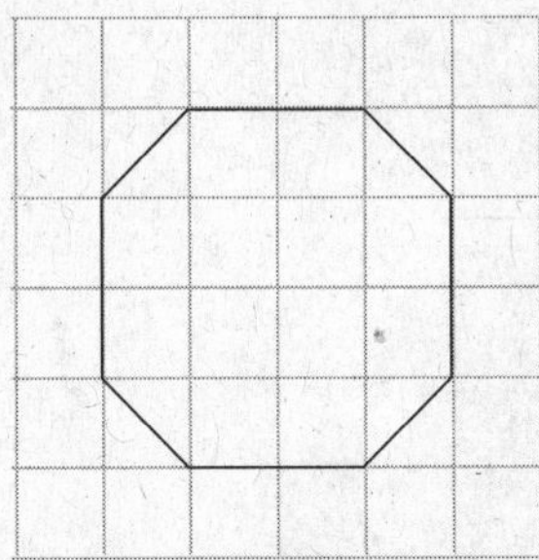

First, count the number of whole squares. There are 12 whole squares.

Then count the partial squares. There are 4 partial squares.

Estimate how many whole squares the partial squares would equal. They equal about 2 whole squares.

Finally, add the whole squares and the estimate for the partial squares to find the total estimated area.

12 + 2 = 14 square units

Subtract from a Larger Area

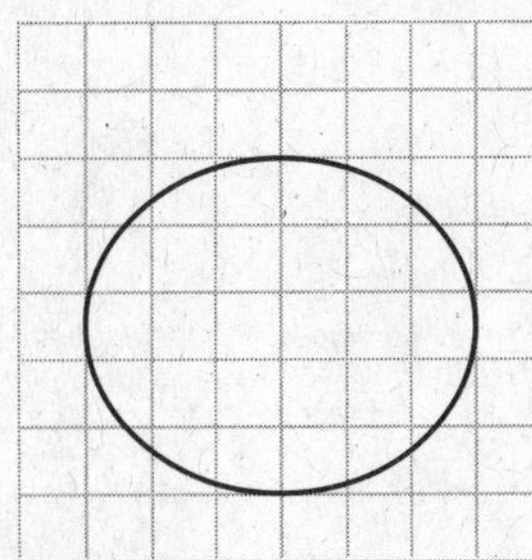

First, find the area of a regular shape that is larger than the irregular shape.

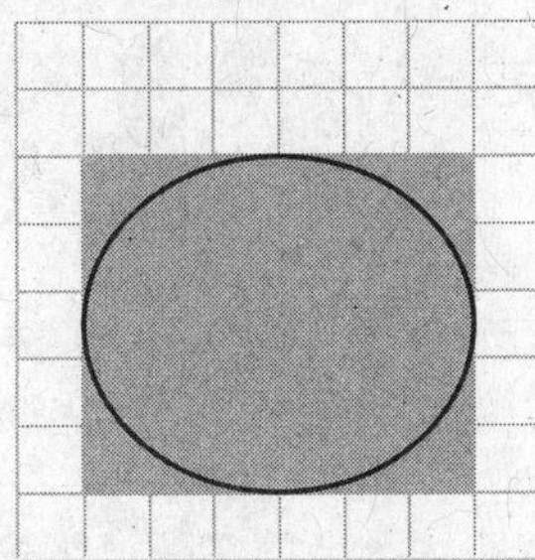

The gray rectangle has an area of 30 square units.

Subtract the squares that are less than the regular area. There is about 1 square subtracted at each corner, so you should subtract 4 squares.

30 − 4 = 26 square units

Find the area of each shape.

1.

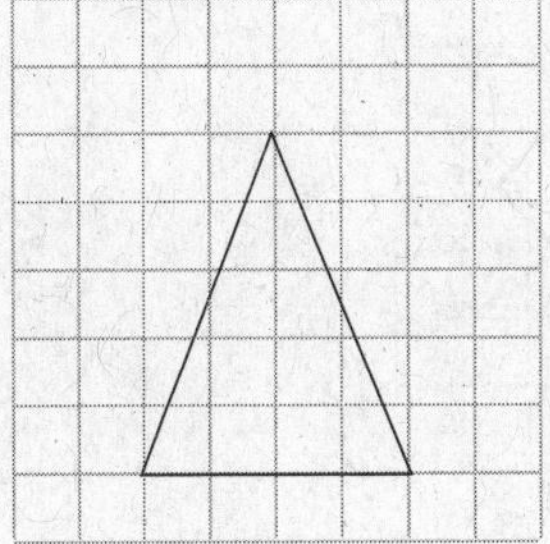

____

2.

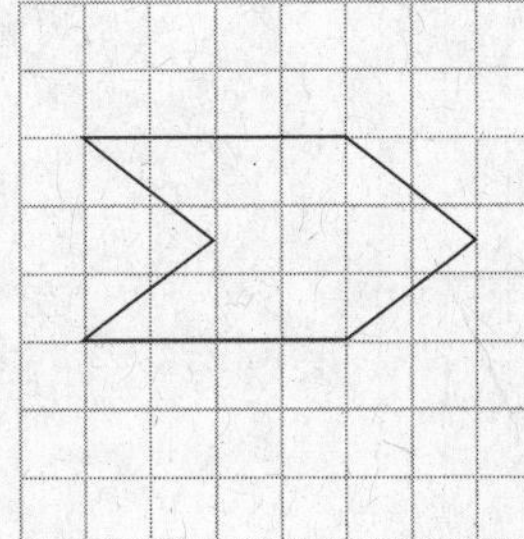

____

Name ________________________

Practice
15-5

Area of Irregular Shapes

Find the area of each shape.

1.

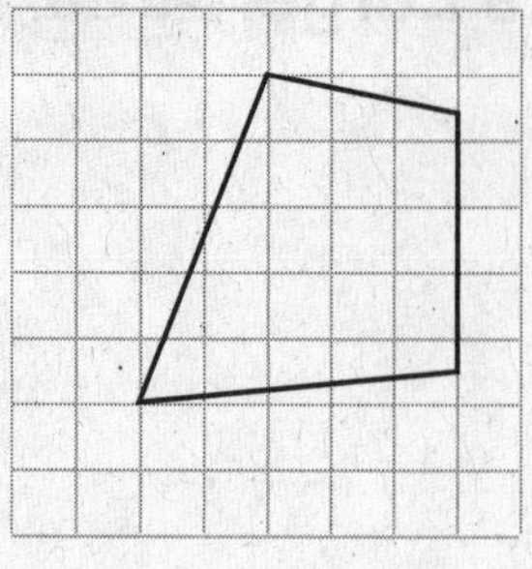

____

2.

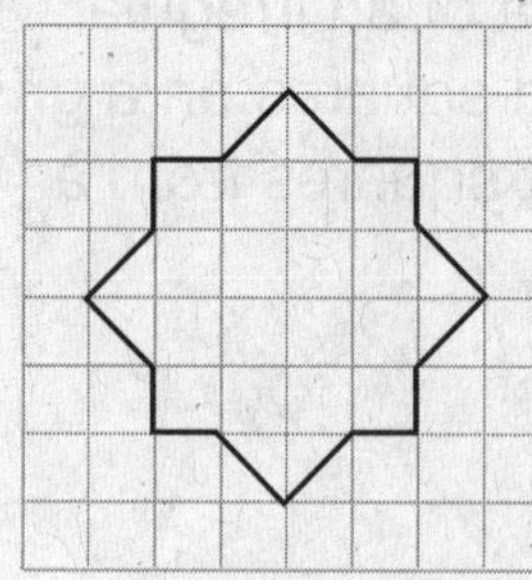

____

3.

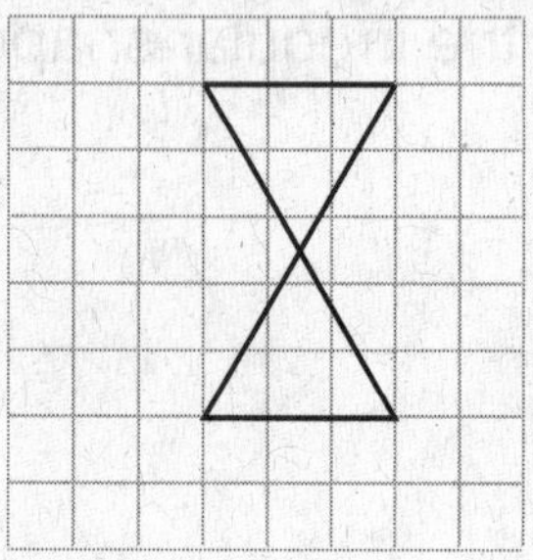

____

4.

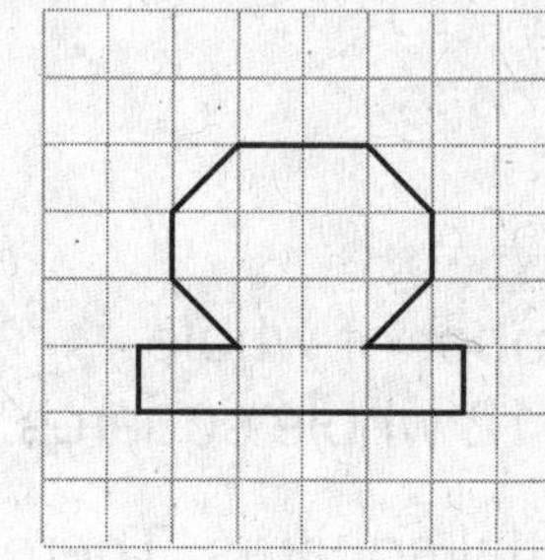

____

5.

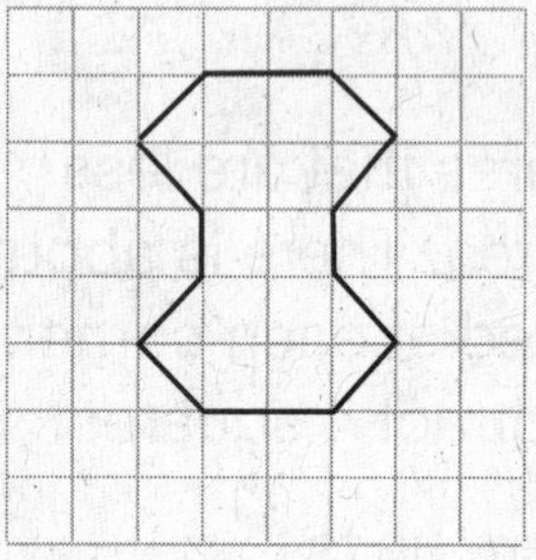

____

6.

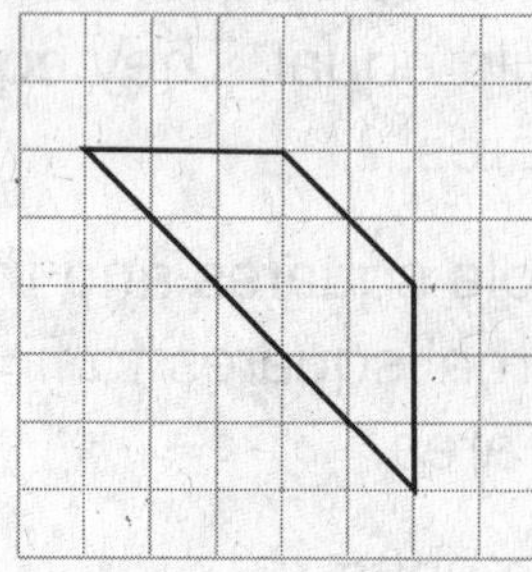

____

7.

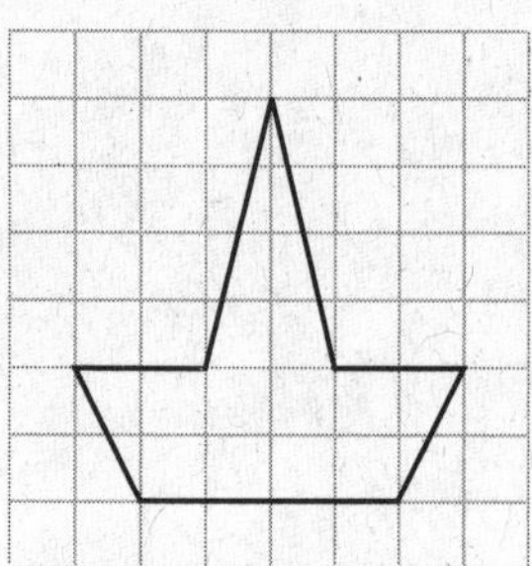

____

8.

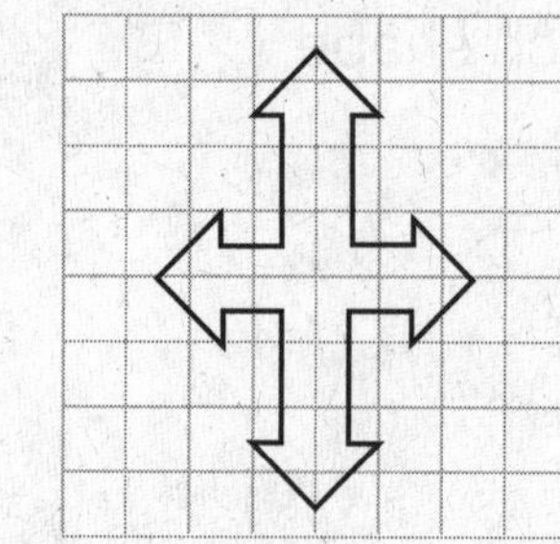

____

Name ____________________

Same Perimeter, Different Area

Rectangles that have the same perimeter can have different areas.

Draw three rectangles that have a perimeter of 12 centimeters. Then find the area of each.

1 cm

5 cm

2 cm

4 cm

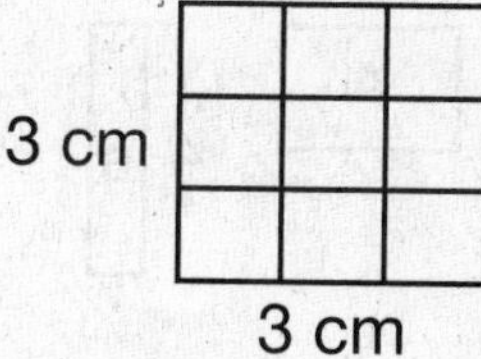

$P = 5 + 1 + 5 + 1 = 12$ cm
$A = 5 \times 1$
$= 5$ square centimeters

$P = 4 + 2 + 4 + 2 = 12$ cm
$A = 4 \times 2$
$= 8$ square centimeters

$P = 3 + 3 + 3 + 3 = 12$ cm
$A = 3 \times 3$
$= 9$ square centimeters

1. Draw two other rectangles with the same perimeter as the one below. Then find the area of each.

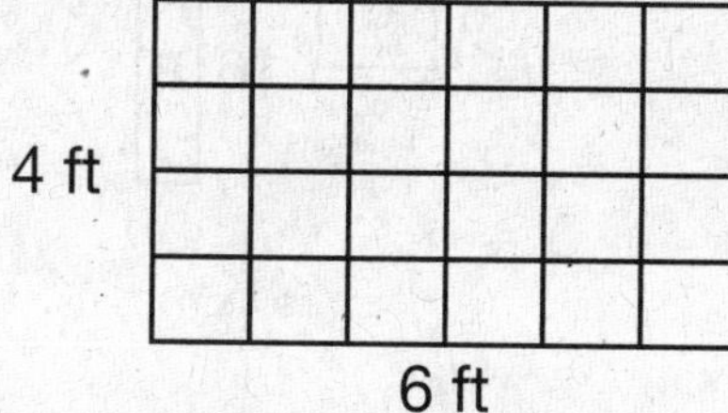

$P =$ ____________

$A =$ ____________

$P =$ ____________

$A =$ ____________

$P =$ ____________

$A =$ ____________

Name ________________________________

Same Perimeter, Different Area

For **1** through **9**, write "Yes" if the 2 rectangles have the same perimeter and "No" if they do not. If they have the same perimeter, tell which one has the greater area.

1.

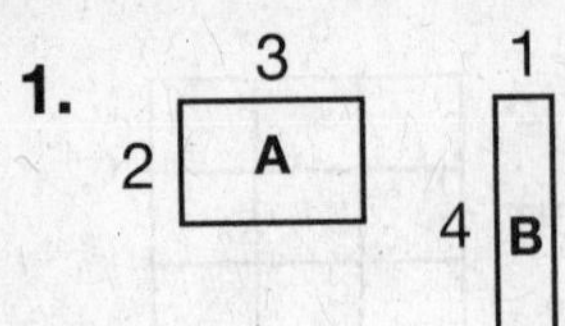

2. C: 5 by 5; D: 10 by 1

3. E: 6 by 6; F: 8 by 4

4. G: 5 by 1; H: 3 by 3

5. I: 4 by 5; J: 2 by 6

6. K: 3 by 1; L: 2 by 2

7. M: 5 by 6; N: 7 by 4

8. O: 5 by 9; P: 7 by 4

9. Q: 8 by 8; R: 4 by 16

10. Two rectangles have a perimeter of 16 inches. Name one possible area for each rectangle. ____________________

11. The length of a rectangle is 12 inches and the width is 6 inches. Which rectangle has the same perimeter?

A 6 by 6

B 5 by 8

C 10 by 8

D 12 by 3

12. Writing to Explain The perimeter of rectangle Z is equal to its area. Rectangle Y has the same perimeter as rectangle Z. The length of rectangle Y is 5 inches and the width is 3 inches. Explain how you can find the length and width of rectangle Z.

____

____

____

Name ______________________________

Same Area, Different Perimeter

Make three rectangles with an area of 36 square feet that have a different perimeter. Use grid paper or color tiles to help you.

1st Rectangle

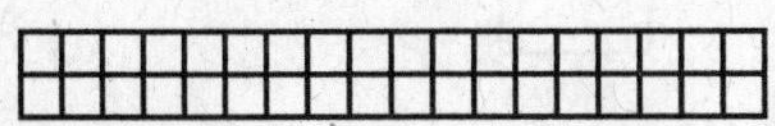

Find the area:
$A = l \times w$
$= 18 \times 2$
$= 36$ square feet

Find the perimeter:
$P = (2 \times l) + (2 \times w)$
$= (2 \times 18) + (2 \times 2)$
$= 36 + 4 = 40$ feet

2nd Rectangle

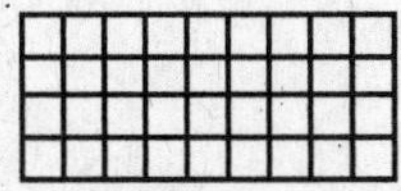

Find the area:
$A = l \times w$
$= 4 \times 9$
$= 36$ square feet

Find the perimeter:
$P = (2 \times l) + (2 \times w)$
$= (2 \times 9) + (2 \times 4)$
$= 18 + 8 = 26$ feet

3rd Rectangle

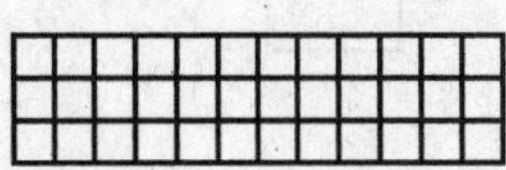

Find the area:
$A = l \times w$
$= 12 \times 3$
$= 36$ square feet

Find the perimeter:
$P = (2 \times l) + (2 \times w)$
$= (2 \times 12) + (2 \times 3)$
$= 24 + 6 = 30$ feet

Solve.

1. Draw two different perimeters of a rectangle with an area of 14 units. Name their dimensions.

2. **Number Sense** A rectangle has an area of 42 square inches. Which has a greater perimeter, the rectangle with the dimensions 21×2 or the dimensions 6×7? ____________

Name ______________________

Practice **15-7**

Same Area, Different Perimeter

For 1 through 9, write "yes" if the 2 rectangles have the same area and "no" if they do not. If they have the same area, tell which one has the smaller perimeter.

1.

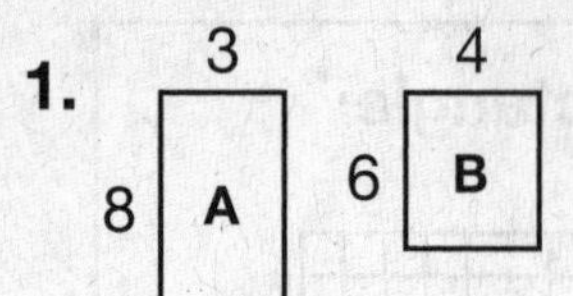

____

2. 10 × 10 **C** 15 × 5 **D**

____

3.

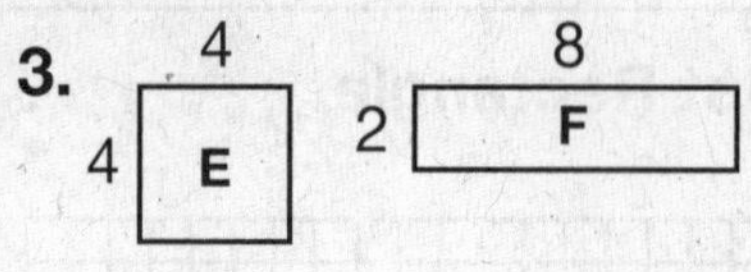

____

4. 5 × 8 **G** 20 × 2 **H**

____

5. 8 × 8 **I** 15 × 1 **J**

____

6. 2 × 6 **K** 3 × 4 **L**

____

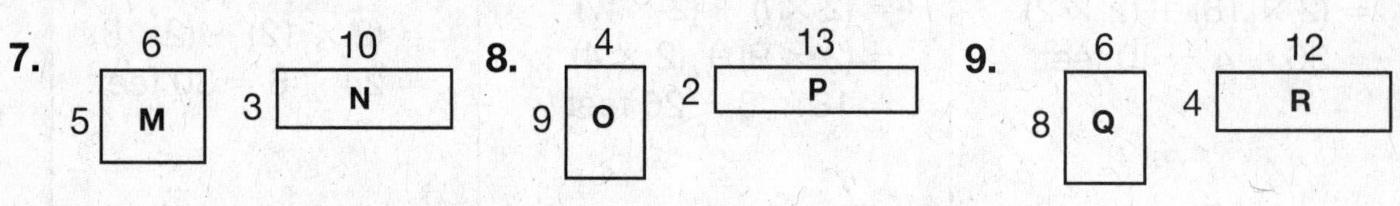

______________________ ______________________ ______________________

10. Two rectangles have an area of 81 square inches. Name one possible perimeter for each rectangle. ______________________

11. The length of a rectangle is 12 inches and the width is 12 inches. Which rectangle has the same area?

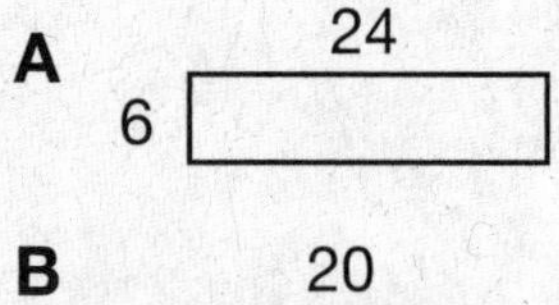

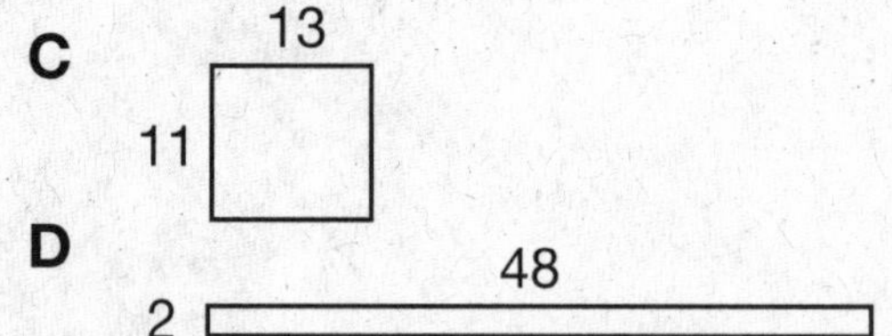

12. Writing to Explain The area of a rectangle is 100 square inches. The perimeter of the rectangle is 40 inches. A second rectangle has the same area but a different perimeter. Is the second rectangle a square? Explain why or why not.

____

____

Name ______________________________

Reteaching **15-8**

Problem Solving: Solve a Simpler Problem and Make a Table

Squares A student is making a pattern of squares out of cotton balls. Each unit on a side of the pattern is made up of 2 cotton balls. How many cotton balls will the student need to make a pattern that is 4 units high and 4 units wide?

1 unit

Read and Understand

Step 1: What do you know?
There are 2 cotton balls in each unit. The square is 4 units high and 4 units wide.

Step 2: What are you trying to find?
How many cotton balls are needed in all?

Plan and Solve

Step 3: What strategy will you use?

Strategy: Solve a simpler problem.

Problem 1: How many cotton balls are needed for a 1-unit by 1-unit square?

8 cotton balls are needed for a 1-unit square.

Problem 2: How many cotton balls are needed for a 2-unit by 2-unit square?

16 cotton balls are needed for a 2-unit square.

There are 2 cotton balls for each unit on the side.
There are always 4 sides, so the pattern is the number of units in each side, multiplied by 2 cotton balls, multiplied by 4 sides.

Square units	1×1	2×2	4×4
Cotton balls needed	8	16	32

Answer: 32 cotton balls are needed.

Look Back and Check

Step 4: Is your work correct?
Yes, all of my computations are correct, and I saw the correct pattern.

1. Joan works for 6 hours each weekday and 8 hours total on the weekends. She earns $6 an hour on weekdays and $9 an hour on weekends. How much money does she earn each week?

____

____

Name ______________________

Practice
15-8

Problem Solving: Solve a Simpler Problem and Make a Table

Sam needs to cut a piece of sheet metal into 8 pieces. It takes him 5 minutes to make each cut.

1. **Writing to Explain** Why would you make a table to find the number of cuts Sam makes?

____

____

2. How many cuts will Sam make? ____________

3. How long will it take Sam to turn the sheet metal into 8 pieces? Write your answer in a complete sentence.

____

Sarah is having a slumber party with her 11 friends and they are telling scary stories. They divide into 3 groups and each group tells a story. Each group member talks for 3 minutes.

4. How many people are in each group? ____________

5. How many minutes does each group take to tell a story? ____________

6. How many minutes does it take for all three groups to tell their stories? ____________

7. If Sarah divided her friends into 4 groups and each person still got the same time to talk, how long would it take to tell the stories?

   A 16 minutes **B** 36 minutes **C** 48 minutes **D** 144 minutes

Name ____________________

Reteaching
16-1

Data from Surveys

To take a survey, you ask different people the same question and record their answers. Heather asked her class, "What is your favorite flavor of frozen yogurt?" Here are her results.

Favorite Flavor of Frozen Yogurt		
Vanilla	////	4
Chocolate	~~////~~ ////	9
Strawberry	///	3
Orange	/	1

We can see that Heather's classmates liked chocolate frozen yogurt the best.

Favorite Winter Olympic Sports		
Bobsledding	~~////~~ //	
Curling	//	
Ice hockey	~~////~~ ~~////~~	
Speed skating	///	

1. How many people in the survey liked bobsledding the best? ____________

2. How many people were surveyed? ____________

3. According to the data, which sport is the favorite of most people? ____________

4. Number Sense From the survey, do you know if people liked figure skating best? Explain.

____

____

____

____

Name ______________________

Practice 16-1

Data from Surveys

Use the data in the tally chart.

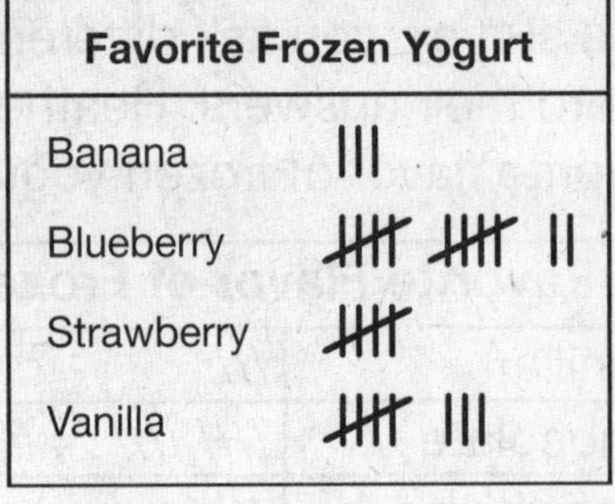

Favorite Frozen Yogurt	
Banana	|||
Blueberry	~~||||~~ ~~||||~~ ||
Strawberry	~~||||~~
Vanilla	~~||||~~ |||

1. How many people in the survey liked strawberry-flavored frozen yogurt best?

____

2. Which flavor of frozen yogurt received the most votes? ______________________

3. How many people liked vanilla frozen yogurt best? ______________________

4. How many people were surveyed? ______________________

5. **Number Sense** Could the frozen yogurt survey help restaurants choose flavors of frozen yogurt? Explain.

____

____

____

6. Which is the last step in taking a survey?

A Explain the results

B Count tallies

C Write a survey question

D Make a tally chart and ask the question

7. **Writing to Explain** Give an example of a topic for a survey question where the results for the answers could be similar.

____

____

____

____

Name ___________________________

Interpreting Graphs

Bar graphs help us compare data.

Data File	
Lengths of U.S. States	
State	**Length**
Florida	500 mi
Georgia	300 mi
Kansas	400 mi
Utah	350 mi

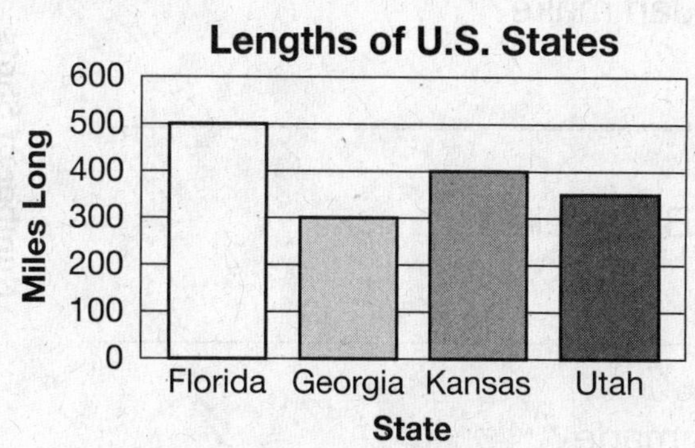

The bar graph shows the information from the table in another way.

Use the bar graph below.

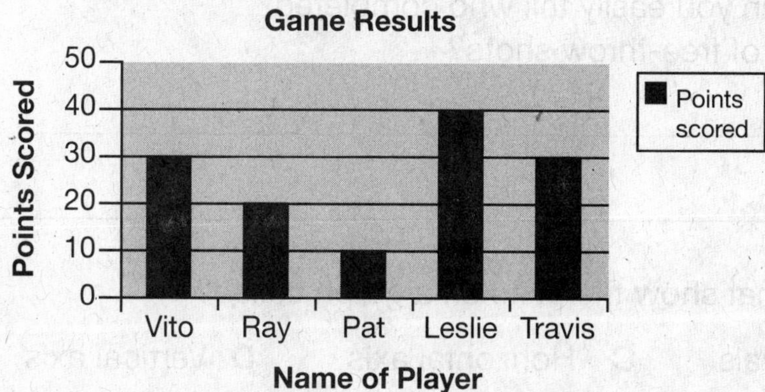

1. How many points did Pat score? ______

2. Who scored more points, Leslie or Travis? ______

3. Which player scored 20 points? ______

4. Which two players scored the same amount of points? ______

Name ____________________

Practice **16-2**

Interpreting Graphs

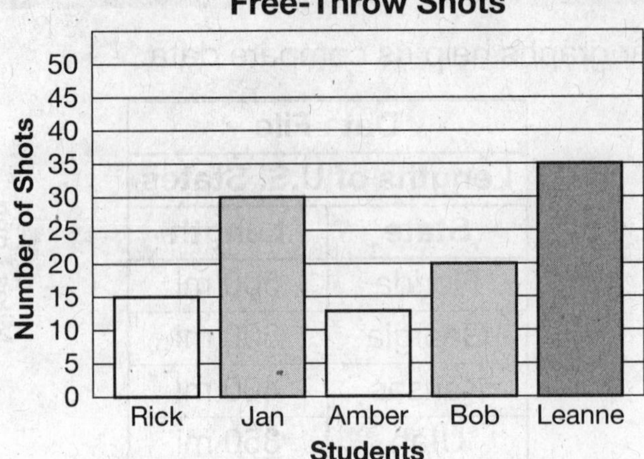

How many free-throw shots did

1. Jan make?

____

2. Bob make?

____

Who made

3. 35 free-throw shots? ____________________

4. 15 free-throw shots? ____________________

5. Number Sense How can you easily tell who completed about the same number of free-throw shots?

____

____

6. What are the numbers that show the units on a graph called?

A Scale **B** Intervals **C** Horizontal axis **D** Vertical axis

7. Writing to Explain Describe the interval you would use for a bar graph if the data ranges from 12 to 39 units.

____

____

____

Name ______________________________

Line Plots

The table below gives the number of miles Freda ran over a period of days. A line plot shows data along a number line. Each X represents one number in the data set.

Miles Run	Day
2	2
3	4
4	5
5	3
6	2
12	1

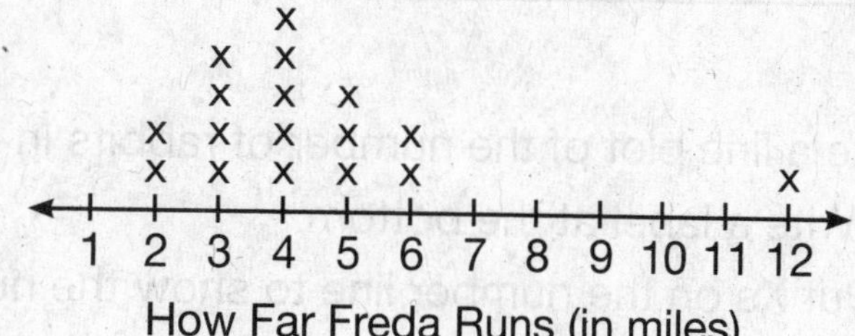

On the line plot each X represents 1 day. An outlier is a number in a data set that is very different from the rest of the numbers.

1. Is there an outlier in the data set above? Explain.

____

2. Complete the line plot to show the data in the table for puppies' weights at birth. Identify the outlier in the data set.

____

Weight (lb)	Number of Puppies
3	5
4	3
5	2
6	0
7	1
13	1

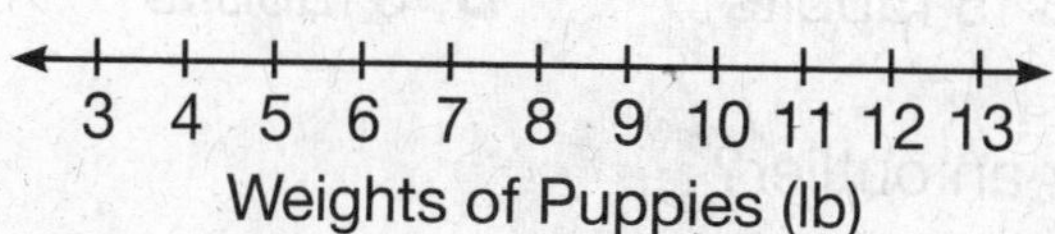

Name ___________________________

Practice
16-3

Line Plots

Number of Rabbits in Each Litter	1	2	3	4	5	6	7	8	9	10	11	12
Litters	/	///	𝍸	𝍸 ////	𝍸 𝍸	𝍸 ///	////	////	///	𝍸	///	/

1. Make a line plot of the number of rabbits in each litter.

a. Write a label at the bottom.

b. Put Xs on the number line to show the number of rabbits in a litter.

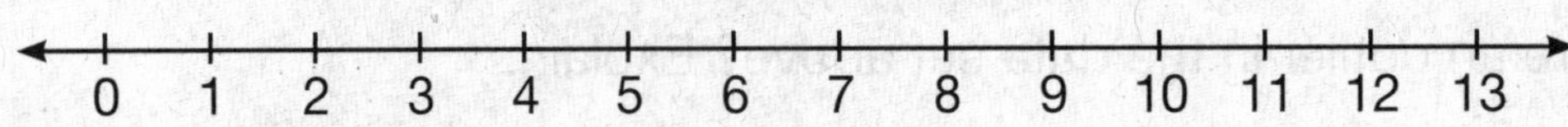

2. How many Xs are shown for 6? ___________

3. What is the greatest number of rabbits in a litter?

4. What is the number of rabbits that appears in a litter most oftwen?

A 3 rabbits **B** 4 rabbits **C** 5 rabbits **D** 6 rabbits

5. Writing to Explain Is the 1-rabbit litter an outlier?

____

____

Name ______________________

Mean

The mean of a set of numbers is the average. You can find the mean of 3, 8, and 7 by adding those three numbers together and then dividing the total by 3.

First, add the three numbers: $3 + 8 + 7 = 18$

Next, divide the total by 3: $18 \div 3 = 6$

The mean of 3, 8, and 7 is 6.

Find the mean.

There are 6 bags of groceries, each with a different number of items.

Bag 1	Bag 2	Bag 3	Bag 4	Bag 5	Bag 6
3 items	9 items	7 items	4 items	8 items	5 items

To find the mean, add the number of items in each bag.

$3 + 9 + 7 + 4 + 8 + 5 = 36$ items

There were 6 numbers in total, so divide 36 by 6 to find the mean.

$36 \div 6 = 6$ The average number of items per bag is 6.

Find the mean of each group of numbers.

1. 8, 5, 8 ____ **2.** 22, 33, 44 ____

3. 1, 6, 9, 4 ____ **4.** 41, 15, 37 ____

5. 8, 13, 90, 17 ____ **6.** 123, 54, 41, 6 ____

7. Number Sense The mean of 26, 26, and 26 is 26. The mean of 25, 26, and 27 is also 26. Find another set of numbers that has the mean of 26.

____

____

Name ______________________________

Practice **16-4**

Mean

In **1** through **18**, find the mean of each group.

1. 6, 2, 4, 8	**2.** 11, 9, 3, 77	**3.** 6, 1, 16, 22, 5
4. 12, 13, 17	**5.** 9, 3, 8, 10, 12, 6	**6.** 2, 5, 8, 7, 12, 8
7. 6, 9, 101, 4	**8.** 3, 2, 1, 6	**9.** 66, 22, 11, 33
10. 53, 22, 16, 61, 73	**11.** 104, 20, 8, 104	**12.** 9, 9, 7, 7
13. 22, 23, 24, 35	**14.** 6, 18, 3, 27, 36	**15.** 3, 12, 66, 18, 16, 11
16. 4, 3, 4, 5	**17.** 44, 1, 6	**18.** 5, 5, 10, 20

19. Donald scored a 99 on a test. Two of his friends scored a 97 and one of his friends scored a 95. What is the mean of their scores? __________

20. Liz caught 8 fish at the lake. Jay caught 4 fish. What is the mean number of fish they caught if Jay catches 2 more fish? __________

21. Michelle is 57 inches tall. Her older sister is 65 inches tall, and her younger brother is 46 inches tall. What is the mean of their heights?

A 46 inches **B** 54 inches **C** 56 inches **D** 62 inches

22. Writing to Explain The mean score for a test is 88. One more score is added to the data. Explain if it is possible for the mean to remain 88.

____

____

Name ______________________________

Median, Mode, and Range

Travelers at an airport were given a survey asking how many trips they take per year.

Trip Survey	
Number of Yearly Trips	**Number of Travelers**
1	///
2	////
3	~~////~~ //
4	///

The **mode** is the number that occurs most often. To find the mode, look for the number that has the most tally marks. The mode is 3 for this data. If all numbers have the same number of tally marks there is **no mode**. The **median** is the middle number of the data listed in order.

1 1 1 2 2 2 2 3 3 3 3 3 3 3 4 4 4

median

The **range** is the difference between the greatest number and the least number: 4 − 1 = 3. The range = 3 for this data.

1. How many travelers at the airport were surveyed? ____________

2. A survey was taken at the park. Children were asked how many times they had visited the park this year. Find the range, mode, and median of the data to the right.

Trips to the Park	
Number of Visits	**Number of Visitors**
3	~~////~~
4	///
5	~~////~~ //
6	~~////~~ /

____

____

3. Find the range, mode, and median of the data set below.
21, 23, 19, 19, 21, 23, 19, 19, 21, 24, 21, 19, 24

____

____

Name ______________________

Practice
16-5

Median, Mode, and Range

In **1** through **9**, find the median, mode, and range of each set of data.

1. 48, 11, 15, 14, 11 median: mode: range:	**2.** 3, 9, 3, 11, 23, 15, 15,12, 3, 9, 14 median: mode: range:	**3.** 5, 2, 1, 1, 3, 7, 6 median: mode: range:
4. 17, 13, 12, 18, 17, 10, 27 median: mode: range:	**5.** 33, 44, 55, 22, 55, 11,66 median: mode: range:	**6.** 21, 63, 22, 18, 35, 29, 63 median: mode: range:
7. 17, 47, 12, 13, 12 median: mode: range:	**8.** 2, 8, 24, 12, 22, 62, 61, 62, 82 median: mode: range:	**9.** 19, 16, 55, 25, 16, 21,19 median: mode: range:

10. Amy determined the number of hours her classmates volunteer each month. Name all the people who volunteer for more than the median of the data.

____

Person	Amy	Bob	Clair	Dave	Erin	Frank	Gina
Hours	7	7	2	4	8	5	6

11. Which person voluteered an amount of time equal to the range?

A Amy **B** Clair **C** Dave **D** Gina

12. Writing to Explain The median score on a test is 90. Is it possible to add two more scores to the data and still have a median score of 90? Explain your answer.

____

____

____

Name ____________________

Reteaching
16-6

Problem Solving: Make a Graph

Pitcher Chris recorded 3 strikeouts in his first game, 5 in his second game, 7 in his third game, 10 in his fourth game, and 11 in his fifth game. How did his number of strikeouts change over the course of the five games he pitched?

Read and Understand

Step 1: What do you know?

I know the number of strikeouts Chris made each game.

Step 2: What are you trying to find?

How the number of strikeouts changed.

Plan and Solve

Step 3: What strategy will you use?

A: Set up the bar graph.
B: Enter the known data.
C: Read the graph. Look for a pattern.

Answer: The number of strikeouts increased each game.

Strategy: Make a bar graph.

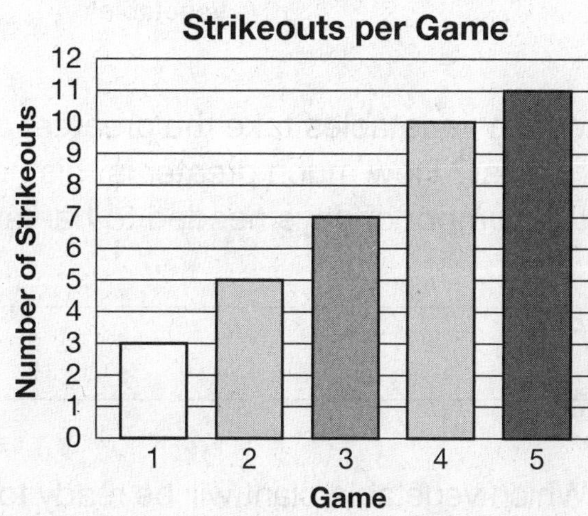

Solve. Write your answer in a complete sentence.

1. How much warmer is it, on average, in April than in January?

____

____

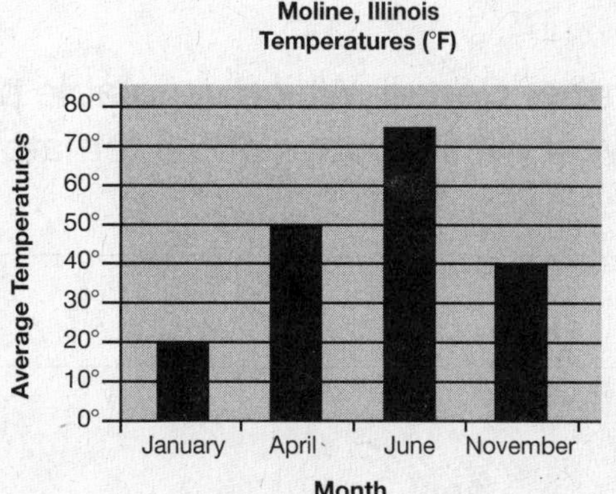

Name ___________________________

Practice 16-6

Problem Solving: Make a Graph

Complete the graph to solve each problem.

1.

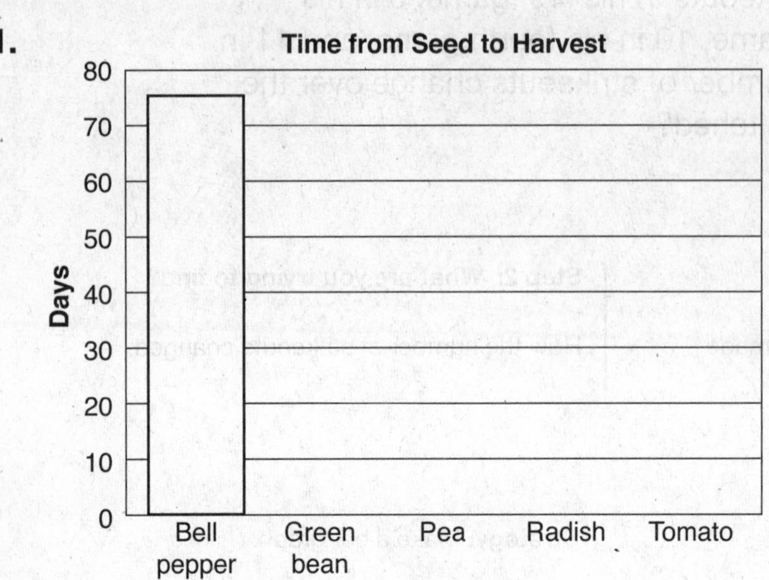

Time from Seed to Harvest	
Vegetable	**Days**
Bell pepper	75
Green bean	56
Pea	75
Radish	23
Tomato	73

2. Which vegetables take the greatest amount of time to harvest? How much greater is this number of days than the number of days needed to harvest radishes?

____

____

3. Which vegetable plant will be ready to harvest earlier, the bell pepper plant or the tomato plant? How many days earlier?

____

4. **Number Sense** Which vegetable plants will be ready to harvest within 5 days of the tomato plant?

____

____

Name ____________________

Graphing Ordered Pairs

A coordinate grid has a horizontal **x-axis** and a vertical **y-axis** that meet at 0. To read a grid, use **ordered pairs** of numbers. You can find the lettered points of the house on the grid by reading the ordered pairs. Start at 0. Move right 3 units. This gives you the first number, or **x-coordinate**. Then move up 2 units. This gives you the second number, or **y-coordinate**, in the ordered pair. The ordered pair for point ***A*** is (3, 2).

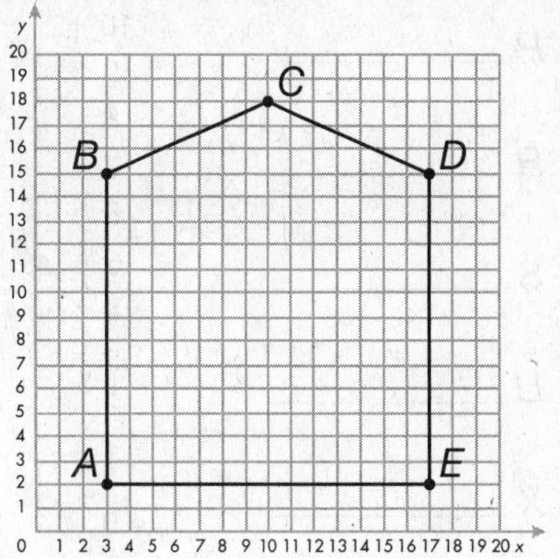

Point	You Move
A (3, 2)	3 → 2↑
B (3, 15)	3 → 15↑
C (10, 18)	10 → 18↑
D (17, 15)	17 → 15↑
E (17, 2)	17 → 2↑

When you **plot** point on a grid, you are graphing it by using the ordered pair for that point. Find each point on the grid and write the correct letter for it on the grid. Then connect the points in the order you found them.

Use the graph above for Exercises **1–7**.

1. Find the ordered pair (8, 2) and mark it with a dot.

2. Find the ordered pair (12, 2) and mark it with a dot.

3. Find the ordered pairs (8, 10) and (12, 10) and mark them with dots.

4. Connect the dots. You have drawn a ________________ .

5. Find the ordered pairs (4, 5) and (7, 5) and mark them with dots.

6. Find the ordered pairs (4, 10) and (7, 10) and mark them with dots.

7. Connect the points you drew in Exercises 5 and 6. You have drawn a ______________ .

Name ____________________

Practice **17-1**

Ordered Pairs

For **1** through **5**, write the ordered pair for each point.

1. *P* 

2. *R* 

3. *S* ____________

4. *U* 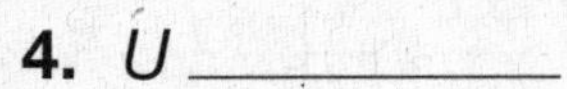

5. *X* ____________

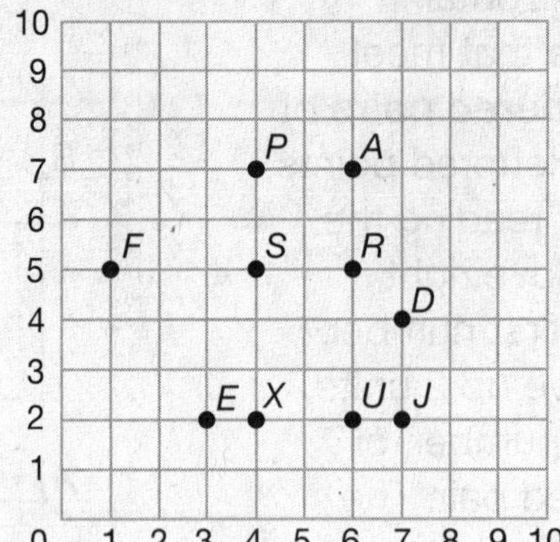

For **6** through **10**, name the point for each ordered pair.

6. (7, 4) ____________

7. (3, 2) ____________

8. (1, 5) ____________

9. (7, 2) ____________

10. (6, 7) ____________

11. Writing to Explain Doug is standing at (2, 1). Susan is standing at (1, 2). Who is farther to the right? How do you know?

____

Name ______________________________

Shapes on Coordinate Grids

Angela is designing a flag for her adventure club. She used the following ordered pairs to create the shape of the flag: (2,2), (8,2), and (5,8).

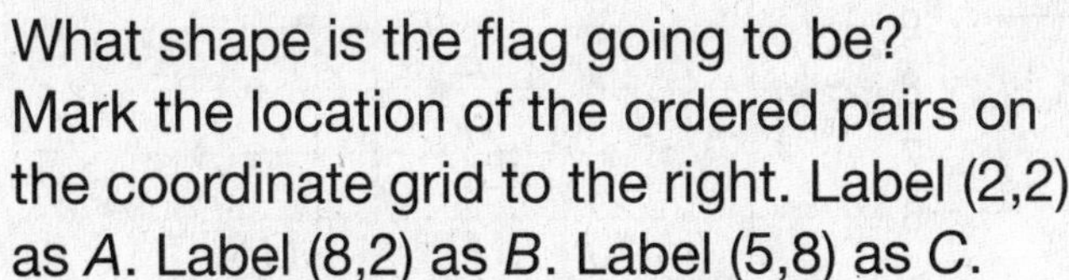
What shape is the flag going to be?
Mark the location of the ordered pairs on the coordinate grid to the right. Label (2,2) as *A*. Label (8,2) as *B*. Label (5,8) as *C*.

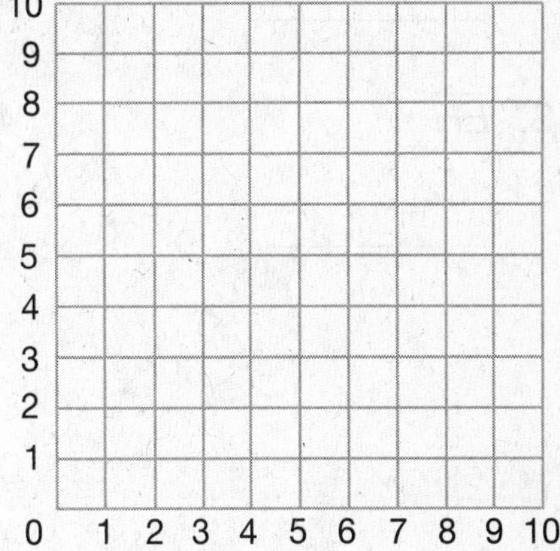

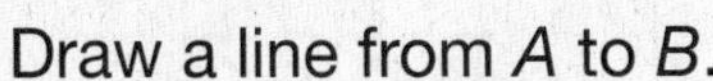
Draw a line from *A* to *B*.
Draw a line from *B* to *C*.
Draw a line from *C* to *A*.

The shape of the flag is a triangle.

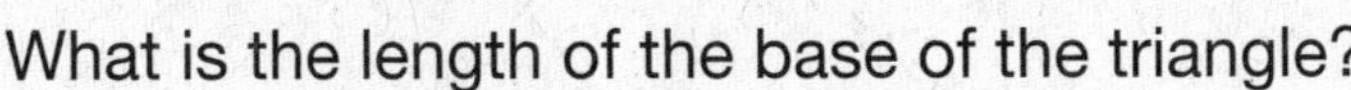
What is the length of the base of the triangle?

Measure the length of $\overline{AB}$.

There are 6 units from (2,2) to (8,2).

The length of the base of the triangle is 6 units.

1. **Number Sense** Can you make a quadrilateral with three ordered pairs? Explain your answer.

____

____

Find each set of ordered pairs using a coordinate grid. Name the shape.

2. (2, 4), (7, 4), (5, 9) ______________________

3. (4, 3), (13, 3), (4, 6), (13, 6) ______________________

4. (2, 6), (6,6), (2, 2), (6, 2) ______________________

Name ______________________

Practice
17-2

Shapes on Coordinate Grids

For **1** through **6**, use the coordinate grid to find the length of each segment.

1. $\overline{AK}$ ________

2. $\overline{EF}$ ________

3. $\overline{EH}$ ________

4. $\overline{JK}$ ________

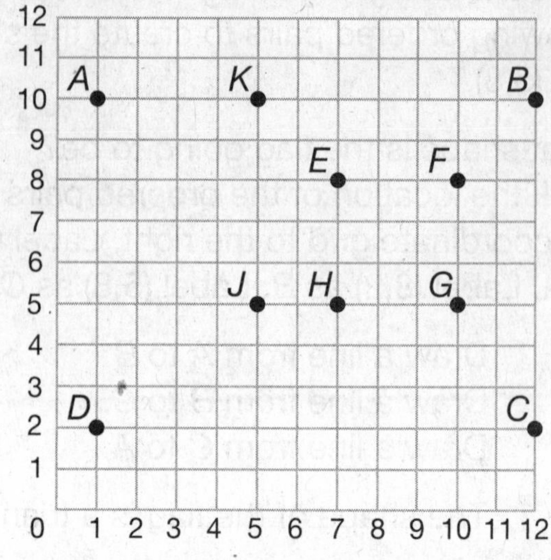

5. The segment from (5, 5) to (12, 5) ________

6. The segment from (7, 5) to (12, 5) ________

7. If you connect the line segments, what is the shape of *KGJ*? ________

8. If you connect the line segments, what is the shape of *ABCD*? ________

9. Which 2 line segments in *ABCD* have a length equal to 8? ________

10. Daryl is making a shape with the ordered pairs (1, 2), (6, 2), (12, 2), and (6, 12). What kind of shape is he making?

A triangle **B** rectangle **C** pentagon **D** octagon

11. Writing to Explain Stacey drew a triangle on a coordinate plane. She wrote down the ordered pair for each vertex. How many ordered pairs did she write down?

____

Name ______________________________

Reteaching
17-3

Lengths of Horizontal and Vertical Line Segments

Jocelyn is going to plant carrots in rows. She is using a coordinate grid to help her arrange the rows.

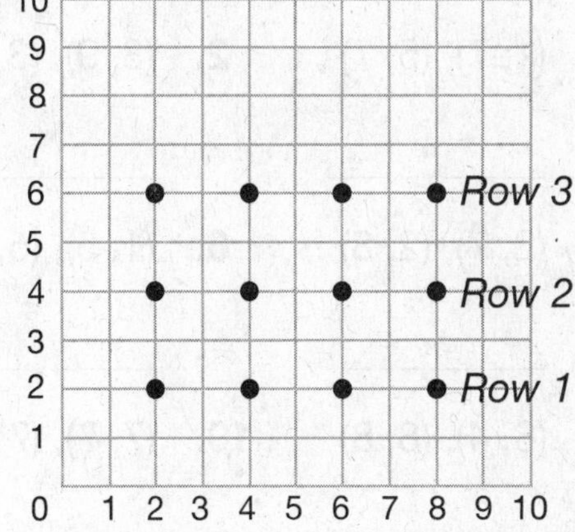

How long is each row?

Compare the ordered pairs at each end of Row 1: (2,2)
(8,2)

The *y*-values are the same, so you know the row is horizontal.
The *x*-values are different. You can subtract the *x*-values to find the length of the row.

$8 - 2 = 6$

The length of Row 1 is 6 units.

How far away is the first row from the third row?

Compare the first ordered pairs from Rows 1 and 3: (2,2)
(2,6)

The *x*-values are the same, so you know the distance is vertical.
To find the distance between the first and third rows, subtract the *y*-values.

$6 - 2 = 4$

The distance between the first row and the third row is 4 units.

Find the distance between the ordered pairs.

1. (2, 2), (8, 2) _______ units

2. (3, 4), (3, 9) _______ units

3. (8, 4), (1, 4) _______ units

4. (1, 9), (9, 9) _______ units

5. (6, 1), (6, 5) _______ units

6. (1, 9), (1, 1) _______ units

7. Number Sense If the ordered pairs (1, 4) and (9, 4) are connected to make a line, is the line vertical or horizontal? ____________________

Name ______________________

Practice
17-3

Lines of Horizontal and Vertical Line Segments

For **1** through **12**, find the distance between the ordered pairs.

1. (1, 7), (5, 7) ______

2. (3, 9), (3, 1) ______

3. (2, 6), (2, 0) ______

4. (12, 2), (1, 2) ______

5. (2, 7), (2, 8) ______

6. (1, 5), (5, 5) ______

7. (0, 1), (0, 3) ______

8. (15, 9), (4, 9) ______

9. (8, 4), (8, 8) ______

10. (7, 7), (7, 9) ______

11. (18, 7), (18, 13) ______

12. (29, 9), (29, 11) ______

13. On a map, a museum is located at (15, 17). A library is located at (2, 17). How many units away is the museum from the library? ______

14. On a map, a costume store is located at (118, 99). A general store is located at (111, 99). How many units away is the costume store from the general store?

A 6 units

B 7 units

C 8 units

D 9 units

15. Writing to Explain On a map, John is standing at (11, 11). His friend Lucy is standing at (1, 11). John took 10 steps to the right. Is he standing with Lucy now?

____

____

Name ________________________________

Reteaching
17-4

Problem Solving: Solve a Simpler Problem

Read	Rena's friend Emma is coming to visit her. Rena made her the map below showing her the way to her house Rena's House Emma's House How far does Emma have to travel to get to Rena's house?
Plan & Solve	First, break the problem into simpler problems. First problem: Emma has to travel north before turning east. How far does she have to travel north? She has to travel 2 blocks north.
Plan & Solve	Second problem: Emma has to travel east before turning north. How far does she have to travel east? She has to travel 5 blocks east.
Plan & Solve	Third problem: Emma now has to travel north to arrive at Rena's house. How far does she have to travel north? She has to travel 3 blocks north.
Check	I can count the blocks and follow the route to make sure my calculations are correct. 2 blocks north, 5 blocks east, and 3 blocks north will get Emma to Rena's house, Emma travels 10 blocks.

Use the information in the graph above to answer the following problems.

1. How many blocks in total does Emma have to travel to get to Rena's house?

____

2. **Number Sense** When Emma returns home, explain how will she travel?

____

____

Name ____________________

Problem Solving: Solve a Simpler Problem

For **1** through **2**, use the graph to the right.

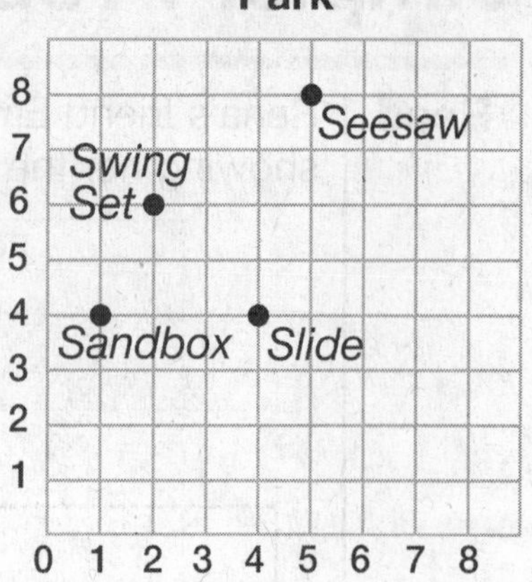

1. Mike is going from the sandbox to the swing set to the slide. How many units does he travel?

____

2. Raja is going from the seesaw to the slide to the sandbox. Does he travel more units than Mike?

____

For **3** through **4** use the graph to the right.

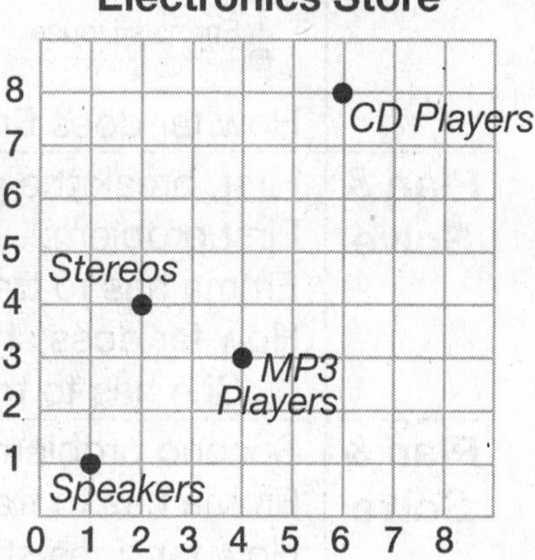

3. Stephanie walked from the CD players to the MP3 players to the stereos. How many units did she walk?

____

4. Jule walked from the speakers to the stereos to the MP3 players. How many units did he walk?

____

5. Sasha is on a hike. Which mountain is furthest from Mt. Grey?

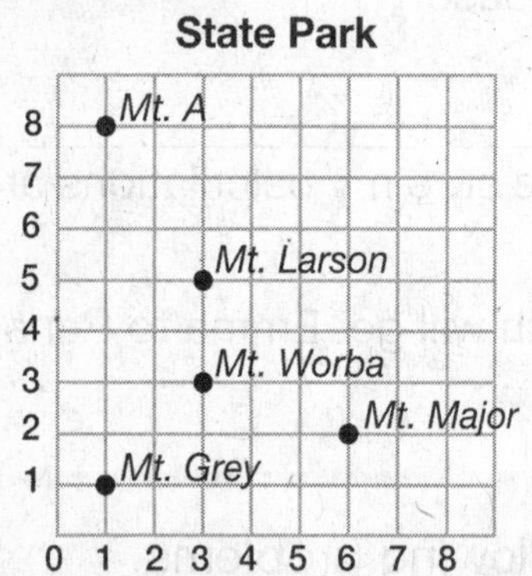

A Mt. A **B** Mt. Worba **C** Mt. Major **D** Mt. Larson

6. **Writing to Explain** Sal made a map of his neighborhood. According to his map, Sal's house is 6 units away from the grocery store. The grocery store is 5 units away from the coffee shop. The coffee shop is 1 unit from Sal's house. How is this possible?

____

Name ________________________

Formulas and Equations

You can use a formula to solve problems about distance.

Marco drove for 4 hours at an average speed of 53 miles per hour. How far did he travel?

Use the formula distance = rate × time.

$d = r \times t$	Find the values for r and t in the problem. Substitute them into the formula to find d.
$d = 53 \times 4$	
$d = 212$	

Marco traveled 212 miles.

Find the distance for the given values of r and t.

1. r = 25 miles per hour
   t = 3 hours
   ____

2. r = 600 feet per minute
   t = 10 minutes
   ____

3. r = 20 kilometers per hour
   t = 4 hours
   ____

4. r = 15 inches per second
   t = 35 seconds
   ____

5. r = 550 miles per hour
   t = 6 hours
   ____

6. r = 250 miles per day
   t = 7 days
   ____

Use the formula $P = (2 \times \ell) + (2 \times w)$ to find the perimeter of each rectangle.

7. ℓ = 11 inches
   w = 5 inches
   ____

8. ℓ = 18 meters
   w = 13 meters
   ____

9. **Writing to Explain** A deer ran for 4 minutes at an average speed of 2,000 feet per minute. An ostrich ran for 3 minutes at an average speed of 3,000 feet per minute. Which animal ran a greater distance?

____

Name ______________________

Practice

18-1

Formulas and Equations

Use the formula below to find each distance.

distance = rate × time $d = r \times t$

1. r = 55 miles per hour
t = 6 hours

____

2. r = 400 kilometers per day
t = 4 days

____

3. r = 32 centimeters per minute
t = 17 minutes

____

4. r = 8 feet per second
t = 22 seconds

____

Use the formula below to find the perimeter of each square.

Perimeter = 4 × length of a side $P = 4 \times s$

5. s = 5 yards

____

6. s = 9 meters

____

7. s = 26 feet

____

8. s = 19 inches

____

9. The length of a rectangle is 14 feet and the width is 7 feet. Use the following formula to find the area of the rectangle.

Area = length × width $A = \ell \times w$

A 21 square feet
B 42 square feet
C 98 square feet
D 196 square feet

10. Number Sense A snail crawled for 40 seconds at an average speed of 15 millimeters per second. Explain how to find the distance the snail traveled in centimeters.

____

____

____

Name ______________________________

Reteaching
18-2

Addition and Subtraction Patterns and Equations

Find a rule and complete the following table.

x	y
12	15
14	17
16	19
18	?

How are x and y related?

Each number in the y column is 3 more than the number in the x column.

The rule is $y = x + 3$

Use the rule to find the missing number.

$x = 18$

$18 + 3 = 21$

The missing number is 21.

1. **Number Sense** If $x + 6 = y$ is the rule, and the value of x is 12, what is the value of y? ____________

Use the following table to answer questions **1** through **4**.

x	y
1	7
3	?
?	11
7	13
?	?

1. What is the value of y when the value of x is 3? ____________
2. What is the value of x when y is 11? ____________
3. What are the values of x and y in the last row of the table? ____________
4. What is the rule for this table?

____

Name ___

Practice **18-2**

Addition and Subtraction Patterns and Equations

For **1** through **6**, complete each table. Find each rule.

1.

x	y
5	14
6	15
7	16
8	?

2.

x	y
36	18
35	17
34	16
33	?

3.

x	y
21	26
23	28
25	30
27	?

4.

x	y
11	8
16	13
21	18
26	?

5.

x	2	4	6	8
y	56	58	60	?

6.

x	19	22	25	28
y	1	4	7	?

7. At a laundromat there is 1 more dryer than there are washers. Write a rule to find the number of d dryers for every w washers

8. Nina walked 15 yards to Paul's house. They then went hiking. Which rule shows how many yards Nina walks for every yard Paul walks?

   A $p = n + 15$ **C** $p = 15 - n$

   B $n = p + 15$ **D** $n = p - 15$

9. **Writing to Explain** Wendy found a rule for a table. The rule she made is $y = x + 2$. She says that means every y-value will be even. Is she correct?

Name ______________________

Reteaching
18-3

Multiplication and Division Patterns and Equations

Ingrid is displaying baskets of pears on a shelf at a fruit market. The following table shows how many pears she is selling if she displays 6, 9, 12, or 15 baskets.

Number of baskets x	**Number of pears** y
6	36
9	54
12	72
15	90

What operation can you use to find the number of pears per basket?

In 6 baskets, there are 36 pears. Divide to find the number of pears per basket.
$36 \div 6 = 6$

In 9 baskets, there are 54 pears.
$54 \div 9 = 6$

In 12 baskets, there are 72 pears.
$72 \div 12 = 6$

The number of pears per basket is 6.

What is the rule in words?

Multiply the number of baskets by 6.

What is the rule in symbols?

$y = x \times 6$

In 15 baskets, each with 6 pears, there are 90 pears in all. $15 \times 6 = 90$

1. **Number Sense** If $x \times 8 = y$ is the rule, and the value of x is 4, what is the value of y? ____________

Name ______________________

Practice 18-3

Multiplication and Division Patterns and Equations

For **1** through **6**, complete each table. Find each rule.

1.

x	*y*
81	9
63	7
45	5
27	?

____

2.

x	*y*
6	42
8	56
10	70
12	?

____

3.

x	*y*
36	6
42	7
48	8
54	?

____

4.

x	*y*
10	30
15	45
20	60
25	?

____

5.

x	2	4	6	8
y	22	44	66	?

____

6.

x	9	12	15	18
y	3	4	5	?

____

7. Lucas recorded the growth of a plant. How tall will the plant be on Day 5?

Day	1	2	3	4	5
Height in inches	6	12	18	24	?

8. Danielle made a table of the rental fees at a video store. What is the rule?

x	1	2	3	4
y	3	6	9	12

A $y = 3x$ **C** $y = x + 3$

B $y = 6x$ **D** $y = 4x$

9. Writing to Explain Curtis found a rule for a table. The rule he made is $y = 7x$. What does the rule tell you about every y-value?

____

Name ______________________________

Graphing Equations

You can graph equations on a grid.

Graph the equation $y = 3x$.

Make a table of ordered pairs. Graph the ordered pairs and draw a line.

x	$y = 3x$	(x, y)
0	$y = 3 \times 0 = 0$	(0, 0)
1	$y = 3 \times 1 = 3$	(1, 3)
2	$y = 3 \times 2 = 6$	(2, 6)
3	$y = 3 \times 3 = 9$	(3, 9)

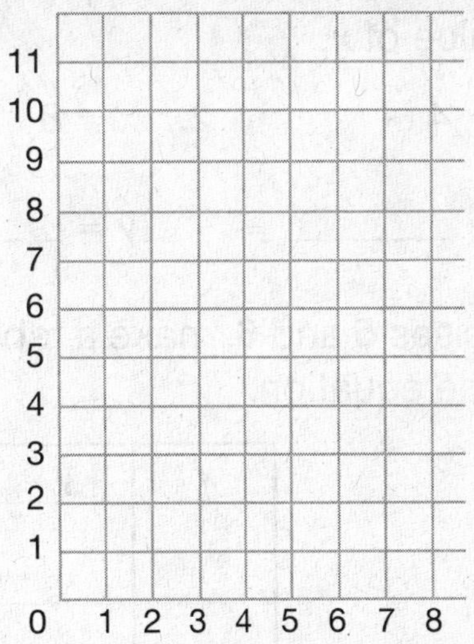

Every x-value determines a y-value. Find the value of y for the value of x.

Use the equation $y = 7x$. If $x = 5$, then $y = 7 \times 5$; $y = 35$.

The ordered pair would be (5, 35).

In Exercises **1–4**, use the equation $y = 4x$. Find the value of y for each value of x.

1. $x = 12$ ____________

2. $x = 7$ ____________

3. $x = 11$ ____________

4. $x = 27$ ____________

5. Complete the table of ordered pairs and graph the equation $y = 4x$.

x	$y = 4x$	(x, y)
0	$y =$	
1	$y =$	
2	$y =$	
3	$y =$	

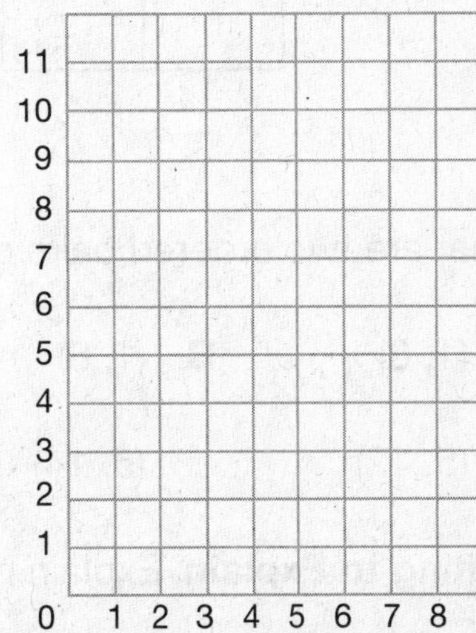

Name ______________________

Graphing Equations

In Exercises **1–4**, use the equation $y = 5x$. Find the value of y for each value of x.

1. $x = 4$ $y =$ ________

2. $x = 8$ $y =$ ________

3. $x = 13$ $y =$ ________

4. $x = 25$ $y =$ ________

In Exercises **5** and **6**, make a table of values for x and y. Then graph the equation.

5. $y = 2x$

x	y

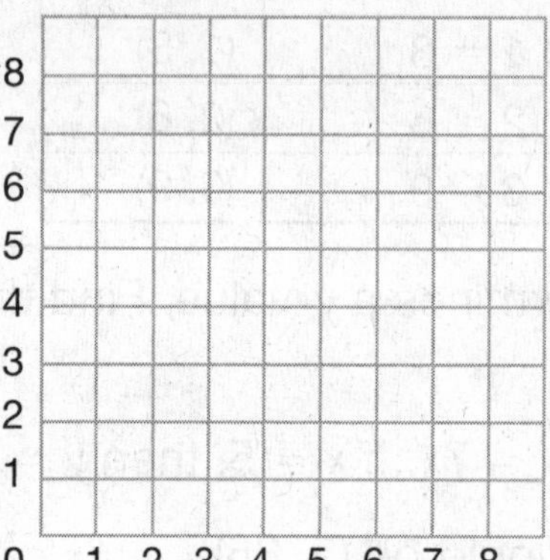

6. $y = x + 5$

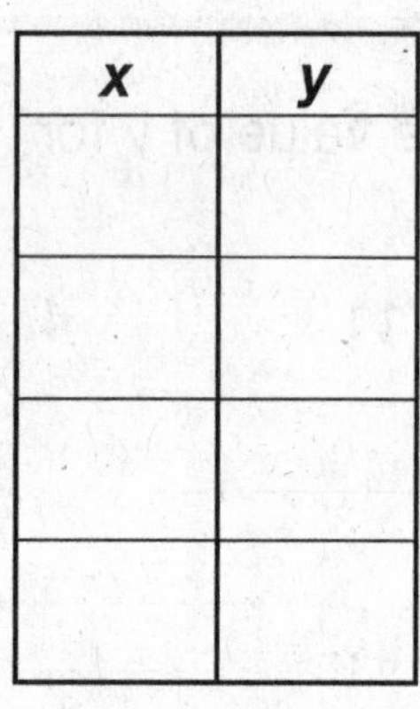

x	y

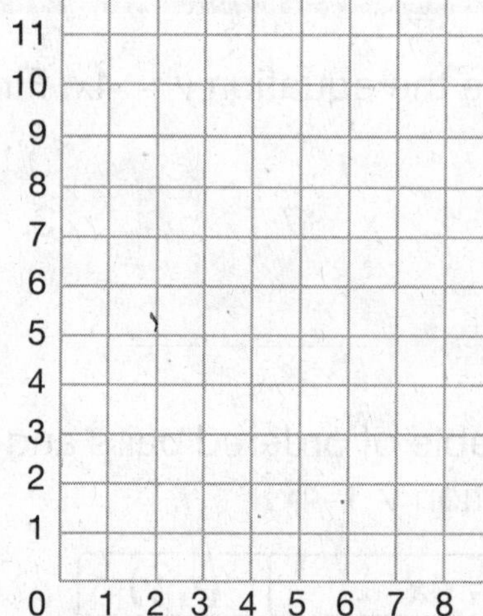

7. What are two ordered pairs on the graph of $y = 2x + 4$?

A (1, 6) (5, 12)

B (1, 6) (5, 14)

C (2, 8) (5, 12)

D (2, 8) (0, 2)

8. Writing to Explain Explain how to evaluate $x - 8$ when $x = 10$.

____

Name ______________________

Reteaching **18-5**

More Graphing Equations

You can graph equations on a grid.

Graph the equation $y = x - 3$

Make a table of ordered pairs.

Graph the ordered pairs and draw a line.

Every x-value determines a y-value, so you can find the value of y for each value of x.

x	$y = x - 3$	**(x, y)**
4	$y = 4 - 3$	(4, 1)
5	$y = 5 - 3$	(5, 2)
6	$y = 6 - 3$	(6, 3)
7	$y = 7 - 3$	(7, 4)
8	$y = 8 - 3$	(8, 5)

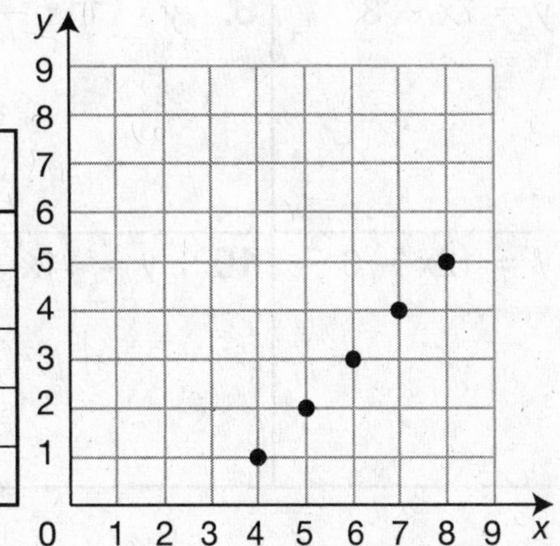

1. **Number Sense** If $y = x - 1$, what are the ordered pairs if the values of x are 8, 9, and 10?

____

For problems **2–4**, find the missing information in the table.

x	$y = x - 4$	**(x, y)**
6	$y = 6 - 4$	(6, 2)
7	$y = 7 - 4$	?
8	$y = 8 - 4$	?
9	$y = 9 - 4$	(9, ?)

2. What is the ordered pair when $x = 7$?

____

3. What is the value of y in the ordered pair when $x = 9$?

____

4. What is the ordered pair when $x = 8$?

____

Name ______________________

Practice 18-5

More Graphing Equations

For **1** through **12**, find five ordered pairs on the graph of each equation.

1. $y = 3x - 2$	**2.** $y = 2x + 2$	**3.** $y = 8x + 1$	**4.** $y = 9x$
5. $y = 7x - 3$	**6.** $y = 11x - 6$	**7.** $y = 9x + 9$	**8.** $y = 5x + 8$
9. $y = 12x - 6$	**10.** $y = 11x - 11$	**11.** $y = 7x - 6$	**12.** $y = 7x + 2$

13. Laura has $2.00. Each week she gets $10.00 for mowing the lawn. Let x = the number of weeks. If she does not spend any money, how much money will she have after 6 weeks? ______________

14. Dean is on a hike. The graph shows how far away he is from a camp site. How far away is he after 4 hours?

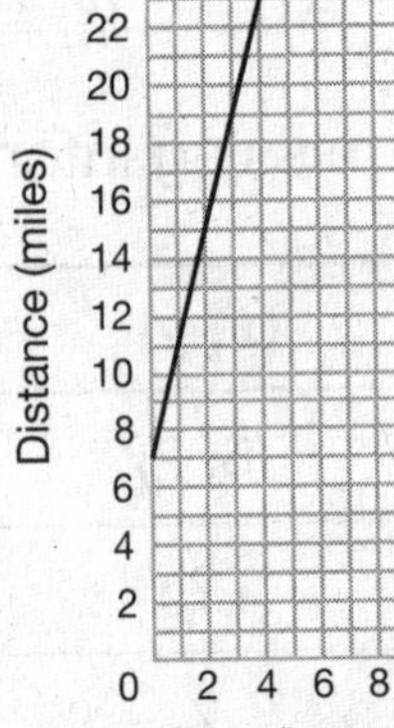

A 16 miles
B 18 miles
C 23 miles
D 30 miles

15. Writing to Explain Ian gets $9.00 for each hour he works. He also gets $10.00 for each day he works. To find out how much he makes in a day, he made the equation $y = 9x + 10x$, where x is the number of hours he works. Explain why Ian's equation will not tell him how much he makes in a day.

____

____

____

Name ______________________________

Reteaching
18-6

Problem Solving: Make a Table

Read and Understand
Todd is making a scrapbook using sports trading cards. He keeps entire teams together. If one scrapbook holds 80 cards, and Todd puts an equal number of baseball and football teams in it, how many of each kind of team is he putting into the book?

Sports Teams		
Number of Each Kind of Team	**Number of Baseball Players**	**Number of Football Players**
1	9	11
2	18	22
3		
4		
5		

What do you need to find? You need to find the equal number of baseball teams and football teams that add to 80 players.

Plan and Solve
How can you solve the problem? You can make a table and find the row in the table that tells you how many football and baseball teams combine to equal 80 players.

Complete the table. Look across the rows. Find the row in which the number of baseball and football players add to 80 players. 4 baseball and 4 football teams add to 80 players.

Check
How did using a table help you solve this problem?

Use the table for Exercises **1** and **2**.

1. What combination of teams adds to 100 players? ______________

2. How many players are on three baseball teams and two football teams? ______________

Name ______________________

Practice 18-6

Problem Solving: Make a Table

Complete the table. Then use it to solve the problems.

Number of Teams	Number of Volleyball Players	Number of Lacrosse Players
1	6	10
2	12	20
3		
4		
5		
6		

1. How many players are there on three volleyball and three lacrosse teams combined? ______

2. Which equal number of volleyball and lacrosse teams results in a number divisible by 10? ______

3. It costs $8 for each T-shirt. They can be bought only in boxes of 3. If there are 16 players on the basketball team, how many shirts can they buy? How much money will the T-shirts cost altogether? ______

4. Carmen spends 20 minutes more each week than the week before painting pictures. If she paints 40 minutes the first week, how long will she work the fifth week? ______

5. **Writing to Explain** Why is making a table a good strategy to know?

____

____

____

Name ____________________

Congruent Figures

When two figures have the same shape and size, they are congruent.

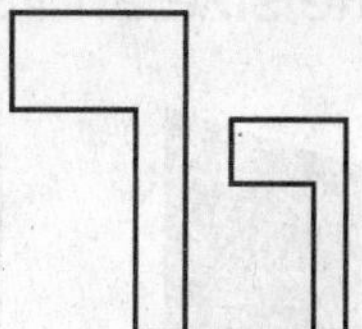

Not congruent
Different size

Congruent
Same size and shape

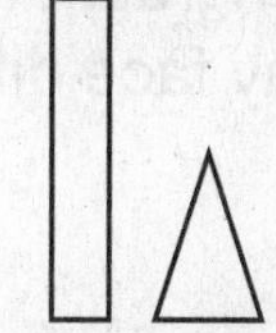

Not congruent
Different shape and size

If figures are congruent, slides, flips, or turns will not change that.

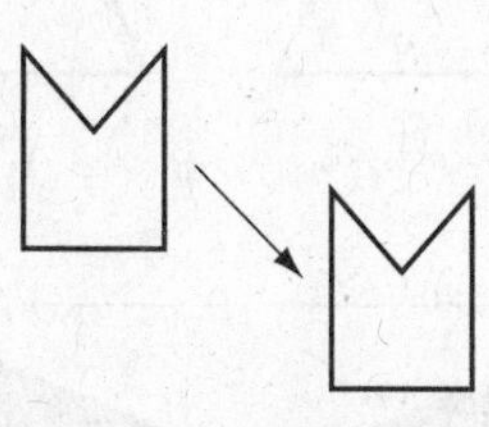

Slide
Moves the figure in a straight direction

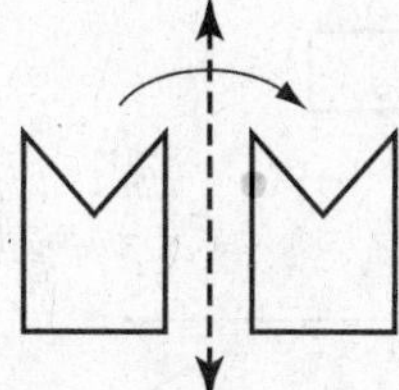

Flip
Gives the figure its mirror image (Sometimes the object looks the same after being flipped.)

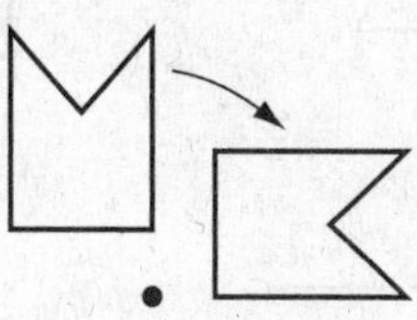

Turn
Moves a figure about a point

Do the figures in each pair appear to be congruent? If so, tell if they are related by a flip, slide, or turn.

1.

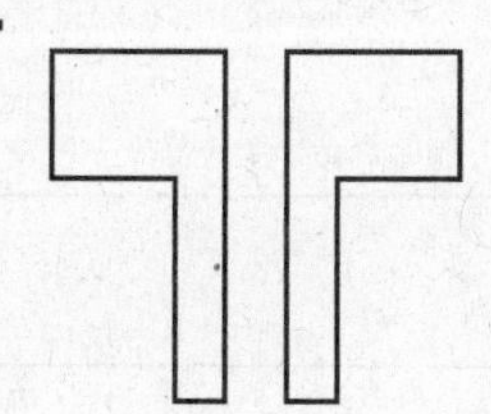

____

____

2.

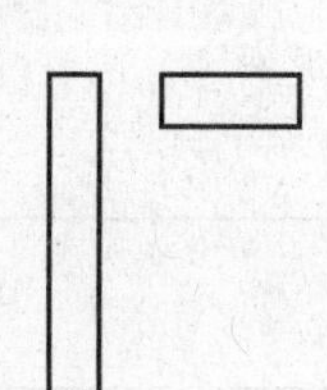

____

____

3.

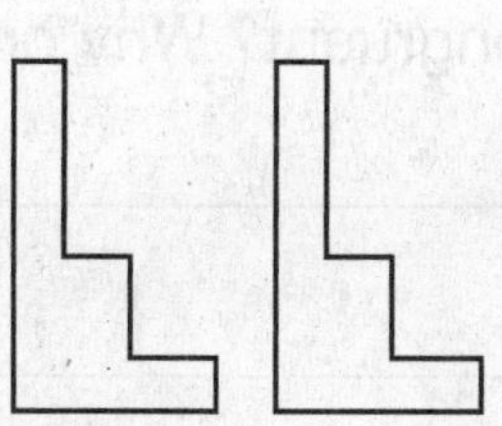

____

____

4. Reasoning Could the letters L and M ever be congruent? Explain.

____

____

____

Name ____________________

Congruent Figures

Congruent figures have the same size and shape, although they may face different directions.

Tell if the figures are congruent.

1. 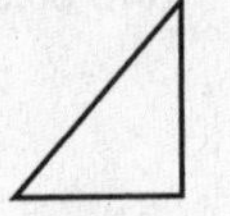 

____

2. 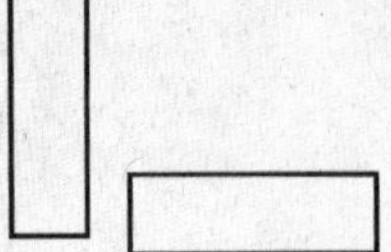

____

3. 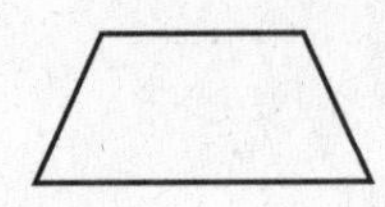

____

4. 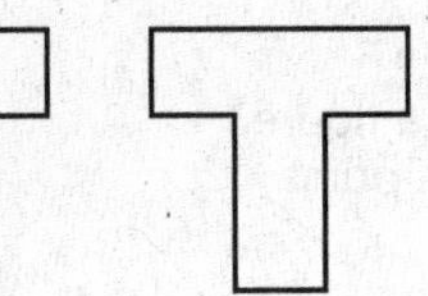

____

5. 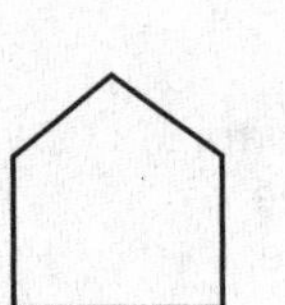 

____

6. 

____

7. Writing to Explain If you divide a 4 in. by 8 in. rectangle from corner to corner, what new shapes do you get? Are they congruent? Why or why not?

____

____

____

____

Name ____________________

Reteaching
19-2

Line Symmetry

Symmetric figures are figures that can be folded to make two halves that fit on top of each other. The lines that divide a symmetric figure into congruent halves are called lines of symmetry.

This square has 4 lines of symmetry. If you fold the square along any of the 4 dashed lines, the two halves will lie on top of each other.

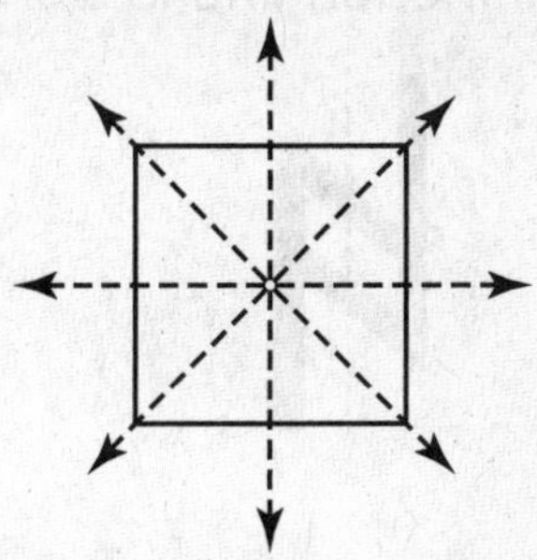

Tell if each line is a line of symmetry.

1. 
____

2. 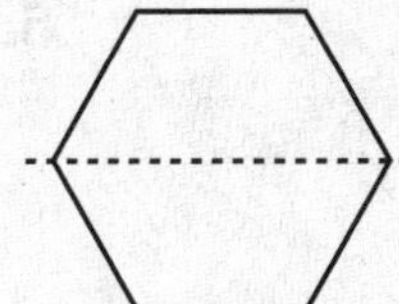
____

3. 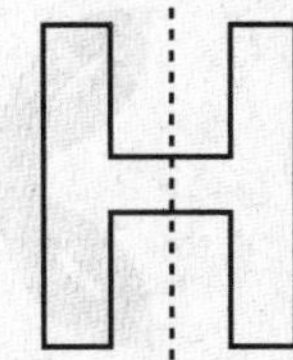
____

4. 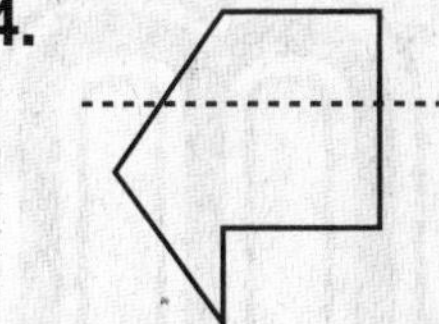
____

Tell how many lines of symmetry each figure has.

5. 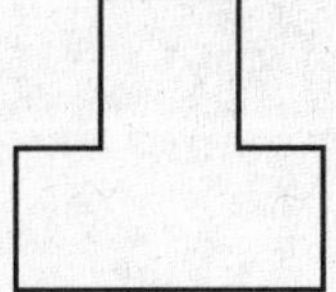
____

6. 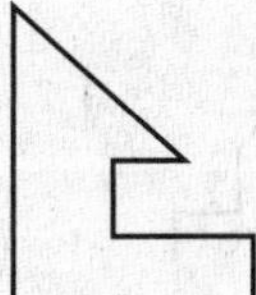
____

7. 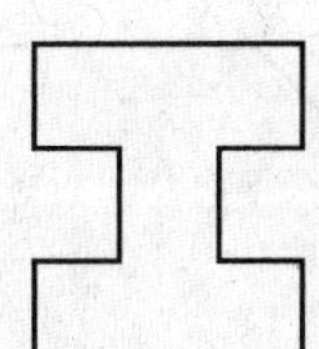
____

8. 
____

9. Reasoning How many lines of symmetry does the letter R have? ____________

10. Complete the drawing so that the figure is symmetric.

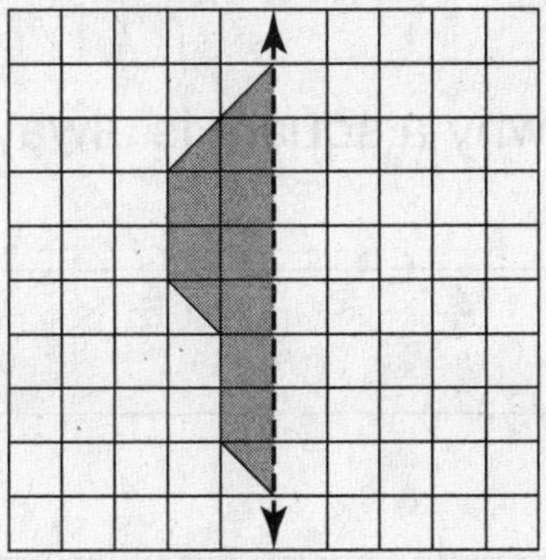

Name ____________________

Line Symmetry

Tell if each line is a line of symmetry.

1. 
____

2. 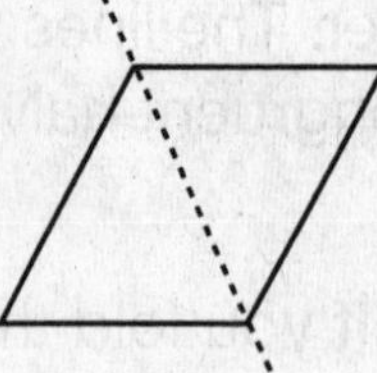
____

3. 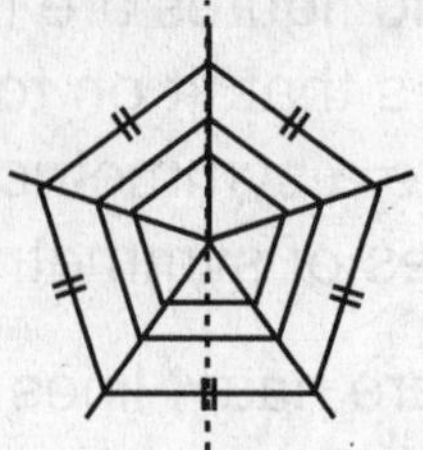
____

Tell how many lines of symmetry each figure has.

4. 
____

5. 
____

6. 
____

7. Draw lines of symmetry.

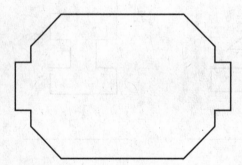

8. How many lines of symmetry does a rhombus that is not a square have?

A 0 **B** 1 **C** 2 **D** 3

9. **Writing to Explain** Explain why a square is always symmetric.

____

____

____

Name ______________________

Rotational Symmetry

An angle is measured in degrees (°).

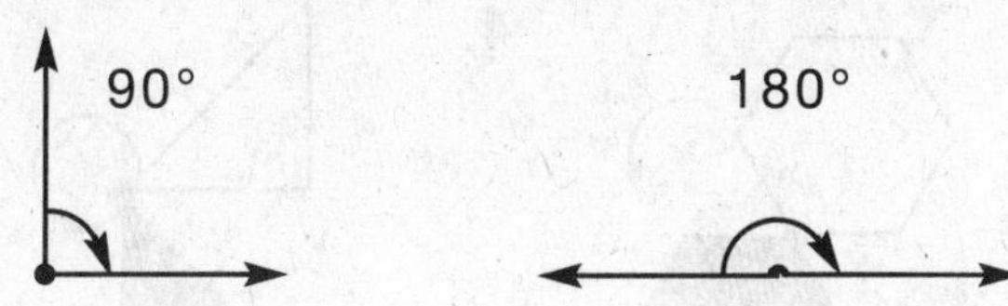

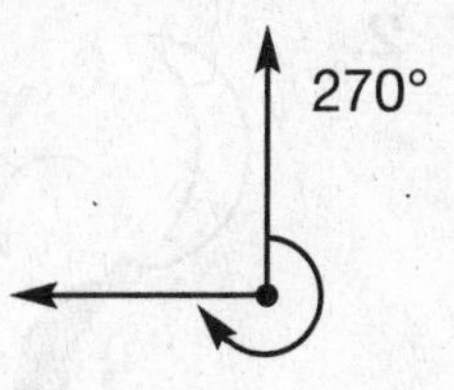

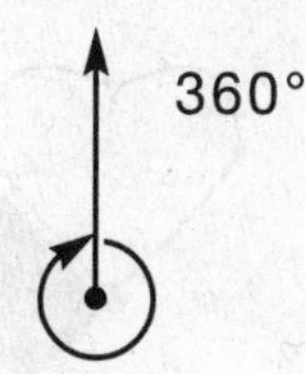

A turn, or rotation, of a figure around a point can be described with an angle measure or a fraction.

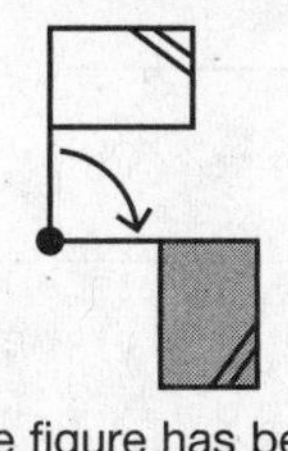

The figure has been rotated 90° or $\frac{1}{4}$ turn.

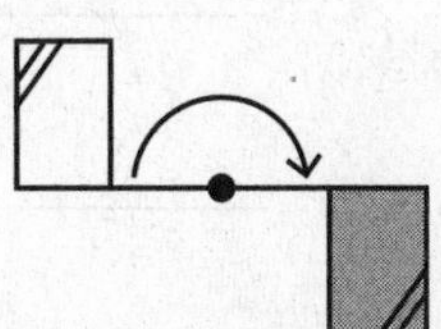

The figure has been rotated 180° or $\frac{1}{2}$ turn.

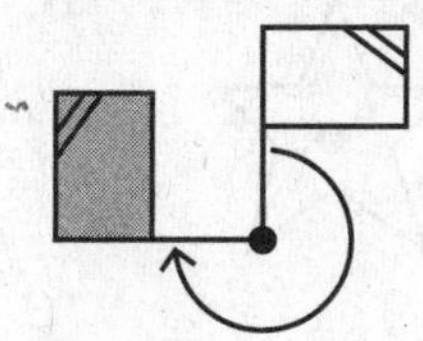

The figure has been rotated 270° or $\frac{3}{4}$ turn.

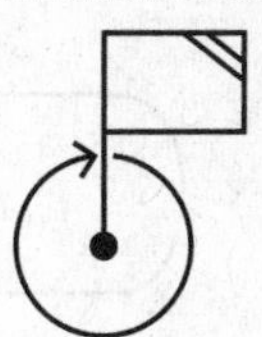

The figure has been rotated 360° or one full turn.

When a figure needs less than a full turn to rotate onto itself, the figure has rotational symmetry.

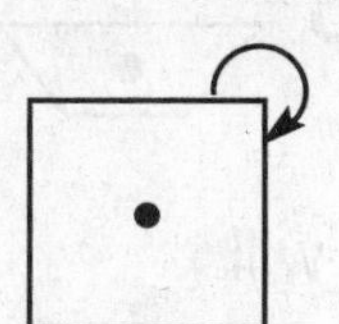

90° rotation, $\frac{1}{4}$ turn

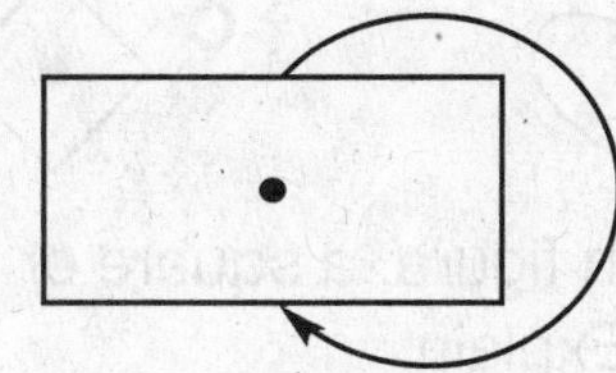

180° rotation, $\frac{1}{2}$ turn

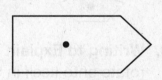

no rotational symmetry

Tell if the figure has rotational symmetry. Write yes or no. If yes, tell what kind of rotational symmetry each figure has.

1. 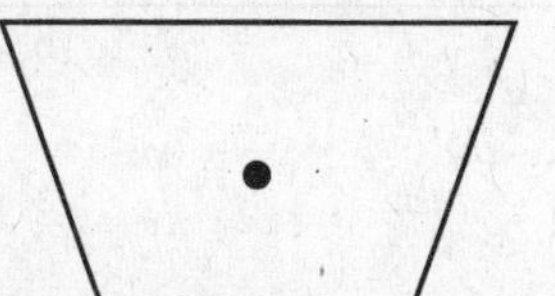 ______________ ______________

2. 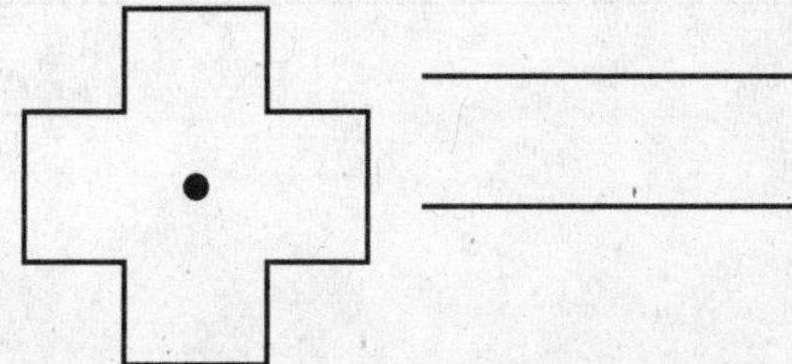 ______________ ______________

Name ______________________

Practice
19-3

Rotational Symmetry

Give an angle measure and a turn to describe the rotation.

1. 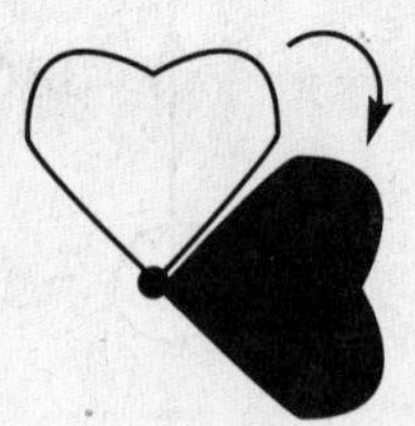

2. 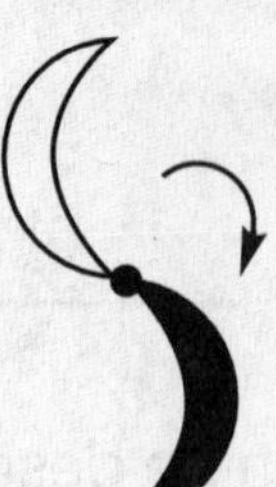

3. 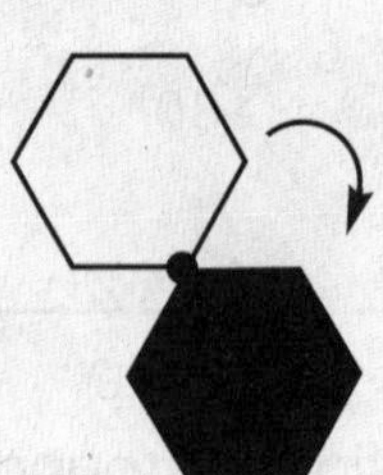

4. 

______________ ______________ ______________ ______________

______________ ______________ ______________ ______________

Tell if the figure has rotational symmetry. Write yes or no.

5. 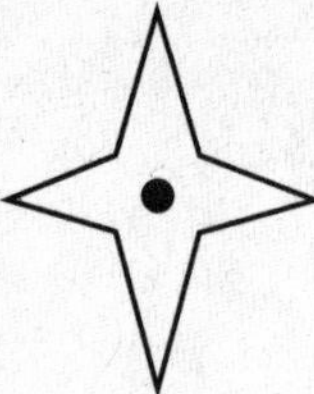

6. 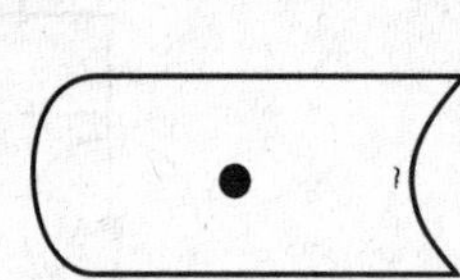

7. 

8. 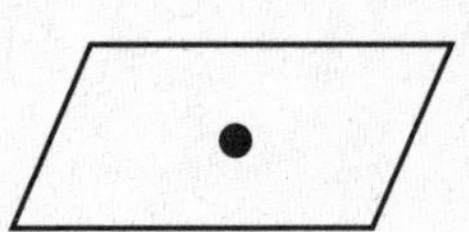

______________ ______________ ______________ ______________

9. Which figure has rotational symmetry?

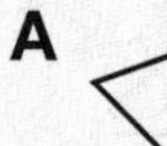

A 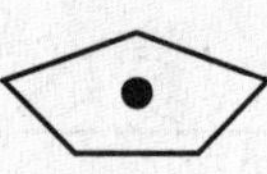

B 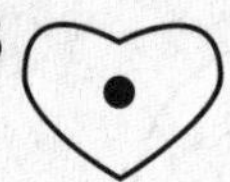

C 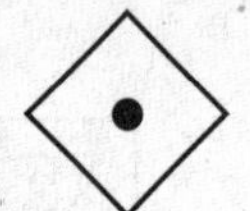

D 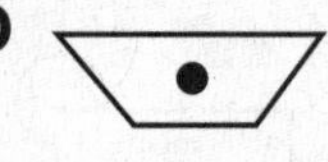

10. Writing to Explain Which figure, a square or a trapezoid, will rotate onto itself in 90°? Explain.

____

____

____

Name ______________________________

Reteaching
19-4

Problem Solving: Draw a Picture

Read	Kristen is hanging paintings in her room. She wants to find a painting that is the same shape as the one shown below, but she needs it to be half the size to fit on her wall. Draw a smaller painting that is the same shape.
Plan	What do I know? The dimensions of the painting are 12 units by 6 units. What am I asked to find? I need to draw a rectangle that is the same shape as the one in the picture, but that is half the size.
Solve	Divide the length of each side by 2. To be the same shape, the new dimensions have to be 6 units by 3 units.

Solve.

1. A fence is 20 ft long. It has posts at each end and at every four feet along its length. How many fence posts are there? Draw a picture.

____

2. **Number Sense** Lee and his family are planning a hiking trip on the Appalachian Trail. They are packing food in 2-lb bundles. How many bundles can they make with 36 lb of food? Write a number sentence to help you solve this problem.

____

Name ______________________

Practice **19-4**

Problem Solving: Draw a Picture

Kacey is making a necklace that is 16 in. long. She uses 5 beads for every inch. How many beads will she need? Draw a picture to solve.

1. **Writing to Explain** Draw a picture and explain how it can help to solve the problem.

____

____

____

2. Write a number sentence based on the picture you drew.

____

3. How many beads will Kacey need? ______________

4. Explain how you can check your answer.

____

____

Roger has a 64-inch piece of wood he needs to cut into 8 pieces.

5. How many cuts does Roger need to make? ______________

6. **Writing to Explain** For Exercise 5, how did drawing a picture help you to solve the problem?

____

____

7. Write a number sentence and solve for how long each piece of board will be if each piece is of equal length.

____

Name ______________________

Finding Combinations

You can organize pictures to help you find possible combinations.

You have 2 scarves and 3 winter hats.

Scarves	Hats
Striped	Black
Polka dot	White
	Grey

First draw all the combination of hats with a striped scarf.

Then draw all the combinations of hats with a polka dot scarf.

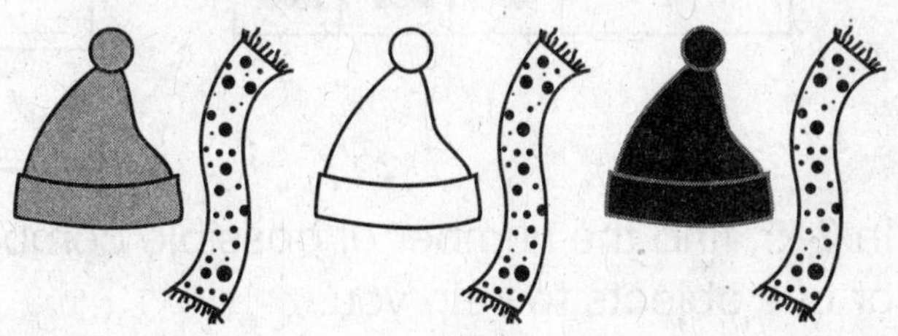

Now count how many groups of hats and scarves you made. There are 6 possible combinations.

Show the possible combinations by filling in the table.

1.

Letter	A	B	C
Number	1	2	3

A, ____	B, ____	____, 1
____, 2	B, ____	C, ____
A, ____	____, 3	C, ____

Find the number of possible combinations by drawing organized pictures.

2. 3 dishes and 2 bowls ____

3. 2 pants and 4 shirts ____

4. 5 paints and 1 wall ____

5. 2 cheeses and 3 crackers ____

6. 4 teas and 4 biscuits ____

7. 3 cups and 5 juices ____

Name ______________________________

Practice
20-1

Finding Combinations

Show the possible combinations by filling in the table.

1.

Mark	✔	✚	✖
Shape	●	■	▲

✔, ___	✖, ___	___, ●
___, ■	✖, ___	✚, ___
✔, ___	___, ▲	✚, ___

In 2–5, find the number of possible combinations. Draw a picture or use objects to help you.

2. Choose one of 3 soups and one of 2 salads. ______________

3. Choose one of 4 cups and one of 2 juices. ______________

4. Choose one of 5 paints and one of 3 trims. ______________

5. Choose one of 7 shirts and one of 3 pants. ______________

6. **Reasoning** June has 1 coat and 7 scarves. How many combinations of coats and scarves does she have? ______________

7. Ross has 3 ties and 4 dress shirts. How many possible combinations of ties and dress shirts does he have?

A 3 **B** 4 **C** 12 **D** 21

8. **Writing to Explain** Carl has 1 kind of bread, crunchy and smooth peanut butter, and several kinds of jellies. What information do you need to find the number of possible combinations of peanut butter and jelly sandwiches he can make?

____

____

Name ____________________

Reteaching **20-2**

Outcomes and Tree Diagrams

List all the possible outcomes for the spinners shown.

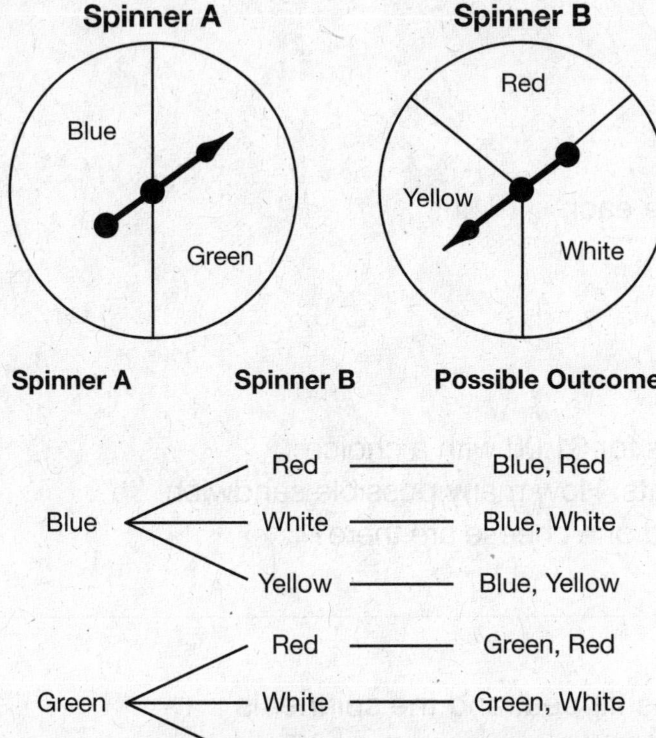

List all the possible outcomes for selecting a marble from each box, without looking.

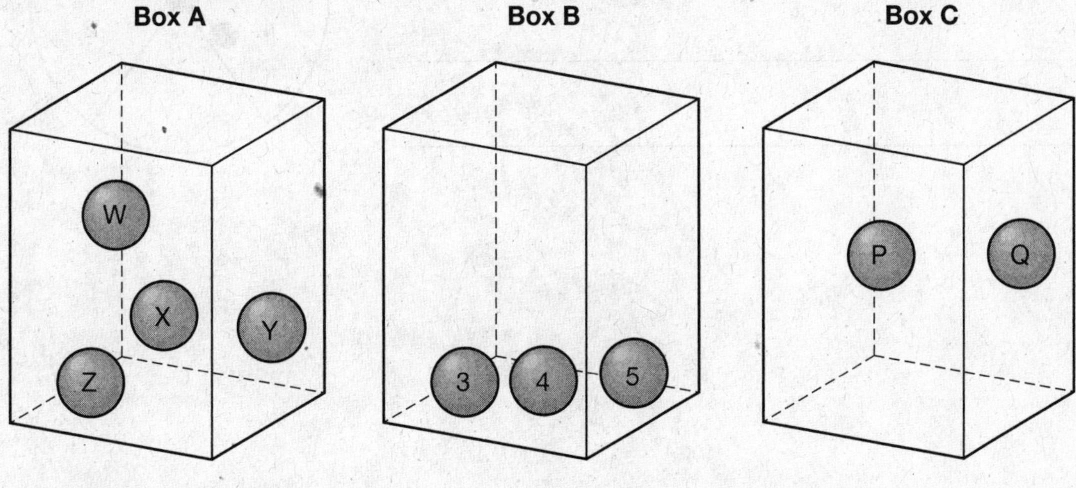

1. Box A ____________________

2. Boxes B and C ____________________

Name ______________________________

Practice
20-2

Outcomes and Tree Diagrams

A coin has two sides, heads and tails. Make a tree diagram to list all the possible outcomes for each situation.

1. Flipping two coins, one time each

2. Flipping three coins, one time each

3. A deli offers lunch sandwiches for $1.00 with a choice of two cheeses and three meats. How many possible sandwich combinations of one meat and one cheese are there?

____

4. Writing to Explain If a coin is flipped, and the spinner is spun, how many total possible outcomes are there? Explain.

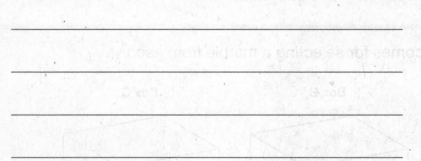

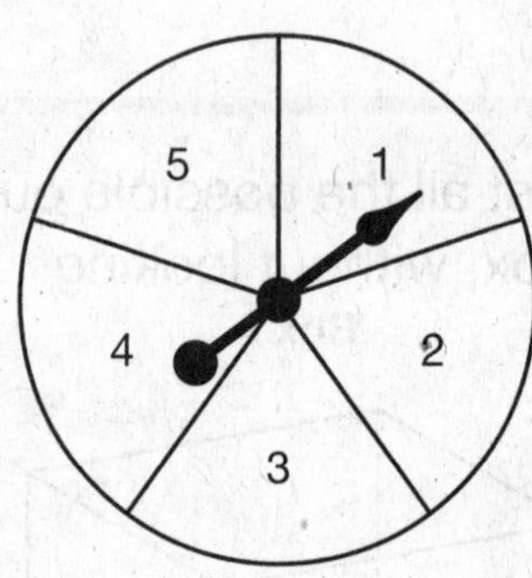

Name ________________________________

Reteaching
20-3

Writing Probability as a Fraction

You can spin a consonant or a vowel on this spinner.

What is the probability of spinning a consonant?

The spinner has 6 equal sections.
So, the total number of possible outcomes is 6.

There are 3 ways to spin a consonant: **R, B, G.**

The probability of spinning

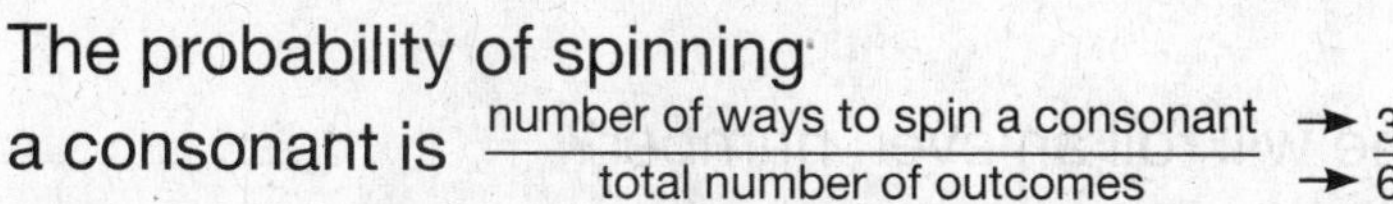

a consonant is $\frac{\text{number of ways to spin a consonant}}{\text{total number of outcomes}} \begin{matrix} \rightarrow 3 \\ \rightarrow 6 \end{matrix}$

So, the probability is $\frac{3}{6} = \frac{1}{2}$, or 1 out of 2.

An impossible event has a probability of 0.

A certain event has a probability of 1.

Any other event has a probability between 0 and 1.

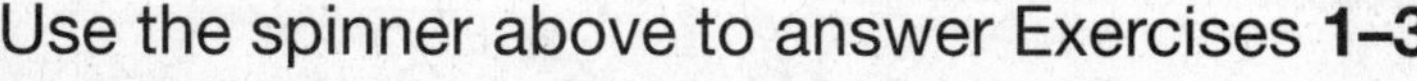

Use the spinner above to answer Exercises **1–3**

1. What is the probability of spinning **B**? ____________

2. What is the probability of spinning **E**? ____________

3. What is the probability of spinning a vowel? ____________

4. A box of markers contains 2 red markers. The probability of selecting a red marker is $\frac{2}{19}$. How many markers are in the box?

____

Name ______________________

Practice
20-3

Writing Probability as a Fraction

Karina is playing a game with a number cube labeled 1, 3, 4, 5, 6, and 9.

1. How many outcomes are possible? ______
2. What is the probability that Karina will roll a 6? ______
3. What is the probability that she will roll an odd number? ______
4. What is the probability that she will roll an even number? ______
5. What is the probability that she will roll a number divisible by 3? ______
6. What is the probability that she will roll a two-digit number? ______
7. What is the probability that she will roll a number other than 1? ______
8. **Writing to Explain** The probability of rolling a 3 on a number cube is $\frac{1}{2}$. How many faces on the cube have a 3?

____

Circle the correct letter for each answer.

9. Lauren spins a spinner numbered 1 through 8. All of the sections are the same size. What is the probability she will not spin an 8?

A $\frac{1}{8}$

B $\frac{3}{8}$

C $\frac{1}{2}$

D $\frac{7}{8}$

10. You toss a number cube labeled 1 through 6. What is the probability you will toss a number greater than 1?

A $\frac{1}{6}$

B $\frac{2}{6}$

C $\frac{4}{6}$

D $\frac{5}{6}$

Name ______________________

Use Reasoning

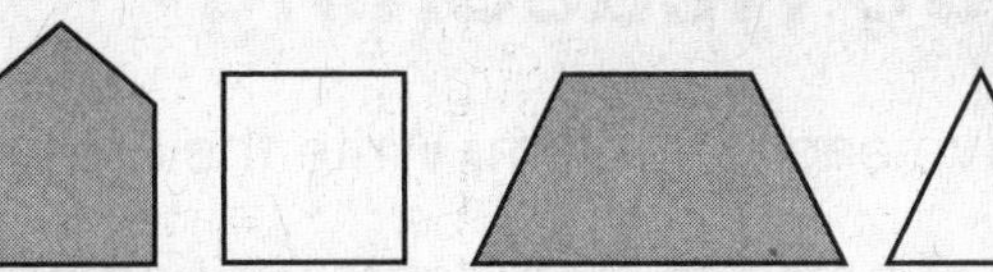

Andrea made a design with the figures shown at the right. She placed all the figures in a row. No figure was next to a figure with the same number of sides as itself. No two shaded figures or unshaded figures were next to each other. The first figure in the design was a trapezoid.

How did Andrea arrange the rest of her design?

Understand You need to find the order of the figures in the design.

Plan You can use the clues you have to place the figures. Draw a picture to help.

Solve Draw four spaces in a row.

You know the trapezoid is first.
It has 4 sides and is shaded.

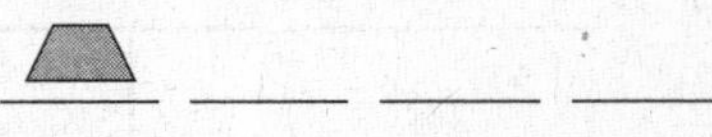

The next figure cannot have 4 sides or be shaded.
The triangle is second. It has 3 sides and is unshaded.

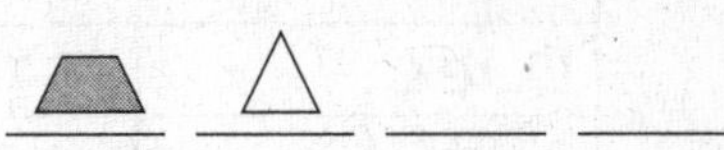

The next figure cannot have 3 sides or be unshaded.
The pentagon is third. It has 5 sides and is shaded.

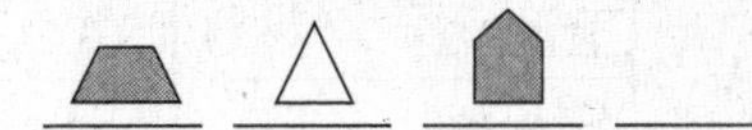

The next figure cannot have 5 sides or be shaded.
The square is fourth. It is the only figure left.
It has 4 sides and is unshaded.

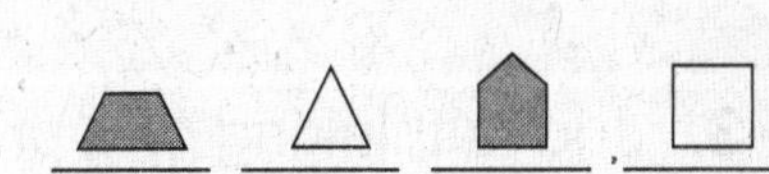

Look Back Is this the only solution to Andrea's design?

List all the possible outcomes for selecting a marble from each box, without looking.

1. Draw a figure that could go after the square in Andrea's design, above. Remember to follow the rules of the design.

2. Look at the design on the right. Fill in the next two figures and then write a description of them.

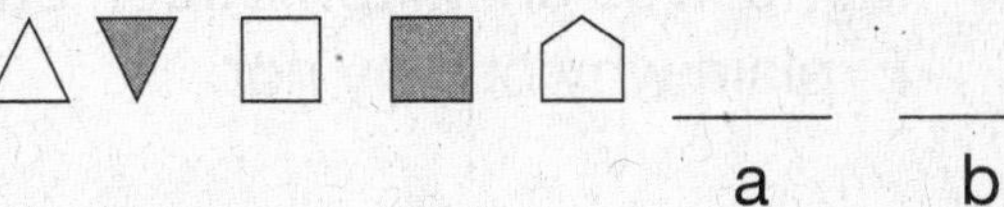

a ______ b ______

a. ______________________________

b. ______________________________

Name ___________________________

Practice 20-4

Problem Solving: Use Reasoning

Solve each problem. Write the answer in a complete sentence.

1. There are 6 students waiting at the bus stop, Donald, Mimi, Wendy, Lance, and Clair. Their ages are 13, 12, 10, 9, and 8. Donald is the oldest and Wendy is the youngest. Lance is 10. Clair is older than Mimi. How old is Mimi?

____

2. Four friends brought sandwiches to a picnic. Who brought the turkey sandwich?

____

	Turkey	Tuna	Peanut Butter and Jelly	Roast Beef
Derek		Y		
Ashley				
Trisha			N	
Steve				Y

3. Jud is thinking of a prime number that is not even. Which number could he be thinking of?

A 0 **B** 2 **C** 5 **D** 9

4. **Writing to Explain** Ingrid lives on either Milton Street or Byron Street. Katie lives on either Byron Street or Whitman Street. Katie does not live on the same street as Ingrid. If Ingrid lives on Milton Street, can Katie live on Byron Street? Explain why or why not.

____

____

____

____

Step Up to Grade 5

F19 Adding Integers 93-94

F33 Graphing Points in the Coordinate Plane 121-122

F34 Graphing Equations in the Coordinate Plane 123-124

F40 Using the Distributive Property 135-136

F43 More Variables and Expressions 141-142

G60 Divisibility by 2, 3, 4, 9, and 10 197-198

G63 Prime Factorization 203-204

G65 Least Common Multiple ... 207-208

G73 Dividing by Multiples of 10 223-224

G75 Dividing by Two-Digit Divisors 227-228

H19 Comparing and Ordering Fractions 121-122

H24 Place Value Through Thousandths 131-132

H31 Decimals to Fractions 145-146

H42 Estimating Sums and Differences of Mixed Numbers 167-168

H46 Multiplying Two Fractions 175-176

I17 Measuring and Classifying Angles 123-124

I20 Constructions 129-130

I33 Converting Customary Units of Length 155-156

I36 Converting Metric Units... 161-162

I49 Area of Parallelograms 187-188

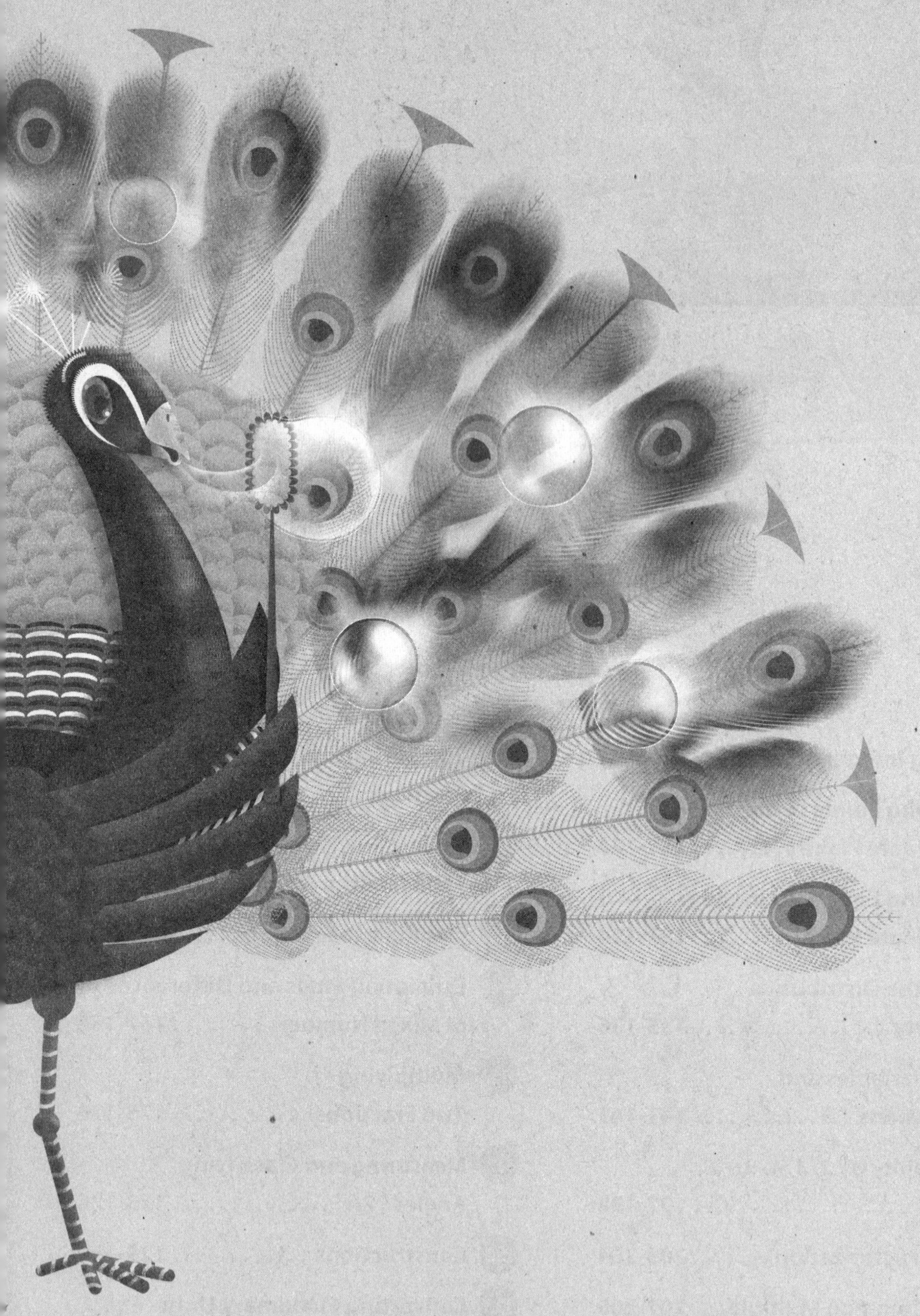

Name ______________________________

Adding Integers

Materials scissors, tape

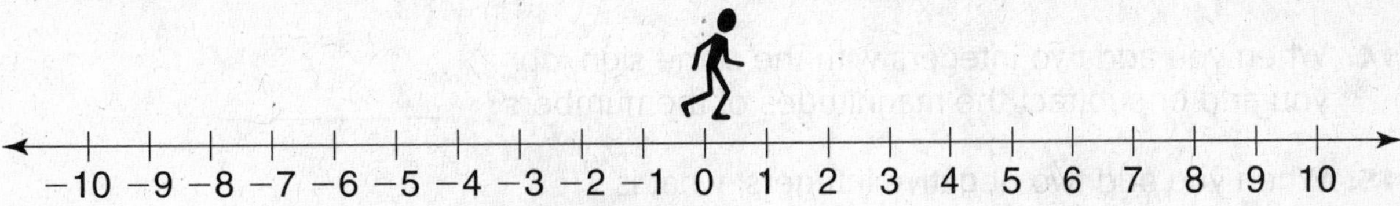

1. Cut out the figure in the lower right corner of the page. Fold on the dashed line, and tape closed.

2. Place the figure in the starting position, at zero. To add $-4 + 7$, move the figure backward 4 spaces to -4. Then move it forward 7 spaces to 3. So $-4 + 7 = 3$.

Adding Integers on the Number Line

- Always start at zero, facing the positive numbers.
- Move forward for positive numbers.
- Move backward for negative numbers.

3. Use the figure to find $-2 + 8$. _______

4. To find $3 + (-8)$, start at zero, move the figure forward 3 spaces to 3. Then move the figure backward 8 spaces to -5.

So $3 + (-8) =$ _______.

5. Use the figure to find $5 + (-9)$. _______

6. To find $-1 + -5$, start at zero, move the figure backward 1 space to -1. Then move the figure backward 5 spaces to -6.

So, $-1 + (-5) =$ _______.

7. Use the figure to find $-3 + (-5)$. _______

8. How many units is -2 from 0 on the number line? _______

The magnitude of a number is its distance from zero.

9. What is the magnitude of -8? _______

10. What is the magnitude of 5? _______

Name ______________________________

Adding Integers (continued)

Use the number line to find each sum. Look for a pattern.

11. $-2 + (-3)$ ______ **12.** $-6 + (-1)$ ______ **13.** $-4 + (-2)$ ______

14. When you add two integers with the same sign, do you add or subtract the magnitudes of the numbers? ______

15. When you add two negative integers, what is the sign of the sum? ______

Use the number line to find each sum. Look for a pattern.

16. $-6 + 3$ ______ **17.** $-5 + 3$ ______ **18.** $1 + (-6)$ ______

19. $9 + (-4)$ ______ **20.** $8 + (-2)$ ______ **21.** $-3 + 9$ ______

22. When you add two integers with different signs, do you add or subtract the magnitudes of the numbers? ______

23. Which has a greater magnitude -6 or 3? ______

24. Is the sum $-6 + 3$ positive or negative? ______

25. When you add a positive and a negative integer and the one with the greater magnitude is negative, what is the sign of the sum? ______

26. Which has a greater magnitude 9 or -4? ______

27. Is the sum $9 + (-4)$ positive or negative? ______

28. When you add a positive and a negative integer and the one with the greater magnitude is positive, what is the sign of the sum? ______

Add. Use rules for adding integers or a number line.

29. $-6 + (-3)$ ______ **30.** $-1 + (-5)$ ______ **31.** $2 + (-5)$ ______ **32.** $-7 + 5$ ______

33. $9 + (-4)$ ______ **34.** $-3 + (-6)$ ______ **35.** $-8 + (-4)$ ______ **36.** $-2 + 7$ ______

Name ______________________

Graphing Points in the Coordinate Plane

Materials red and blue crayons, markers, or colored pencils

To graph a point in the coordinate plane always start at the origin. You can use a red crayon to show negative numbers and a blue crayon to show positive numbers.

Plot point *A* at (3, −4) by doing the following.

1. Since the *x*-coordinate, 3, is positive, draw a blue line from the origin right 3 units on the *x*-axis to (3, 0).
2. Since *y*-coordinate, −4, is negative, draw a red line from (3, 0) down 4 units and plot a point. This point is (3, −4). Label it *A*.

Find the coordinates of point *B,* by doing the following.

3. From the origin, you must go left, so use the red crayon. Draw a red line from the origin, along the *x*-axis, to the point directly below point *B*.

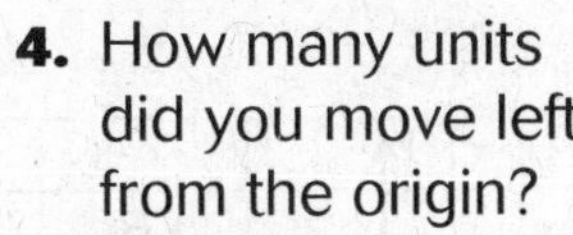

4. How many units did you move left from the origin?

____

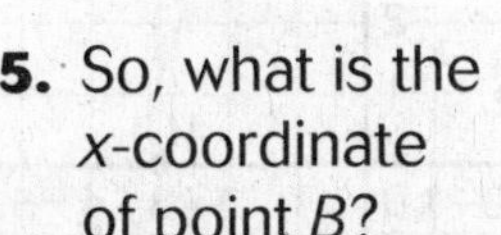

5. So, what is the *x*-coordinate of point *B*?

____

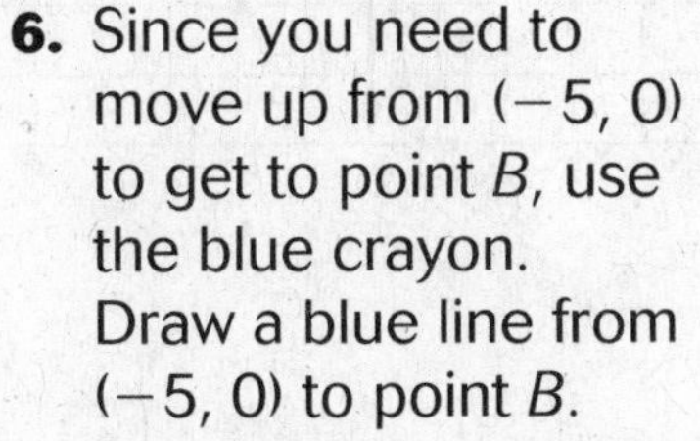

6. Since you need to move up from (−5, 0) to get to point *B*, use the blue crayon. Draw a blue line from (−5, 0) to point *B*.

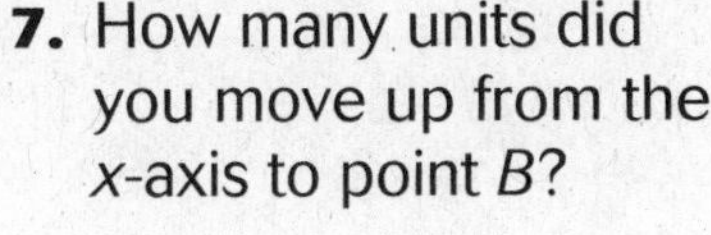

7. How many units did you move up from the *x*-axis to point *B*?

____

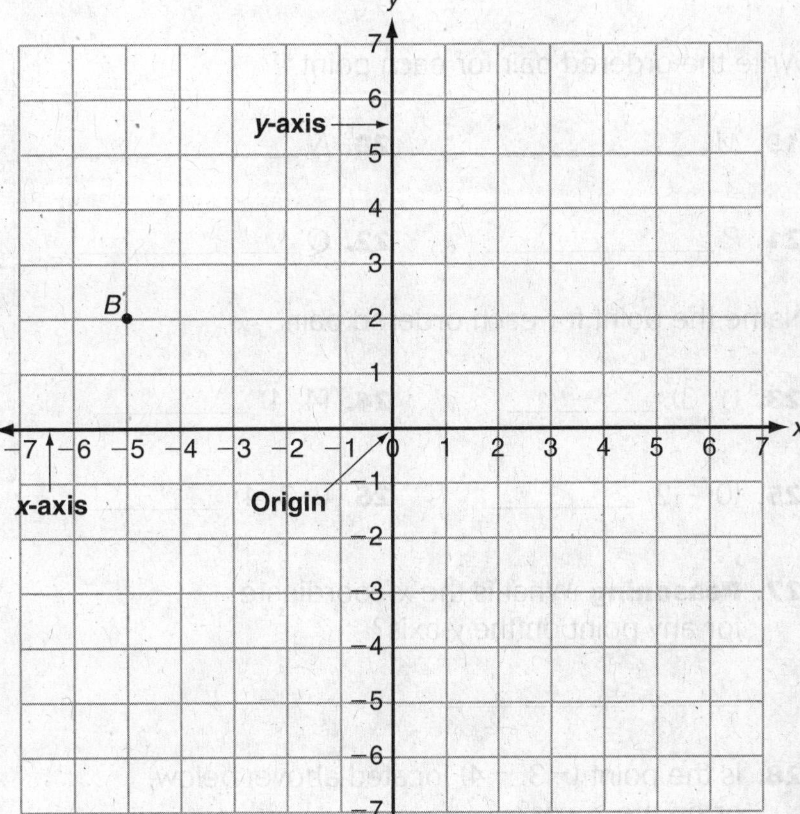

8. So, what is the *y*-coordinate of point *B*? ______________

9. What are the coordinates of point *B*? ______________

Name ____________________

Graphing Points in the Coordinate Plane (continued)

Write the ordered pair for each point.

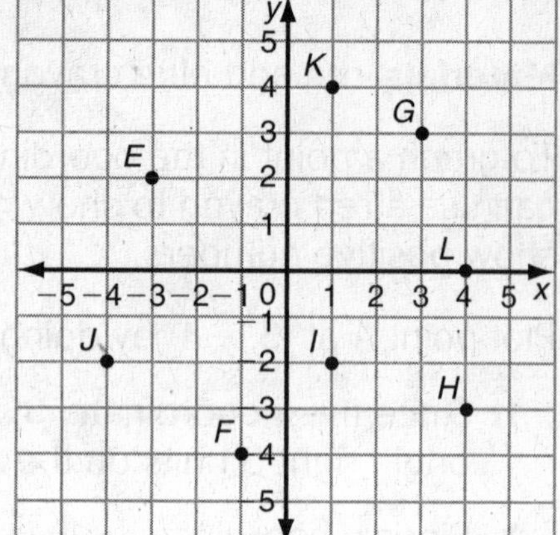

10. *E* __________ **11.** *F* __________

12. *G* __________ **13.** *H* __________

Name the point for each ordered pair.

14. (4, 0) __________ **15.** (1, −2) __________

16. (1, 4) __________ **17.** (−4, −2) __________

18. Reasoning What is the *y*-coordinate for any point on the *x*-axis?

____

Write the ordered pair for each point.

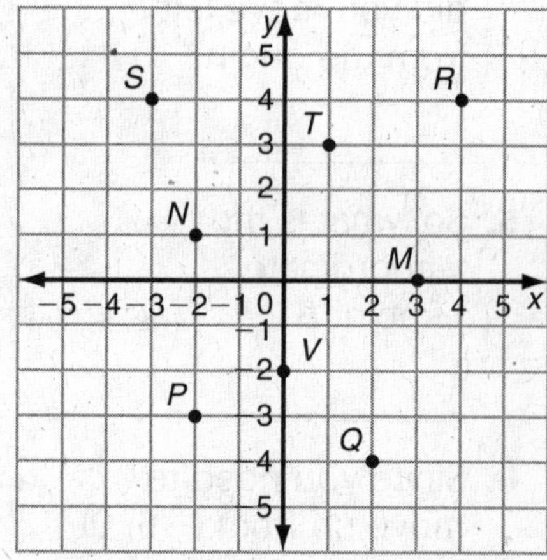

19. *M* __________ **20.** *N* __________

21. *P* __________ **22.** *Q* __________

Name the point for each ordered pair.

23. (1, 3) __________ **24.** (4, 4) __________

25. (0, −2) __________ **26.** (−3, 4) __________

27. Reasoning What is the *x*-coordinate for any point on the *y*-axis?

____

28. Is the point (−3, −4) located above, below, or on the *x*-axis? __________

29. Is the point (0, −8) located above, below, or on the *x*-axis? __________

Name ______________________________

Graphing Equations in the Coordinate Plane

Graph the equation $y = x - 1$ by doing the following.

1. Find y when $x = -2$, $x = 0$, and $x = 4$. Complete.

When $x = -2$:
$y = x - 1$
$y = -2 - 1$
$y = -2 + (-1)$
$y =$ ______

When $x = 0$:
$y = x - 1$
$y =$ ______ $- 1$
$y =$ ______ $+ (-1)$
$y =$ ______

When $x = 4$:
$y = x - 1$
$y =$ ______ $- 1$
$y =$ ______

2. Complete the table of ordered pairs.

x	***y***
−2	−3
0	
4	

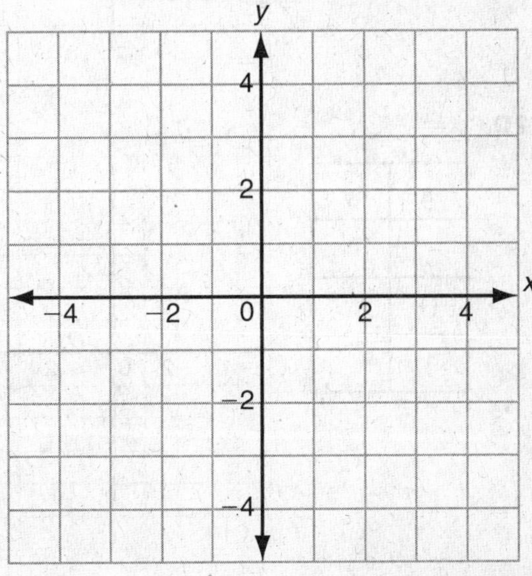

3. Plot each ordered pair.

4. Draw a line through the points. If the points are not on a line, check your work above.

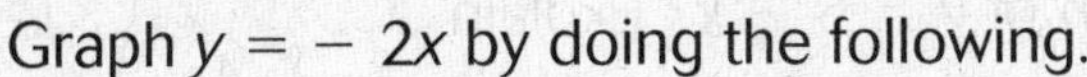

Graph $y = -2x$ by doing the following.

5. Complete the table of ordered pairs for the equation $y = -2x$.

x	***y***
−2	
0	
2	

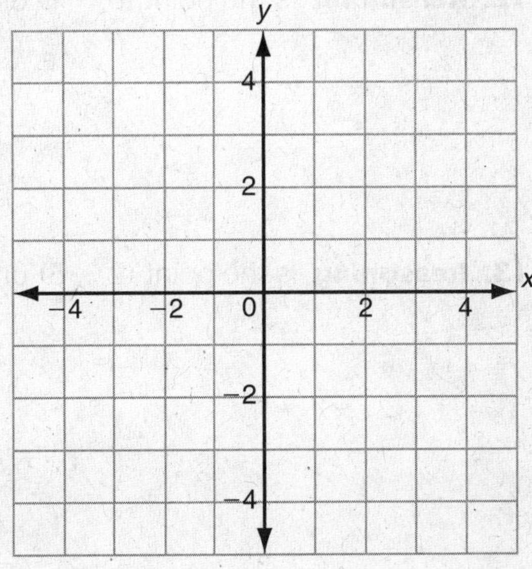

6. Plot each ordered pair.

7. Draw a line through the points. If the points are not on a line, check your work above.

Name ______________________________

Graphing Equations in the Coordinate Plane (continued)

Complete each table of ordered pairs. Then graph the equation.

8. $y = x + 2$

x	y
−4	
0	
2	

9. $y = 2x$

x	y
−2	
0	
2	

10. $y = -3x$

x	y
−1	
0	
1	

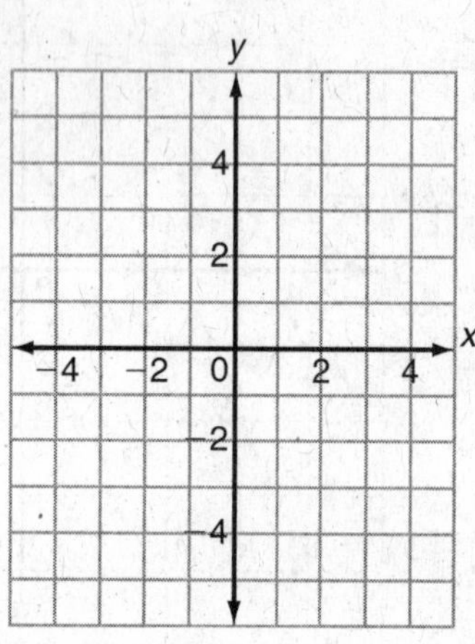

11. $y = 2 - x$

x	y
−2	
0	
3	

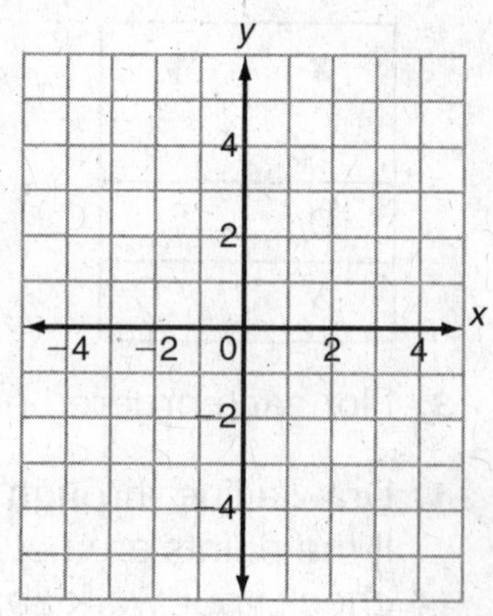

12. Reasoning Is the point (6, −1) on the graph of $y = 5 - x$? Explain.

13. Reasoning Is the point (2, −8) on the graph of $y = 4x$? Explain.

Name ______________________________

Using the Distributive Property

Materials counters, 100 per pair or group

Discover the Distributive Property by following 1–8.

1. Make an array with 4 rows and 5 counters in each row.

2. The array shows 4 × 5 = ______.

3. Make another array with 4 rows and 3 counters in each row.

4. The second array shows 4 × ______ = ______.

5. Put the two arrays together.

How many counters in all? ______ + ______ = ______

6. Fill in the blanks, using your answers above.

(4 × 5) + (4 × 3) = ______ + ______ = ______

7. After putting the two arrays together, how many counters are in each of the 4 rows? 5 + 3 = ______

8. Fill in the blanks.

(4 × 5) + (4 × 3) = ______ × (5 + 3) = ______ × 8 = ______

Name. ______________________

Using the Distributive Property (continued)

9. Make an array with 5 rows and 19 in each row. Separate the array into one that is 5 by 10 and one that is 5 by 9.

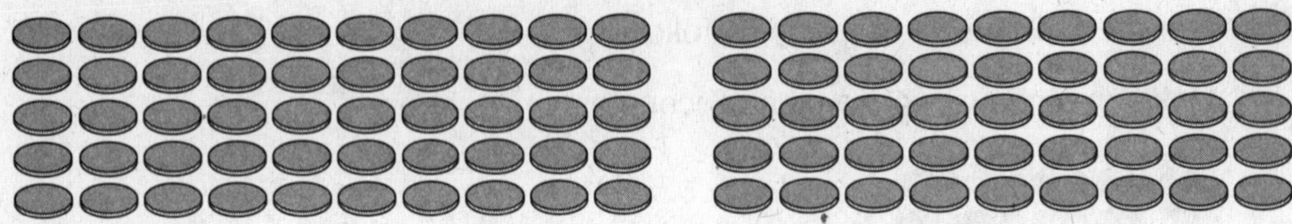

10. Use the array above to fill in the blanks.

5 × 19 = 5 × (______ + 9) = (5 × ______) + (5 × ______)

= ______ + ______

= ______

Fill in the blanks using the Distributive Property.

11. 6 × 9 = 6 × (4 + ______) = (6 × 4) + (6 × ______)

12. 3 × 14 = 3 × (______ + 4) = (3 × ______) + (______ × 4)

13. 2 × 27 = ______ × (20 + ______) = (______ × 20) + (______ × ______)

14. 12 × 8 = (10 + ______) × 8 = (10 × ______) + (______ × 8)

15. 9 × 47 = (9 × 40) + (9 × ______) = ______ × (40 + ______)

16. 16 × 105 = (16 × 100) + (16 × ______) = ______ × (100 + ______)

17. 25 × 204 = (______ × 200) + (25 × ______) = 25 × (______ + ______)

18. 8 × 96 = ______ × (100 − 4) = (______ × 100) − (______ × 4)

19. 7 × 48 = ______ × (50 − ______) = (______ × 50) − (______ × ______)

20. Reasoning Describe two different ways to find 4 × 49 with mental math.

Name ______________________________

More Variables and Expressions

To evaluate an expression, place the known value in place of the variable. Then use the order of operations to simplify.

1. Find $3n - 5$, when $n = 7$.

$3 \times$ ______ $- 5$ Put 7 in place of *n*.

$=$ ______ $- 5$ Use the order of operations, multiply first.

$=$ ______ Subtract.

2. Find $3k - \frac{k}{4}$, when $k = 8$.

$3 \times$ ______ $- \frac{\square}{4}$ Put 8 in place of *k*.

$=$ ______ $-$ ______ Multiply and divide first.

$=$ ______ Subtract.

3. Find $4y + 2z$, when $y = 5$ and $z = 7$.

$4 \times$ ______ $+ 2 \times$ ______ Put 5 in place of *y* and 7 in place of *z*.

$=$ ______ $+$ ______ Multiply first.

$=$ ______ Add.

4. Find $(3a - b) \div c$, when $a = 10$, $b = 6$, and $c = 2$.

$(3 \times$ ______ $-$ ______$) \div$ ______ Put 10 in place of *a*, 6 in place of *b*, and 2 in place of *c*

$= ($______ $-$ ______$) \div$ ______ Use the order of operations, do parentheses first. Inside the parentheses, multiply first.

$=$ ______ $\div$ ______ Subtract inside the parentheses.

$=$ ______ Divide.

Name ______________________

More Variables and Expressions (continued)

Evaluate each expression for $x = 3$.

5. $\left(\frac{x}{3}\right) + 15$ ________

6. $24 - (2x)$ ________

7. $(3x) + 5$ ________

8. $(4x) - 12$ ________

9. $(5x) - \left(\frac{15}{x}\right)$ ________

10. $35 + \left(\frac{21}{x}\right)$ ________

11. $(19 + x) \div 11$ ________

12. $(6x) + x - 12$ ________

13. $5x \div 3$ ________

Evaluate each expression for $a = 9$, $b = 2$, and $c = 0$.

14. $(a + 7b) + c$ ________

15. $13c + a$ ________

16. $(a + b) \times 3$ ________

17. $12b - 14c$ ________

18. $(a + b + c) \times 2$ ________

19. $(11 + a) \div b$ ________

20. $c \times (b + c)$ ________

21. $4a - 5b$ ________

22. $(a - b - c) \times 4$ ________

23. $7b - 12c$ ________

24. $(2a + b) \div 5$ ________

25. $a \times (b - c)$ ________

Use the data at the right to answer Exercises 26–28.

Veggie Pizza House		
Size	**Pizza**	**Beverages**
small	$5.00	$1
large	$8.00	$2

26. The cost of x small pizzas with y small beverages is given by the expression $5x + y$. How much do 3 small pizzas and 2 small beverages cost? ________

27. The cost of x large pizzas with y large beverages is given by the expression $8x + 2y$. How much do 2 large pizzas with 3 large beverages cost? ________

28. Reasoning Micka purchases 4 small veggie pizzas and 3 large beverages. Romano purchases 3 large pizzas and 4 small beverages. Who spent more money? Explain.

Name ______________________________

Divisibility by 2, 3, 5, 9, and 10

A number such as 256 is divisible by a number like 2 if 256 ÷ 2 has no remainder. If 256 is a multiple of 2, then 256 is divisible by 2.

Use the divisibility rules and answer 1 to 10 to determine if 256 is divisible by 2, 3, 5, 9, or 10.

Divisibility Rules	
Number	**Rule**
2	The last digit is even: 0, 2, 4, 6, 8.
3	The sum of the digits is divisible by 3.
5	The last digit ends in a 0 or 5.
9	The sum of the digits is divisible by 9.
10	The ones digit is a 0.

1. Is the last digit in 256 an even number? ______

2. Is 256 divisible by 2? ______

3. Is the last digit in 256 a 0 or 5? ______

4. Is 256 divisible by 5? ______

5. Is 256 divisible by 10? ______

6. What is the sum of the digits of 256? $2 + 5 + 6 =$ ______

7. Is the sum of the digits of 256 divisible by 3? ______

8. Is 256 divisible by 3? ______

9. Is the sum of the digits of 256 divisible by 9? ______

10. Is 256 divisible by 9? ______

Use the divisibility rules to determine if 720 is divisible by 2, 5, 9, or 10.

11. Is 720 divisible by 2? ______

12. Is 720 divisible by 5? ______

13. Is 720 divisible by 10? ______

14. Is 720 divisible by 9? ______

Name ______________________________

Divisibility by 2, 3, 5, 9, and 10 (continued)

Test each number to see if it is divisible by 2, 3, 5, 9, or 10. List the numbers each is divisible by.

15. 56 ____________
16. 78 ____________
17. 182 ____________

18. 380 ____________
19. 105 ____________
20. 126 ____________

21. 4,311 ____________
22. 8,356 ____________
23. 2,580 ____________

24. 7,265 ____________
25. 4,815 ____________
26. 630 ____________

27. Feliz has 225 baseball trophies. He wants to display his trophies on some shelves with an equal number of trophies on each. He can buy shelves in packages of 5, 9, or 10. Which shelf package should he NOT buy? Explain.

28. Reasoning Are all numbers that are divisible by 5 also divisible by 10? Explain your reasoning.

29. Reasoning Are all numbers that are divisible by 10 also divisible by 5? Explain your reasoning.

Name ______________________________

Prime Factorization

1. Use the two factor trees shown to factor 240. For the first circle, think of what number times 6 is 24. For the next two circles, factor 10. Continue factoring each number. Do not use the number 1.

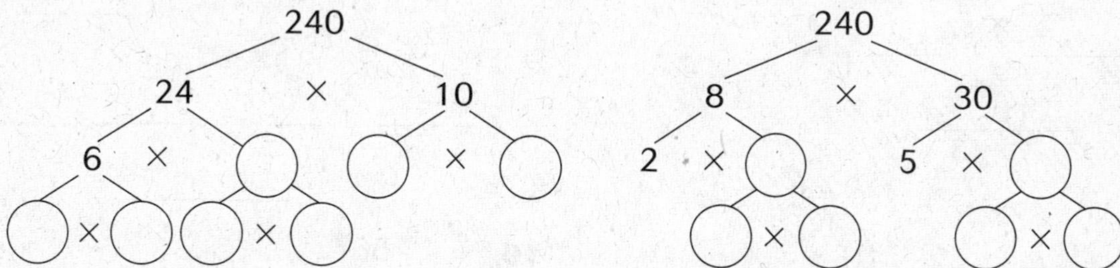

2. What are the numbers at the ends of the branches for each tree?

______________________________ ______________________________

3. Reasoning What do all the numbers at the end of each branch have in common?

4. Reasoning What do you notice about the numbers in the two groups?

5. Arrange the numbers from least to greatest and include a multiplication sign between each pair of numbers.

Your answer to 5 above shows the prime factorization of 240. If you multiply all the factors back together, you get 240.

6. Write the prime factorization of 240 using exponents.

______ × 3 × 5

Name ___________________________

Prime Factorization (continued)

Complete each factor tree. Write the prime factorization with exponents, if you can. Do not use the number 1 as a factor.

7.

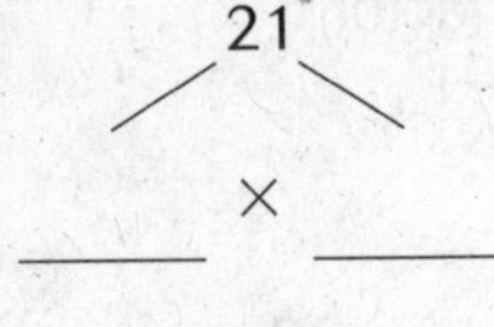

8.

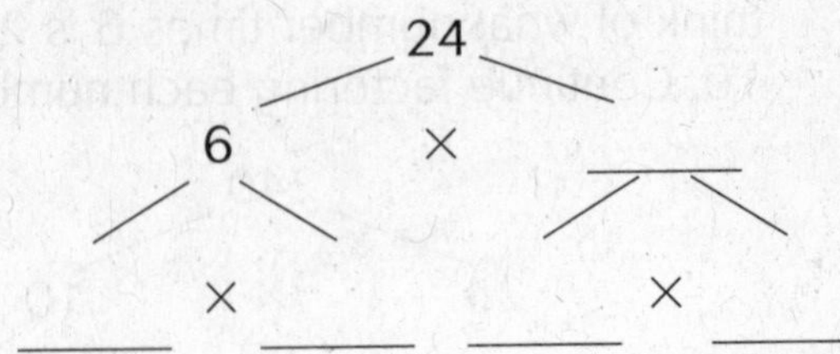

9.

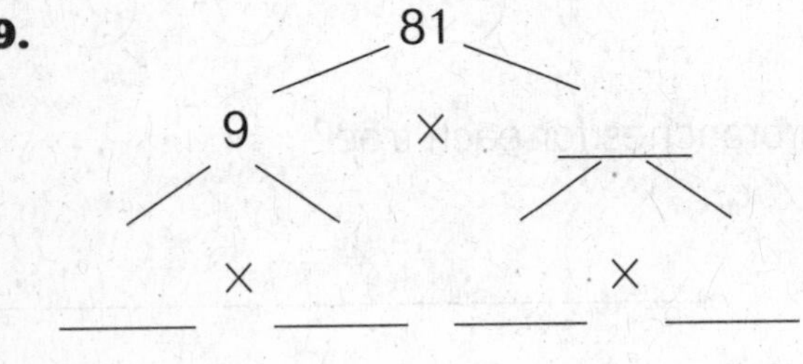

10.

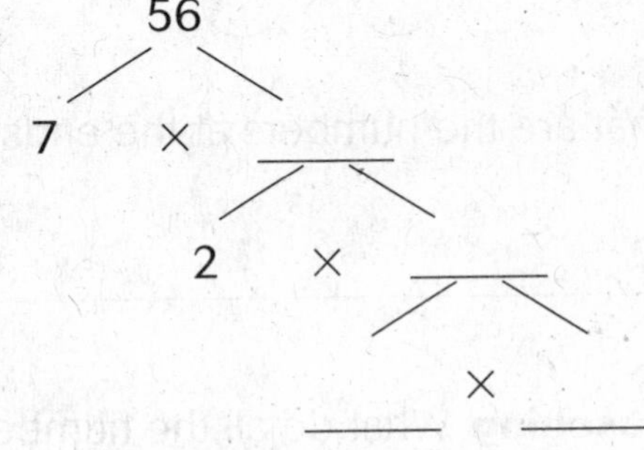

For Exercises 11 to 22, if the number is prime, write prime. If the number is composite, write the prime factorization of the number.

11. 11 ________

12. 18 ________

13. 41 ________

14. 40 ________

15. 16 ________

16. 17 ________

17. 80 ________

18. 95 ________

19. 35 ________

20. 72 ________

21. 48 ________

22. 55 ________

23. Reasoning Holly says that the prime factorization for 44 is 4×11. Is she right? Why or why not?

Name ______________________

Least Common Multiple

A student group is having a large cookout. They wish to buy the same number of hamburgers and hamburger buns. Hamburgers come in packages of 12 and buns come in packages of 8. What is the least amount of each they can buy in order to have the same amount?

Follow 1 to 4 below to answer the question.

1. Complete the table.

Packages	**1**	**2**	**3**	**4**	**5**	**6**
Hamburgers	12	24				
Buns	8	16				

2. What are some common multiples from the table? ______

3. What is the least of these common multiples? ______

So, the least common multiple (LCM) of 12 and 8 is 24.

4. What is the least amount of hamburgers and buns that the students can buy and have the same amount of each? ______

Find the least common multiple of 6 and 15 by following the steps below.

5. Complete the table.

	2 ×	**3 ×**	**4 ×**	**5 ×**	**6 ×**	**7 ×**	**8 ×**	**9 ×**	**10 ×**
6	12	18							
15	30	45							

6. What are the common multiples from the table? ______

7. What are the next three common multiples that are not in the table? ______

8. What is the least common multiple of 6 and 15? ______

Name ______________________________

Least Common Multiple (continued)

Find the least common multiple (LCM).

9. 30, 4 ________

10. 18, 9 ________

11. 12, 36 ________

12. 6, 12 ________

13. 8, 20 ________

14. 3, 14 ________

15. 6, 25 ________

16. 8, 12, 15 ________

17. 3, 4, 5 ________

18. Maria and her brother Carlos both got to be hall monitors today. Maria is hall monitor every 16 school days. Carlos is hall monitor every 20 school days. What is the least number of school days before they will both be hall monitors again?

19. Reasoning Find two numbers whose least common multiple is 12.

20. Reasoning Can you find the greatest common multiple of 6 and 15? Explain.

Name ______________________________

Dividing by Multiples of 10

Use the multiplication sentences to find each quotient. Look for a pattern.

1. 4 × 20 = ______ 80 ÷ 20 = ______

40 × 20 = ______ 800 ÷ 20 = ______

400 × 20 = ______ 8,000 ÷ 20 = ______

2. What basic division fact is used in each quotient above?

______ ÷ ______ = ______

Use basic facts and a pattern to find 2,400 ÷ 80. Answer 3 to 5.

3. What basic division fact can be used to find 2,400 ÷ 80?

______ ÷ ______ = ______

In 24 ÷ 8 = 3, 24 is the dividend, 8 is the divisor, and 3 is the quotient.

4. Look for a pattern.

Number Sentence	Zeros in the Dividend	Zeros in the Divisor	Zeros in the Quotient
240 ÷ 80 = ______	1	1	0
240 ÷ 8 = ______			
2,400 ÷ 8 = ______			
2,400 ÷ 80 = ______			

Complete.
Zeros in the dividend – Zeros in the divisor = ________ in the quotient

5. Reasoning Use the pattern to explain why 2,400 ÷ 80 has one zero.

Name ____________________

Dividing by Multiples of 10 (continued)

Divide. Use mental math.

6. 300 ÷ 30 = ______ **7.** 60 ÷ 20 = ______ **8.** 200 ÷ 40 = ______

9. 240 ÷ 60 = ______ **10.** 490 ÷ 70 = ______ **11.** 450 ÷ 90 = ______

12. 100 ÷ 50 = ______ **13.** 2,700 ÷ 90 = ______ **14.** 1,800 ÷ 60 = ______

15. 3,500 ÷ 70 = ______ **16.** 1,500 ÷ 30 = ______ **17.** 800 ÷ 40 = ______

18. 640 ÷ 80 = ______ **19.** 3,600 ÷ 60 = ______ **20.** 140 ÷ 70 = ______

21. 1,200 ÷ 20 = ______ **22.** 8,100 ÷ 90 = ______ **23.** 560 ÷ 80 = ______

24. 600 ÷ 30 = ______ **25.** 400 ÷ 20 = ______ **26.** 2,400 ÷ 60 = ______

27. 1,200 ÷ 40 = ______ **28.** 2,500 ÷ 50 = ______ **29.** 2,100 ÷ 70 = ______

30. 4,500 ÷ 90 = ______ **31.** 480 ÷ 80 = ______ **32.** 450 ÷ 50 = ______

33. Dan has a coin collection. His sister Michaela has just started collecting. Michaela has 20 coins, and Dan has 400 coins. About how many times larger is Dan's collection?

____

34. Hector must store computer CDs in cartons that hold 40 CDs each. How many cartons will he need to store 2,000 CDs?

____

35. Reasoning Write another division problem with the same answer as 2,700 ÷ 90.

Name ______________________________

Dividing by Two-Digit Divisors

A carpenter cut a board that is 144 inches long. He cut pieces 32 inches long. How many pieces did he get and how much of the board was left?

Find 144 ÷ 32 by answering 1 to 11.

1. First, estimate to find the approximate number of pieces.

150 ÷ 30 = ______

2. Write the estimate in the ones place of the quotient, on the right.

$$32\overline{)1\ 4\ 4}$$ with quotient 5

3. Multiply. 32 × 5 = ______

4. Compare the product to the dividend. Write > or <.

160 ◯ 144

Since 160 is too large, 5 was too large. Try 4.

5. Multiply. 32 × 4 = ______

6. Compare the product to the dividend. Write > or <.

128 ◯ 144

Since 128 is less than 144, 4 is not too large. Write 4 in the ones place of the quotient on the right. Write 128 below 144.

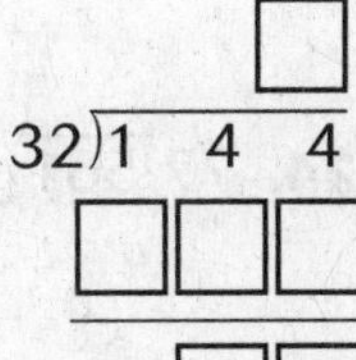

7. Subtract. 144 − 128 = ______

8. Compare the remainder to the divisor. Write > or <.

16 ◯ 32

Since the remainder is less than the divisor, the division is finished.

9. What is 144 ÷ 32? ______ R ______

10. How many 32-inch pieces did the carpenter cut? ______ pieces

11. How much of the board was left? ______ inches

Name ______________________________

Dividing by Two-Digit Divisors (continued)

Divide.

12. $32\overline{)202}$ **13.** $94\overline{)260}$ **14.** $45\overline{)345}$

15. $62\overline{)137}$ **16.** $28\overline{)212}$ **17.** $58\overline{)552}$

18. $82\overline{)657}$ **19.** $32\overline{)131}$ **20.** $93\overline{)824}$

21. $89\overline{)465}$ **22.** $74\overline{)204}$ **23.** $78\overline{)637}$

24. $77\overline{)561}$ **25.** $61\overline{)181}$ **26.** $73\overline{)419}$

27. $63\overline{)564}$ **28.** $82\overline{)718}$ **29.** $57\overline{)318}$

30. A vegetable stand sells 192 cucumbers and 224 squash during the month of July. About how many cucumbers did they sell each day? ______________

31. Reasoning To start dividing 126 by 23, Miranda used the estimate 120 ÷ 20 = 6. How could she tell 6 is too high?

Name ____________________

Comparing and Ordering Fractions

Jen ate $\frac{7}{9}$ of a salad. Jack ate $\frac{5}{9}$ of a salad. Find out who ate the greater part of a salad by answering 1–3.

Compare $\frac{7}{9}$ and $\frac{5}{9}$.

1. Are the denominators the same? _______

If the denominators are the same, then compare the numerators. The fraction with the **greater** numerator is **greater than** the other fraction.

2. Compare. Write >, <, or =. $7 \bigcirc 5$

$\frac{7}{9} \bigcirc \frac{5}{9}$

3. Who ate the greater part of a salad, Jen or Jack? ____________

Compare $\frac{3}{5}$ and $\frac{3}{4}$ by answering 4 to 6

4. Are the denominators the same? _______

5. Are the numerators the same? _______

If the numerators are the same, compare the denominators. The fraction with the **greater** denominator is **less than** the other fraction.

6. Compare. Write >, <, or =. $5 \bigcirc 4$

$\frac{3}{5} \bigcirc \frac{3}{4}$

Compare $\frac{3}{4}$ and $\frac{2}{3}$ by answering 7 to 11.

7. Are the denominators the same? _______

8. Are the numerators the same? _______

If neither the numerators or the denominators are the same, change to equivalent fractions with the same denominator.

9. What is the LCM of 3 and 4? _______

Name ______________________

Comparing and Ordering Fractions (continued)

10. Rewrite $\frac{3}{4}$ and $\frac{2}{3}$ as equivalent fractions with a denominator of 12.

$\frac{3}{4} = \frac{\square}{12}$ $\frac{2}{3} = \frac{\square}{12}$

11. Compare. Write >, <, or =. $\frac{9}{12} \bigcirc \frac{8}{12}$

$\frac{3}{4} \bigcirc \frac{2}{3}$

Write $\frac{5}{6}$, $\frac{5}{9}$, and $\frac{1}{3}$ in order from least to greatest by answering 12 to 15.

12. Use the denominators to compare. Write >, <, or =. $\frac{5}{6} \bigcirc \frac{5}{9}$

13. Rewrite $\frac{1}{3}$ so that it has a denominator common with $\frac{5}{9}$. $\frac{1}{3} = \frac{\square}{9}$

14. Compare the numerators. Write >, <, or =. $\frac{5}{9} \bigcirc \frac{3}{9}$

$\frac{5}{9} \bigcirc \frac{1}{3}$

15. Use the comparisons to write $\frac{5}{6}$, $\frac{5}{9}$, and $\frac{1}{3}$ in order from least to greatest.

_______ < _______ < _______

Compare. Write >, <, or =.

16. $\frac{3}{7} \bigcirc \frac{1}{7}$ **17.** $\frac{5}{8} \bigcirc \frac{10}{16}$ **18.** $\frac{3}{11} \bigcirc \frac{4}{10}$ **19.** $\frac{3}{4} \bigcirc \frac{2}{3}$

20. $\frac{3}{5} \bigcirc \frac{9}{15}$ **21.** $\frac{5}{6} \bigcirc \frac{5}{8}$ **22.** $\frac{5}{8} \bigcirc \frac{7}{12}$ **23.** $\frac{7}{9} \bigcirc \frac{4}{9}$

Write the fractions in order from least to greatest.

24. $\frac{1}{4}, \frac{6}{7}, \frac{3}{5}$ **25.** $\frac{5}{8}, \frac{8}{10}, \frac{2}{7}$ **26.** $\frac{5}{9}, \frac{10}{12}, \frac{5}{7}$ **27.** $\frac{3}{9}, \frac{12}{15}, \frac{5}{6}$

__________ __________ __________ __________

28. Reasoning Mario has two pizzas the same size. He cuts one into 4 equal pieces and the other into 5 equal pieces. Which pizza has larger pieces? Explain.

Name ______________________

Place Value Through Thousandths

1. Write 5.739 in the place-value chart below.

ones		tenths	hundredths	thousandths
	.			

2. What is the value of the 5 in 5.739? ________

3. What is the value of the 7 in 5.739? ________

4. What is the value of the 3 in 5.739? ________

5. What is the value of the 9 in 5.739? ________

6. Write 5.739 in expanded form. ________ + 0.7 + ________ + 0.009

7. Write 5.739 in words.

________ and seven hundred ________________ thousandths

Write seven and two hundred four thousandths in standard from by answering 8 to 14.

8. How many ones are in seven and two hundred four thousandths? ________

Write 7 in the ones place of the place-value chart below.

ones		tenths	hundredths	thousandths
	.			

9. Write two hundred, thousandths as a fraction. ________

10. Write an equivalent fraction. $\frac{200}{1{,}000} = \frac{\square}{10}$

11. How many tenths are in seven and two hundred four thousandths? ________

Write 2 in the tenths place of the place-value chart above.

12. How many hundredths are in seven and two hundred four thousandths? ________

Write 0 in the hundredths place of the place-value chart above.

Name ______________________________

Place Value Through Thousandths (continued)

13. How many thousandths are in seven and two hundred four thousandths? __________

Write 4 in the thousandths place of the place-value chart.

14. Write 7.204 in expanded form. ________ + ________ + ________

15. **Reasoning** What is 1 thousandth less than 7.204? ________

Write each value in standard form.

16. 507 thousandths __________

17. 5 and 6 thousandths __________

18. 9 and 62 thousandths __________

Write the value of the underlined digit.

19. $2.5\underline{5}3$ __________

20. $0.38\underline{1}$ __________

21. $6.\underline{6}47$ __________

22. $9.0\underline{9}7$ __________

Write each decimal in expanded form.

23. 4.685 ______________________

24. 3.056 ______________________

25. 0.735 ______________________

26. 4.004 ______________________

Write each decimal in word form.

27. 2.598

____

28. 0.008

____

29. 0.250

____

Name ________________

Decimals to Fractions

Materials crayons, markers, or colored pencils

Write 0.45 as a fraction by answering 1 to 5.

1. Color the grid to show 0.45.

2. How many squares did you color? ______

3. How many squares are in the grid? ______

4. What fraction represents the part of the grid that you colored? ______

5. Write a fraction equal to 0.45. 0.45 = ______

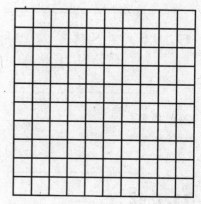

You can also use place value to change a decimal to a fraction.

Write 0.3 as a fraction by answering 6 to 9

6. Write 0.3 in words. ______

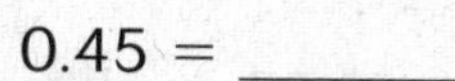

7. What is the place value of the 3 in 0.3? ______

8. What fraction represents three tenths? ______

Since the 3 is in the tenths place, you write 3 over 10.

9. Write a fraction equal to 0.3. 0.3 = ______

Write 3.07 as a mixed number by answering 10 to 13.

10. What is the whole number part of the decimal 3.07? ______

11. What is the place value of the last digit in 3.07? ______

12. Write the place value as the denominator and write 7 as the numerator. $3.07 = 3\frac{7}{\square}$

13. Write a mixed number equal to 3.07. 3.07 = ______

Name ______________________

Decimals to Fractions (continued)

Write each decimal as a fraction or mixed number.

14. 0.4 ________

15. 3.7 ________

16. 5.27 ________

17. 0.8 ________

18. 1.2 ________

19. 4.03 ________

20. 0.12 ________

21. 10.5 ________

22. 0.19 ________

23. 0.42 ________

24. 5.75 ________

25. 8.6 ________

26. 19.09 ________

27. 0.01 ________

28. 28.37 ________

29. Jaime put 13.9 gallons of gas in the car.
What is 13.9 written as a mixed number? ________

30. Candice ran 2.75 miles.
What is 2.75 written as a mixed number? ________

31. Justin's mom bought a 12.57 pound turkey.
What is 12.57 written as a mixed number? ________

32. Reasoning Marco says $0.08 = \frac{8}{10}$. Is he correct? Explain why.

33. Reasoning $2.37 = 2\frac{37}{100}$ and $2.3 = 2\frac{3}{10}$. Explain why the 3 in 2.37 represents $\frac{3}{10}$.

Name ______________________

Estimating Sums and Differences of Mixed Numbers

Last week, Dwayne spent $4\frac{1}{3}$ hours playing basketball and $1\frac{2}{3}$ hours playing soccer. Answer 1 to 9 to estimate how much time Dwayne spent in all playing these two sports.

Estimate $4\frac{1}{3} + 1\frac{2}{3}$.

1. What two whole numbers is $4\frac{1}{3}$ between? _______ and _______

2. Use the number line.
Is $4\frac{1}{3}$ closer to 4 or 5? _______

$4\frac{1}{3}$

4 $4\frac{1}{6}$ $4\frac{2}{6}$ $4\frac{3}{6}$ $4\frac{4}{6}$ $4\frac{5}{6}$ 5

3. What is the number halfway between 4 and 5? _______

4. Compare. Write >, <, or =. $\frac{1}{3}$ ◯ $\frac{1}{2}$

By comparing $\frac{1}{3}$ and $\frac{1}{2}$, you can tell that $4\frac{1}{3}$ is closer to 4 than 5, without using a number line. So, $4\frac{1}{3}$ rounded to the nearest whole number is 4.

5. What two whole numbers is $1\frac{2}{3}$ between? _______ and _______

6. Compare. Write >, <, or =. $\frac{2}{3}$ ◯ $\frac{1}{2}$

7. What is $1\frac{2}{3}$ rounded to the nearest whole number? _______

8. Use the rounded numbers to estimate $4\frac{1}{3} + 1\frac{2}{3}$.

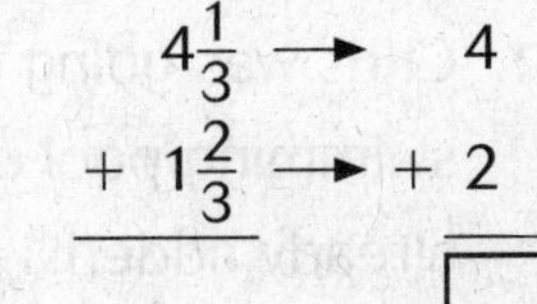

9. About how much time did Dwayne spend playing basketball and soccer? _______

About how much more time did Dwayne spend playing basketball than soccer?

10. Estimate $4\frac{1}{3} - 1\frac{2}{3}$ at the right.

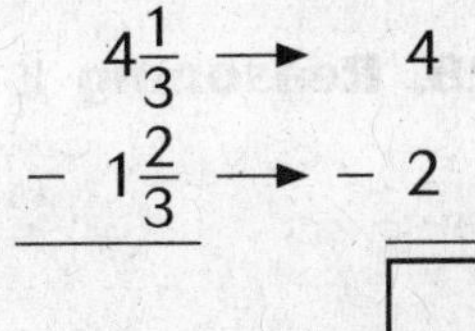

11. About how much more time did Dwayne spend playing basketball than soccer? _______

Estimating Sums and Differences of Mixed Numbers (continued)

Estimate each sum or difference.

12. $2\frac{2}{3} - 1\frac{1}{3}$ ________

13. $2\frac{9}{10} - 1\frac{5}{10}$ ________

14. $5 + 4\frac{2}{4}$ ________

15. $6\frac{4}{6} + 1\frac{5}{6}$ ________

16. $6\frac{7}{8} - 5\frac{3}{8}$ ________

17. $6 - 3\frac{3}{9}$ ________

18. $4\frac{9}{14} + 2\frac{11}{14}$ ________

19. $6 + 4\frac{2}{16}$ ________

20. $2\frac{3}{4} - 1$ ________

21. $7\frac{2}{6} + 6\frac{5}{6}$ ________

22. $3\frac{2}{5} + 1\frac{2}{5}$ ________

23. $6\frac{1}{8} - 1\frac{5}{8}$ ________

24. $7 - 2\frac{3}{7}$ ________

25. $3\frac{4}{8} + 1\frac{7}{8}$ ________

26. Yolanda walked $2\frac{3}{5}$ miles on Monday, $1\frac{1}{5}$ miles on Tuesday, and $3\frac{4}{5}$ miles on Wednesday. Estimate her total distance walked. ________

27. Chris was going to add $2\frac{1}{4}$ cups of a chemical to the swimming pool until he found out that Richard already added $1\frac{1}{8}$ cups of the chemical. Estimate how much more Chris should add so that the total is his original amount. ________

28. Reasoning Is $3\frac{1}{2}$ closer to 3 or 4? Explain.

Name ______________________

Multiplying Two Fractions

Materials crayons, markers, or colored pencils, paper to fold

Pablo's yard is $\frac{3}{4}$ of an acre. One-half of the yard is woods. What part of an acre is wooded?

Find $\frac{1}{2}$ of $\frac{3}{4}$ or $\frac{1}{2} \times \frac{3}{4}$ by answering 1 to 5.

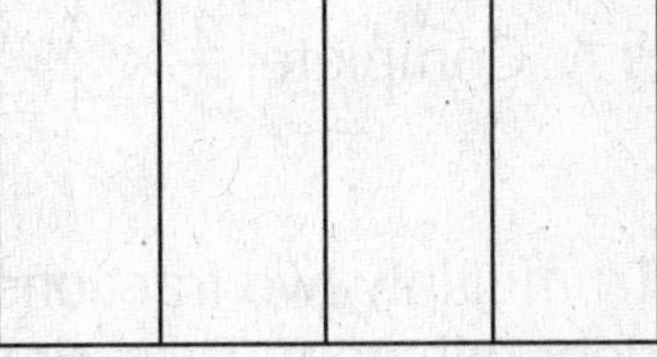

1. Fold a sheet of paper into 4 equal parts, as shown at the right. Color 3 parts with slanted lines to show $\frac{3}{4}$. Color the rectangle at the right to show what you did.

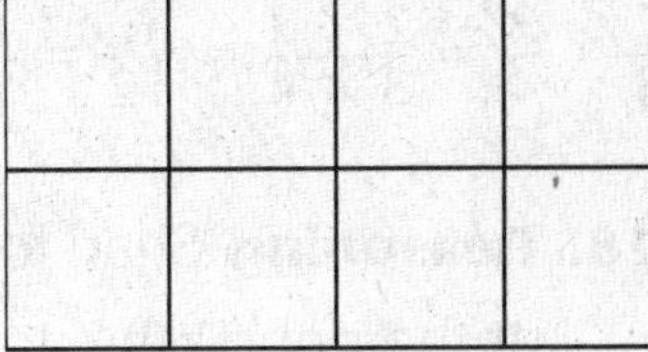

2. Now fold the paper in half the other way. Shade one half with lines slanted the opposite direction of the first set. Color the rectangle at the right to show what you did.

3. What fraction of the paper is shaded with crisscrossed lines? ______

4. The part shaded with crisscrossed lines shows $\frac{1}{2}$ of $\frac{3}{4}$ or $\frac{1}{2} \times \frac{3}{4}$.
So, what is $\frac{1}{2} \times \frac{3}{4}$? ______

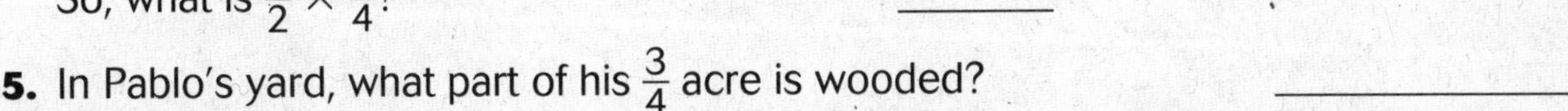

5. In Pablo's yard, what part of his $\frac{3}{4}$ acre is wooded? ______

6. To find $\frac{1}{2} \times \frac{3}{4}$, how many sections did you divide the paper into? ______

7. What is the product of the denominators in $\frac{1}{2} \times \frac{3}{4}$? $2 \times 4 =$ ______

8. To find $\frac{1}{2} \times \frac{3}{4}$, how many sections did you crisscross? ______

9. What is the product of the numerators in $\frac{1}{2} \times \frac{3}{4}$? $1 \times 3 =$ ______

10. Write the product of the numerators over the product of the denominators. $\frac{1 \times 3}{2 \times 4} =$

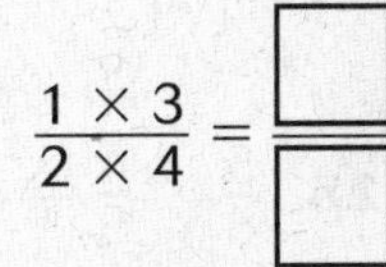

11. Is your answer to item 10 the same as item 4? ______

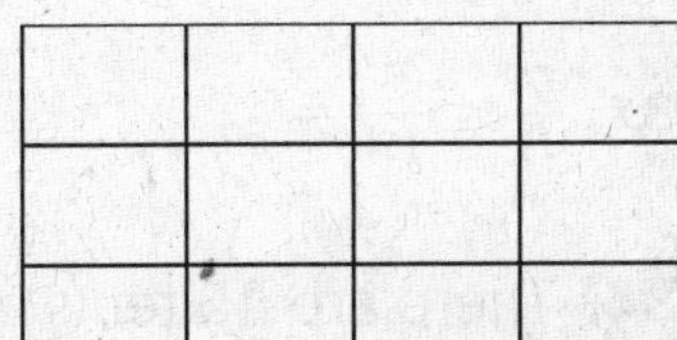

12. Use paper folding to find $\frac{2}{3} \times \frac{3}{4}$. Color the rectangle at the right to show what you did. So, $\frac{2}{3} \times \frac{3}{4} =$ ______

13. To find $\frac{2}{3} \times \frac{3}{4}$, how many sections did you divide the paper into? ______

Name ____________________

Multiplying Two Fractions (continued)

14. What is the product of the denominators in $\frac{2}{3} \times \frac{3}{4}$? $3 \times 4 =$ ______

15. To find $\frac{2}{3} \times \frac{3}{4}$ how many sections did you crisscross? ______

16. What is the product of the numerators in $\frac{2}{3} \times \frac{3}{4}$? $2 \times 3 =$ ______

17. Complete: $\frac{2}{3} \times \frac{3}{4} = \frac{2 \times 3}{3 \times 4} = \frac{\square}{\square}$

To multiply two fractions, you can multiply the numerators and then the denominators. Then simplify, if possible.

$$\frac{2}{3} \times \frac{3}{4} = \frac{2 \times 3}{3 \times 4} = \frac{6}{12} = \frac{1}{2}$$

18. Reasoning Shari found $\frac{3}{10} \times \frac{5}{9}$ as shown at the right. Why does Shari's method work?

$$\frac{3}{10} \times \frac{5}{9} = \frac{\overset{1}{\cancel{3}} \times \overset{1}{\cancel{5}}}{\underset{2}{\cancel{10}} \times \underset{3}{\cancel{9}}} = \frac{1}{6}$$

Multiply. Simplify, if possible.

19. $\frac{1}{8} \times \frac{2}{3} =$ ______

20. $\frac{5}{6} \times \frac{1}{2} =$ ______

21. $\frac{1}{4} \times \frac{3}{5} =$ ______

22. $\frac{6}{7} \times \frac{1}{3} =$ ______

23. $\frac{3}{4} \times \frac{3}{8} =$ ______

24. $\frac{1}{5} \times \frac{4}{5} =$ ______

25. $\frac{2}{3} \times \frac{4}{7} =$ ______

26. $\frac{3}{7} \times \frac{3}{10} =$ ______

27. $\frac{4}{9} \times \frac{3}{4} =$ ______

28. $\frac{5}{8} \times \frac{4}{5} =$ ______

29. $\frac{7}{9} \times \frac{3}{5} =$ ______

30. $\frac{1}{10} \times \frac{5}{7} =$ ______

31. $\frac{7}{8} \times \frac{5}{14} =$ ______

32. $\frac{3}{11} \times \frac{1}{9} =$ ______

33. $\frac{1}{12} \times \frac{4}{5} =$ ______

34. There are 45 tents at the summer camp. Girls will use $\frac{2}{3}$ of the tents. How many tents will the girls use? ______

Name ________________________________

Measuring and Classifying Angles

Materials protractor, straightedge, and crayons, markers, or colored pencils

A protractor can be used to measure and draw angles. Angles are measured in degrees.

Use a protractor to measure the angle shown by answering 1 to 2.

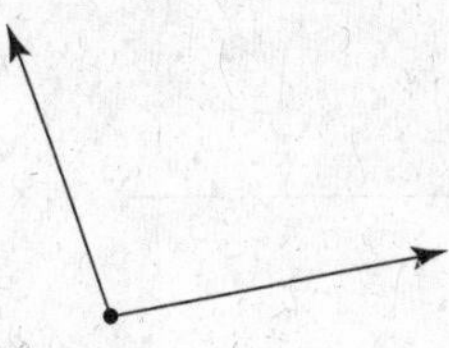

1. Place the protractor's center on the angle's vertex and place the 0° mark on one side of the angle.

2. Read the measure where the other side of the angle crosses the protractor. What is the measure of the angle? ________

Use a protractor to draw an angle with a measure of 60° by answering 3 to 5.

3. Draw $\overrightarrow{AB}$ by connecting the points shown with the endpoint of the ray at point *A*.

4. Place the protractor's center on point *A*. Place the protractor so the the 0° mark is lined up with $\overrightarrow{AB}$.

A B

5. Place a point at 60°. Label it *C* and draw $\overrightarrow{AC}$.

Use a protractor to measure the angles shown, if necessary, to answer 6 to 9.

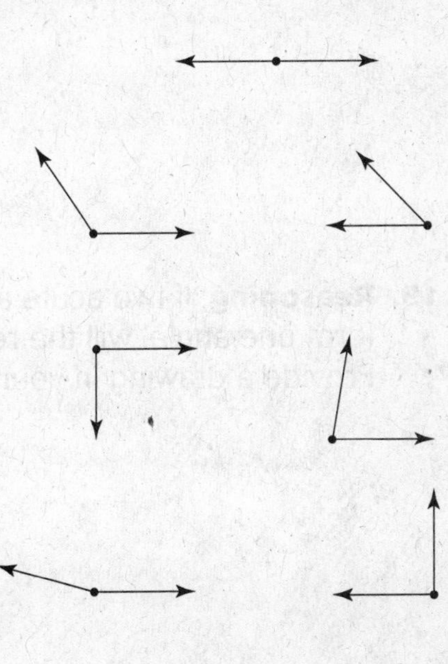

6. **Acute** angles have a measure between 0° and 90°. Trace over the acute angles with blue.

7. **Right** angles have a measure of 90°. Trace over the right angles with red.

8. **Obtuse** angles have a measure between 90° and 180°. Trace over the obtuse angles with green.

9. **Straight** angles have a measure of 180°. Trace over the straight angles with orange.

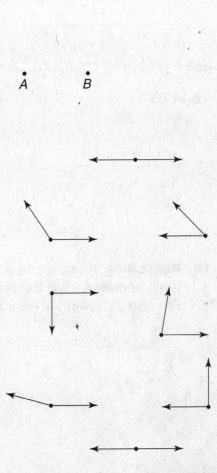

Name ______________________________

Measuring and Classifying Angles (continued)

Classify each angle as acute, right, obtuse, or straight. Then measure the angle.

10.

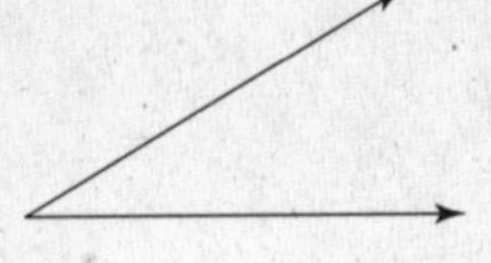

____

____

11.

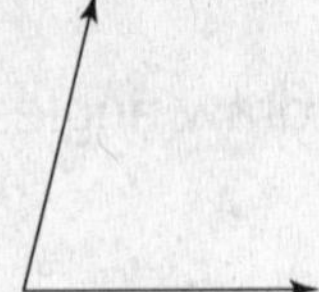

____

____

12.

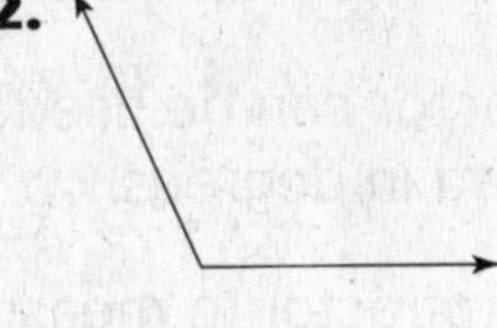

____

____

13.

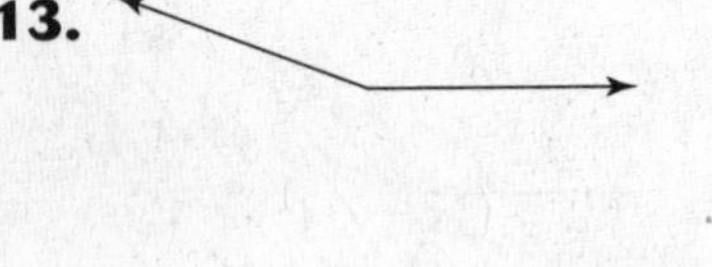

____

____

14.

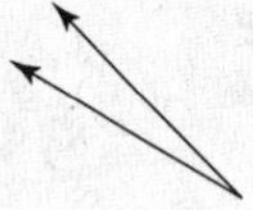

____

____

15.

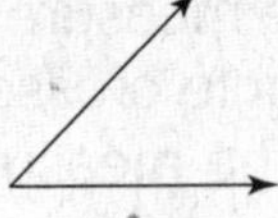

____

____

Use a protractor to draw an angle with each measure.

16. 120°

17. 35°

18. 70°

19. Reasoning If two acute angles are placed next to each other to form one angle, will the result always be an obtuse angle? Explain. Provide a drawing in your explanation.

Name ______________________________

Constructions

Materials compass and straightedge

Construct a segment congruent to $\overline{XY}$ by answering 1 to 3.

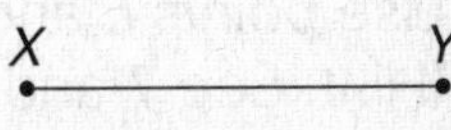

1. Use a compass to measure the length of $\overline{XY}$, by placing one point on X and the other on Y.

2. Draw a horizontal ray with endpoint W. Place the compass point on point W. Use the compass measure of $\overline{XY}$ to draw an arc intersecting the ray drawn. Label this intersection J.

3. Are $\overline{XY}$ and $\overline{WJ}$ congruent? ____________

Construct an angle congruent to $\angle A$ by answering 4 to 6.

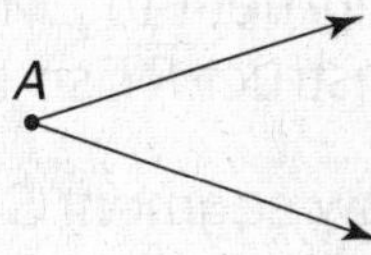

4. Place the compass point on A, and draw an arc intersecting both sides of $\angle A$. Draw a ray with endpoint S. With the compass point on S, use the same compass setting from $\angle A$ to draw an arc intersecting the ray at point T.

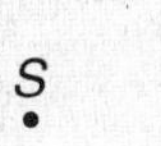

5. Use a compass to measure the length of the arc intersecting both sides of $\angle A$. Place the compass point on T. Use the same measure from $\angle A$ to draw an arc that intersects the first arc. Label the point of intersection R and draw the $\overrightarrow{SR}$.

6. Are $\angle A$ and $\angle RST$ congruent? ____________

Construct a line perpendicular to $\overleftrightarrow{AB}$ by answering 7 to 9.

7. Open the compass to more than half the distance between A and B. Place the compass point at A and draw arcs above and below the line.

8. Without changing the compass setting, place the point at B. Draw arcs that intersect the arcs made from point A. Label the point of intersection above the line as C and below the line as D. Draw line CD.

9. Are $\overleftrightarrow{AB}$ and $\overleftrightarrow{CD}$ perpendicular? ____________

Name ____________________

Constructions (continued)

Construct a line that is parallel to $\overleftrightarrow{AB}$ on the previous page, by answering 10 to 12.

10. Draw point *E* on $\overleftrightarrow{CD}$ above point *C*.

11. Use points *E* and *D* to construct a line perpendicular to $\overleftrightarrow{CD}$. (Hint: See 7 and 8.) Label this line *FG*.

12. Are $\overleftrightarrow{AB}$ and $\overleftrightarrow{FG}$ parallel? ____________

Construct a triangle congruent to triangle *LMN* by answering 13 to 16.

13. Construct $\angle R$ congruent to $\angle L$.

14. On one side of $\angle R$, construct $\overline{RS}$ so that it is congruent to $\overline{LM}$. On the other side of $\angle R$, construct $\overline{RT}$ so that it is congruent to $\overline{LN}$.

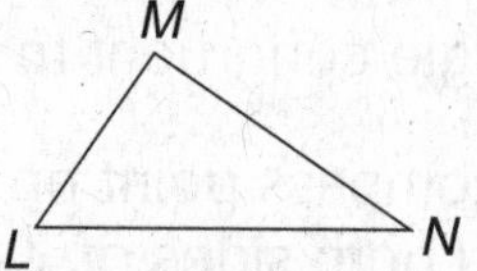

15. Draw segment *ST*.

16. Are $\triangle LMN$ and $\triangle RST$ congruent? ____________

Construct a rectangle by answering 17 to 21.

17. Construct a line that is perpendicular to $\overleftrightarrow{PQ}$. Label the point of intersection *G*.

18. Use points *P* and *G* to construct another line perpendicular to $\overleftrightarrow{PG}$. Label the point of intersection *H*.

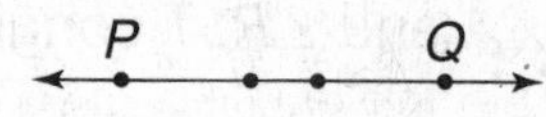

19. Choose a point on the first line and label it *K*. Construct segment *HJ* on the second line so that it is congruent to $\overline{GK}$.

20. Draw segment *JK*.

21. **Reasoning** How do you know that *GHJK* is a rectangle?

Name ____________________

Converting Customary Units of Length

Customary Units of Length
1 foot (ft) = 12 inches (in.)
1 yard (yd) = 36 (in.)
1 yard (yd) = 3 feet (ft)
1 mile (mi) = 5,280 feet (ft)
1 mile (mi) = 1,760 yards (yd)

Mayla bought 6 yards of ribbon. How many feet of ribbon did she buy?

Answer 1 to 4 to change 6 yards to feet.

To change larger units to smaller units, multiply. To change smaller units to larger units, divide.

1. 1 yard = _____ feet

2. Do you need to multiply or divide to change from yards to feet? __________

3. What is 6 × 3 feet? _____ feet

4. How many feet of ribbon did Mayla buy? ______

Deidra bought 60 inches of ribbon. How many feet of ribbon did she buy? Change 60 inches to feet by answering 5 to 8.

5. 1 foot = _____ inches

6. Do you need to multiply or divide to change from inches to feet? __________

7. What is 60 ÷ 12? _____

8. How many feet of ribbon did Deidra buy? ______

Troy ran 4 miles. How many yards did he run? Change 4 miles to yards by answering 9 to 12.

9. 1 mile = _______ yards

10. Do you need to multiply or divide to change from miles to yards?

11. 4 miles = yards

12. How many yards did Troy run? __________

Name ______________________________

Converting Customary Units of Length (continued)

Find each missing number.

13. 1 yd = _______ ft **14.** 72 in. = _______ ft **15.** 3 mi = _______ ft

16. 5,280 ft = _______ mi **17.** 5 mi = _______ yd **18.** 4 yd = _______ ft

19. 48 in. = _______ ft **20.** 1 yd = _______ in. **21.** 6 mi = _______ ft

22. 5 yd = _______ ft **23.** 3 mi = _______ yd **24.** 2 ft = _______ in.

25. 21 ft = _______ yd **26.** 3 yd = _______ in. **27.** 4 yd = _______ in.

For Exercises 28 to 32 use the information in the table.

Turtle Crawl Results

Turtle	Distance
Snapper	38 inches
Speedy	3 feet
Pokey	2 yards
Pickles	4 feet

28. How many inches did Speedy crawl?

_______ inches

29. How many inches did Pokey crawl?

_______ inches

30. How many inches did Pickles crawl?

_______ inches

31. Reasoning Which turtle crawled the greatest distance? _______

32. Reasoning Which turtle crawled the least distance? _______

33. Reasoning Explain how you could use addition to find how many yards are in 72 inches.

Name ______________________________

Converting Metric Units

The table shows how metric units are related. Every unit is 10 times greater than the next smaller unit. Abbreviations are shown for the most commonly used units.

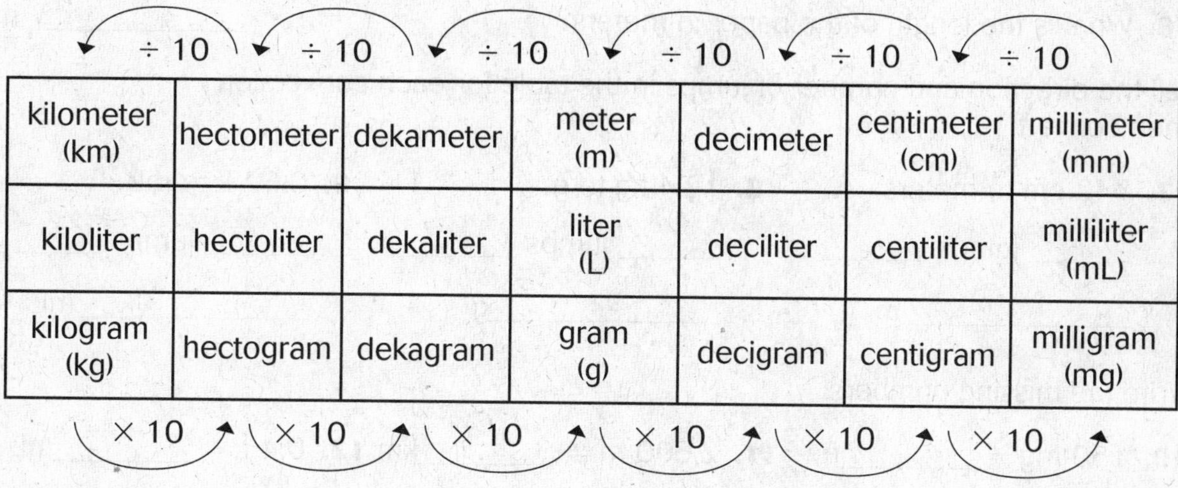

kilometer (km)	hectometer	dekameter	meter (m)	decimeter	centimeter (cm)	millimeter (mm)
kiloliter	hectoliter	dekaliter	liter (L)	deciliter	centiliter	milliliter (mL)
kilogram (kg)	hectogram	dekagram	gram (g)	decigram	centigram	milligram (mg)

To change from one metric unit to another, move the decimal point to the right or to the left to multiply or divide by 10, 100, or 1,000.

The length of a sheet of paper is 27.9 centimeters. Convert 27.9 cm to millimeters by answering 1 to 3.

1. To move from centimeters to millimeters in the table, do you move right or left? ____________

2. How many jumps are there between centimeters and millimeters in the table? ____________

Move the decimal one place to the right to convert from centimeters to millimeters. This is the same as multiplying by 10.

3. What is the length of the paper in millimeters? ____________ mm

Convert 27.9 cm to meters by answering 4 to 6.

4. To move from centimeters to meters in the table, do you move right or left? ____________

Name ______________________________

Converting Metric Units (continued)

5. How many jumps are there between centimeters and meters in the table?

Move the decimal two places to the left to convert from centimeters to meters. This is the same as dividing by 100.

6. What is the length of the paper in meters? ________ m

Tell the direction and number of jumps in the table for each conversion. Then convert.

7. 742 cm to meters
____ jumps ____
________ m

8. 12.4 kg to g
____ jumps ____
________ g

9. 0.62 L to mL
____ jumps ____
________ mL

Write the missing numbers.

10. 150 mg = ________ g **11.** 2,600 m = ________ km **12.** 0.4 L = ________ mL

13. 300 mL = ________ L **14.** 4 kg = ________ mg **15.** 2.6 m = ________ mm

16. 2,670 mg = ________ g **17.** 34 cm = ________ mm **18.** 16 L = ________ mL

For Exercises 19 to 21 use the table at the right.

Building	Height
John Hancock Center	344 m
Petronas Towers	452 m
Sears Tower	44,200 cm
CN Tower	553,000 mm

19. What is the height of the Petronas Towers in centimeters?

____

20. What is the height of the CN Tower in meters?

____

21. What is the height of the John Hancock Center in km?

____

22. Reasoning Which is shorter, 15 centimeters or 140 millimeters? Explain.

Name ______________________________

Area of Parallelograms

Materials grid paper, colored pencils or markers, scissors

Find the area of the parallelogram on the grid by answering 1 to 10.

1. Trace the parallelogram below on a piece of grid paper. Then cut out the parallelogram.

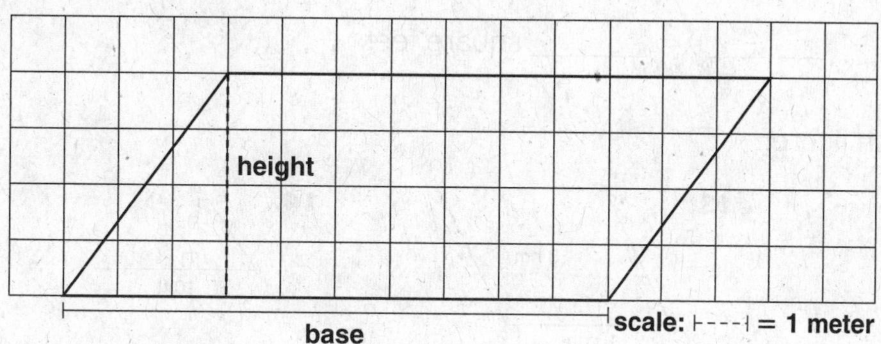

2. Cut out the right triangle created by the dashed line.

3. Take the right triangle and move it to the right of the parallelogram.

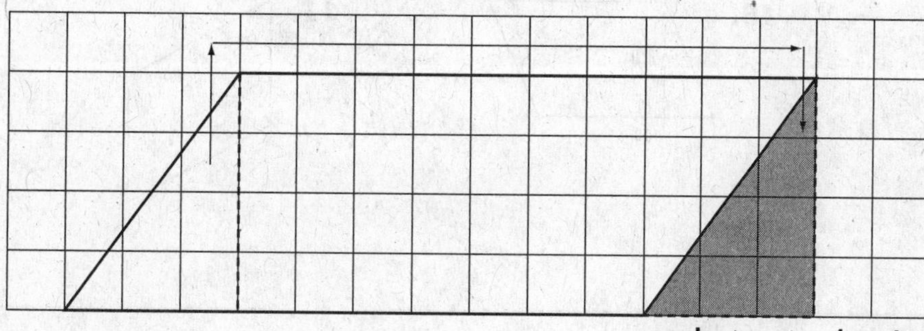

4. What shape did you create? ________________

5. Is the area of the parallelogram the same as the area of the rectangle? ________

6. What is the area of the rectangle? $A = \ell \times w =$ ________ $\times 4 =$ ________ sq meters

7. What is the base *b* of the parallelogram? ________ meters

8. What is the height *h* of the parallelogram? ________ meters

9. What is the base times the height of the parallelogram? ________

10. Is this the same as the area of the rectangle? ________

Name ______________________________

Area of Parallelograms (continued)

The formula for the area of a parallelogram is $A = bh$.

11. Use the formula to find the area of a parallelogram with a base of 9 ft and a height of 6 feet.

$A = \quad b \quad \times \quad h$

$\downarrow \qquad \downarrow$

$A =$ (______) × (______) = ______ square feet

Find the area of each figure.

12.

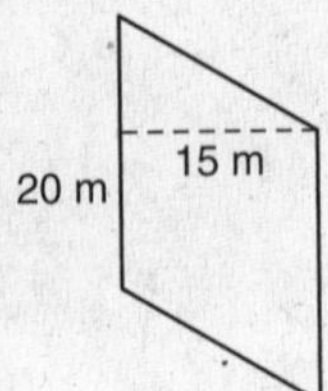

13.

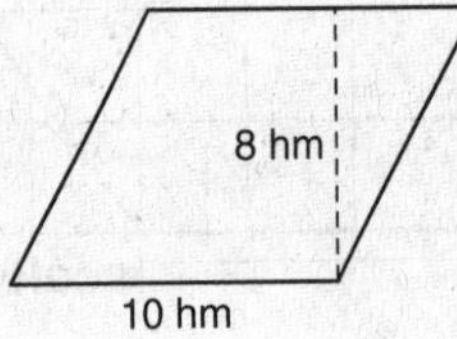

14.

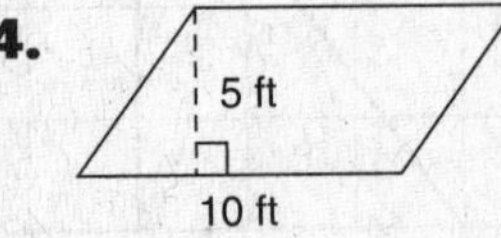

______ ______ ______

15.

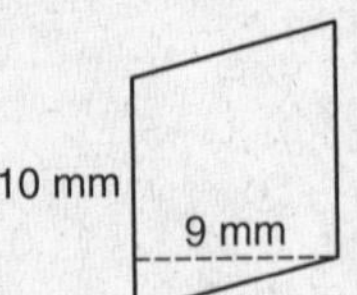

16.

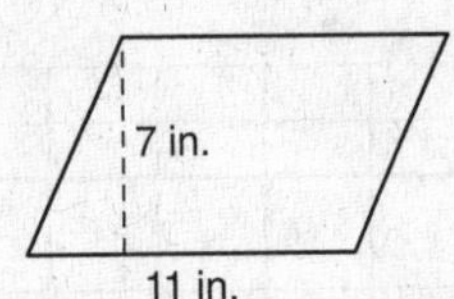

17.

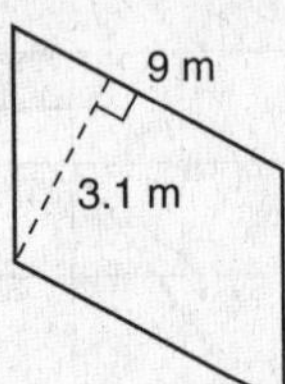

______ ______ ______

18.

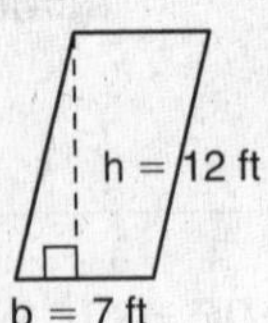

19.

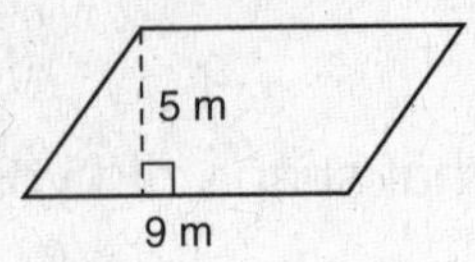

20.

5 m

9 m

______ ______ ______

21. Reasoning The area of a parallelogram is 100 square millimeters. The base is 4 millimeters. Find the height. ______